The Essential Cosmic Perspective

Taken from:

The Essential Cosmic Perspective, Eighth Edition
by Jeffrey Bennett, Megan Donahue, Nicholas Schneider, and Mark Voit

PEARSON

Cover Art: Courtesy of Denis Belitsky. Shutterstock.

Taken from:

The Essential Cosmic Perspective, Eighth Edition
by Jeffrey Bennett, Megan Donahue, Nicholas Schneider, and Mark Voit
Copyright © 2018, 2015, 2012, 2009, 2007 by Pearson Education, Inc.
New York, New York 10013

This special edition published in cooperation with Pearson Education, Inc.

Pearson Education, Inc., 330 Hudson Street, New York, New York 10013
A Pearson Education Company
www.pearsoned.com

Printed in the United States of America

000200010272097324

BJ

ISBN 10: 1-323-74778-8
ISBN 13: 978-1-323-74778-0

Dedication

TO ALL WHO HAVE EVER WONDERED about the mysteries of the universe. We hope this book will answer some of your questions—and that it will also raise new questions in your mind that will keep you curious and interested in the ongoing human adventure of astronomy.

And, especially, to Michaela, Emily, Sebastian, Grant, Nathan, Brooke, and Angela. The study of the universe begins at birth, and we hope that you will grow up in a world with far less poverty, hatred, and war so that all people will have the opportunity to contemplate the mysteries of the universe into which they are born.

Brief Contents

Contents

Preface

We humans have gazed into the sky for countless generations. We have wondered how our lives are connected to the Sun, Moon, planets, and stars that adorn the heavens. Today, through the science of astronomy, we know that these connections go far deeper than our ancestors ever imagined. This book tells the story of modern astronomy and the new perspective, *The Essential Cosmic Perspective*, that astronomy gives us on ourselves and our planet.

Who Is This Book For?

The Essential Cosmic Perspective is designed as a textbook for college courses in introductory astronomy, but is suitable for anyone who is curious about the universe. We assume no prior knowledge of astronomy or physics, and the book is especially written for students who do not intend to major in mathematics or science.

The Essential Cosmic Perspective is the mid-level of the three general astronomy textbooks we offer. Our longer book, *The Cosmic Perspective*, provides a comprehensive survey of modern astronomy with enough depth to fill a two-semester introductory astronomy sequence. This book, *The Essential Cosmic Perspective*, is trimmed down to fit what can realistically be covered in a one-semester survey of astronomy, though it may also be used with two-semester sequences. Our shortest textbook, *The Cosmic Perspective Fundamentals*, covers only the most fundamental topics in astronomy and is designed for courses that address a more limited set of topics.

New to This Edition

The underlying philosophy, goals, and structure of *The Essential Cosmic Perspective* remain the same as in past editions, but we have thoroughly updated the text and made a number of other improvements. Here, briefly, is a list of the significant changes you'll find in this eighth edition:

- **Major Chapter-Level Changes:** We have made numerous significant changes both to update the science and to improve the pedagogical flow in this edition. The full list is too long to put here, but major changes include the following:
  - **Chapter 7** has been significantly rewritten to reflect new results from *MESSENGER* at Mercury, *Curiosity* and *MAVEN* at Mars, and the latest data on global warming.
  - **Chapter 9** has been reorganized and rewritten to reflect recent developments in the study of small bodies, particularly the revolutionary new views provided by recent spacecraft including *Dawn*, *Rosetta*, and *New Horizons*.
  - **Chapter 10** has been heavily revised in light of thousands of new discoveries of extrasolar planets since the prior edition.
  - In **Chapter 14,** we have almost completely rewritten Section 14.4 to focus on events in which black holes can form and neutron star mergers.

- **Chapter 15** has been revised to reduce jargon and to include a new full-page figure showing the Milky Way in different wavelengths. In addition, Section 15.4 on the galactic center has been rewritten and features a new two-page Cosmic Context spread.
  - **Chapter 16** has been significantly revised in light of new research into galactic evolution.
  - **Chapter 19** has been significantly rewritten, particularly in Sections 19.2 and 19.3 (which has also been completely reorganized), thanks to new understanding of the potential habitability of Mars, Titan, and extrasolar planets.

- **Fully Updated Science:** Astronomy is a fast-moving field, and numerous new developments have occurred since the prior edition was published. In addition to the major chapter-level changes above, other scientific updates in this edition include the following:
  - New results and images from spacecraft exploring our solar system, including *Curiosity* and *MAVEN* at Mars, *Cassini* at Saturn, *MESSENGER* at Mercury, *Dawn* at Ceres, *New Horizons* at Pluto, and more
  - Recent results from major space observatories, including *Hubble* and *Kepler*, and from powerful ground-based observatories such as ALMA
  - Updated data and models on topics including the formation of planetary systems, global warming, and galaxy formation and evolution
  - Major new discoveries and statistics relating to the study of extrasolar planets, new research on the timing and possible origin of life on Earth, and much more

- **Reinforced Focus on Critical Thinking:** We have always placed a strong emphasis on helping students develop critical thinking skills, both by showing students the process through which we have acquired our current understanding of the universe and through features that encourage critical thinking, such as our Think About It and See It for Yourself questions and many of our exercises. To further reinforce the importance of critical thinking, we have added the following new features to this edition:
  - **New Feature—Extraordinary Claims boxes:** Carl Sagan made famous the statement "extraordinary claims require extraordinary evidence." With this new feature, we provide students with examples of extraordinary claims about the universe and how they were either supported or debunked as scientists collected more evidence. The first of these features appears in Chapter 3, where the context of Sagan's dictum is also explained. Nine additional Extraordinary Claims boxes are sprinkled throughout the rest of the text. Instructors will find assignable tutorials based on these boxes on the Mastering Astronomy® site.
  - **New Feature—My Cosmic Perspective:** As in prior editions, every chapter ends with a feature titled "The

Big Picture," designed to help students put the chapter content into the context of a larger cosmic perspective. For this edition, we have added in each of these sections a final entry entitled "My Cosmic Perspective," which aims to focus on a more personal connection between students and the cosmos. We believe that such a personal connection encourages students to think more critically about the meaning of all that they learn in their astronomy course.

- **New Icons:** You'll see a new icon designed to call attention to a few of the features that promote critical thinking: ⟳ (a "C" for "critical"). While we believe the entire structure of the book promotes critical thinking, you can use the features identified by these icons for special assignments to help students with these skills.

- **New Content in MasteringAstronomy®:** We have reached the point where *The Essential Cosmic Perspective* is no longer just a textbook; rather, it is a "learning package" that combines a printed book with deeply integrated, interactive media developed to support every chapter of our book. For students, the MasteringAstronomy® Study Area provides a wealth of tutorials and activities to build understanding, while quizzes and exercises allow them to test what they've learned. For instructors, the MasteringAstronomy® Item Library provides the unprecedented ability to quickly build, post, and automatically grade pre- and post-lecture diagnostic tests, weekly homework assignments, and exams of appropriate difficulty, duration, and content coverage. It also provides the ability to record detailed information on the step-by-step work of every student directly into a powerful and easy-to-use gradebook, and to evaluate results with a sophisticated suite of diagnostics. Among the changes you'll find to the MasteringAstronomy® site for this edition are numerous new narrated video tours of key figures from the textbook; numerous new tutorials in the Item Library; and a fully updated set of reading, concept, and visual quizzes in both the Study Area and the Item Library.

Themes of *The Essential Cosmic Perspective*

The Essential Cosmic Perspective offers a broad survey of our modern understanding of the cosmos and of how we have built that understanding. Such a survey can be presented in a number of different ways. We have chosen to interweave a few key themes throughout the book, each selected to help make the subject more appealing to students who may never have taken any formal science courses and who may begin the course with little understanding of how science works. Our book is built around the following five key themes:

- **Theme 1:** *We are a part of the universe and thus can learn about our origins by studying the universe.* This is the overarching theme of *The Essential Cosmic Perspective,* as we continually emphasize that learning about the universe helps us understand ourselves. Studying the intimate connections between human life and the cosmos gives students a

reason to care about astronomy and also deepens their appreciation of the unique and fragile nature of our planet.

- **Theme 2:** *The universe is comprehensible through scientific principles that anyone can understand.* We can understand the universe because the same physical laws appear to be at work in every aspect, on every scale, and in every age of the universe. Moreover, while professional scientists generally have discovered the laws, anyone can understand their fundamental features. Students can learn enough in one or two terms of astronomy to comprehend the basic reasons for many phenomena that they see around them—ranging from seasonal changes and phases of the Moon to the most esoteric astronomical images that appear in the news.

- **Theme 3:** *Science is not a body of facts but rather a process through which we seek to understand the world around us.* Many students assume that science is just a laundry list of facts. The long history of astronomy shows that science is a process through which we learn about our universe—a process that is not always a straight line to the truth. That is why our ideas about the cosmos sometimes change as we learn more, as they did dramatically when we first recognized that Earth is a planet going around the Sun rather than the center of the universe. In this book, we continually emphasize the nature of science so that students can understand how and why modern theories have gained acceptance and why these theories may change in the future.

- **Theme 4:** *A course in astronomy is the beginning of a lifelong learning experience.* Building on the prior themes, we emphasize that what students learn in their astronomy course is not an end but a beginning. By remembering a few key physical principles and understanding the nature of science, students can follow astronomical developments for the rest of their lives. We therefore seek to motivate students to continue to participate in the ongoing human adventure of astronomical discovery.

- **Theme 5:** *Astronomy affects each of us personally with the new perspectives it offers.* We all conduct the daily business of our lives with reference to some "world view"—a set of personal beliefs about our place and purpose in the universe that we have developed through a combination of schooling, religious training, and personal thought. This world view shapes our beliefs and many of our actions. Although astronomy does not mandate a particular set of beliefs, it does provide perspectives on the architecture of the universe that can influence how we view ourselves and our world, which can potentially affect our behavior. In many respects, the role of astronomy in shaping world views may represent the deepest connection between the universe and the everyday lives of humans.

Pedagogical Principles of *The Essential Cosmic Perspective*

No matter how an astronomy course is taught, it is very important to present material according to a clear set of pedagogical principles. The following list briefly summarizes the major pedagogical principles that we apply throughout this book. (The Instructor Guide describes these principles in more detail.)

- **Stay focused on the big picture.** Astronomy is filled with interesting facts and details, but they are meaningless unless they fit into a big picture view of the universe. We therefore take care to stay focused on the big picture (essentially the themes discussed above) at all times. A major benefit of this approach is that although students may forget individual facts and details after the course is over, the big picture framework should stay with them for life.

- **Always provide context first.** We all learn new material more easily when we understand why we are learning it. We therefore begin the book (in Chapter 1) with a broad overview of modern understanding of the cosmos so that students know what they will be studying in the rest of the book. We maintain this "context first" approach throughout the book by always telling students what they will be learning, and why, before diving into the details.

- **Make the material relevant.** It's human nature to be more interested in subjects that seem relevant to our lives. Fortunately, astronomy is filled with ideas that touch each of us personally. By emphasizing our personal connections to the cosmos, we make the material more meaningful, inspiring students to put in the effort necessary to learn it.

- **Emphasize conceptual understanding over the "stamp collecting" of facts.** If we are not careful, astronomy can appear to be an overwhelming collection of facts that are easily forgotten when the course ends. We therefore emphasize a few key concepts that we use over and over again. For example, the laws of conservation of energy and conservation of angular momentum (introduced in Section 4.3) reappear throughout the book, and we find that the wide variety of features found on the terrestrial planets can be understood through just a few basic geological processes. Research shows that, long after the course is over, students are far more likely to retain such conceptual ideas than individual facts or details.

- **Emphasize critical thinking and understanding of the process of science.** One of the major problems in public understanding of science is that too many people don't understand the difference between evidence-based science and opinion or faith. For that reason, we place particular focus on making sure students can think critically about scientific evidence and how we have arrived at current scientific understanding. For example, we discuss the nature of science in detail in Chapter 3 and then continue to show examples of how science has progressed throughout the book, while also encouraging students to think critically about the evidence that has led to this progression.

- **Proceed from the more familiar and concrete to the less familiar and abstract.** It's well known that children learn best by starting with concrete ideas and then generalizing to abstractions. The same is true for many adults. We therefore always try to "build bridges to the familiar"— that is, to begin with concrete or familiar ideas and then gradually develop more general principles from them.

- **Use plain language.** Surveys have found that the number of new terms in many introductory astronomy books is larger than the number of words taught in many first-year foreign language courses. This means that most books are teaching astronomy in what looks to students like a foreign language! It is much easier for students to understand key astronomical concepts if they are explained in plain English without resorting to unnecessary jargon. We have gone to great lengths to eliminate jargon as much as possible or, at minimum, to replace standard jargon with terms that are easier to remember in the context of the subject matter.

- **Recognize and address student misconceptions.** Students do not arrive as blank slates. Most students enter our courses not only lacking the knowledge we hope to teach but often holding misconceptions about astronomical ideas. Therefore, to teach correct ideas, we must also help students recognize the paradoxes in their prior misconceptions. We address this issue in a number of ways, most overtly with Common Misconceptions boxes. These summarize commonly held misconceptions and explain why they cannot be correct.

The Topical (Part) Structure of *The Essential Cosmic Perspective*

The Essential Cosmic Perspective is organized into six broad topical areas (the six parts in the table of contents), each approached in a distinctive way designed to help maintain the focus on the themes discussed earlier. Here, we summarize the guiding philosophy through which we have approached each topic. Every part concludes with a two-page Cosmic Context figure, which ties together into a coherent whole the diverse ideas covered in the individual chapters.

PART I Developing Perspective (Chapters 1–3)

Guiding Philosophy Introduce the big picture, the process of science, and the historical context of astronomy.

The basic goal of these chapters is to give students a big picture overview and context for the rest of the book and to help them develop an appreciation for the process of science and how science has developed through history. Chapter 1 outlines our modern understanding of the cosmos, so that students gain perspective on the entire universe before diving into its details. Chapter 2 introduces basic sky phenomena, including seasons and phases of the Moon, and provides perspective on how phenomena we experience every day are tied to the broader cosmos. Chapter 3 discusses the nature of science, offering a historical perspective on the development of science and giving students perspective on how science works and how it differs from nonscience.

The Cosmic Context for Part I appears on pp. 80–81.

PART II Key Concepts for Astronomy (Chapters 4–5)

Guiding Philosophy Connect the physics of the cosmos to everyday experiences.

These chapters lay the groundwork for understanding astronomy through what is sometimes called the "universality of physics"— the idea that a few key principles governing matter, energy, light, and motion explain both the phenomena of our daily lives and the mysteries of the cosmos. Chapter 4 covers the laws of motion, the crucial conservation laws of angular momentum and energy, and the universal law of gravitation. Chapter 5 covers the nature of light and matter, spectra, and telescopes.

The Cosmic Context for Part II appears on pp. 134–135.

PART III Learning from Other Worlds (Chapters 6–10)

Guiding Philosophy Learn about Earth by studying other planets in our solar system and beyond.

This set of chapters begins in Chapter 6 with a broad overview of the solar system and its formation, including a 10-page tour that highlights some of the most important and interesting features of the Sun and each of the planets. Chapters 7 to 9 focus, respectively, on the terrestrial planets, the jovian planets, and the small bodies of the solar system. Finally, Chapter 10 turns to the exciting topic of other planetary systems that have been discovered in recent years. Note that Part III is essentially independent of Parts IV and V, and can be covered either before or after them.

The Cosmic Context for Part III appears on pp. 286–287.

PART IV Stars (Chapters 11–14)

Guiding Philosophy We are intimately connected to the stars.

These are our chapters on stars and stellar life cycles. Chapter 11 covers the Sun in depth, so that it can serve as a concrete model for building an understanding of other stars. Chapter 12 describes the general properties of stars, how we measure these properties, and how we classify stars using the H-R diagram. Chapter 13 covers stellar evolution, tracing the birth-to-death lives of both low- and high-mass stars. Chapter 14 covers the end points of stellar evolution: white dwarfs, neutron stars, and black holes.

The Cosmic Context for Part IV appears on pp. 384–385.

PART V Galaxies and Beyond (Chapters 15–18)

Guiding Philosophy Present galaxy evolution and cosmology together as intimately related topics.

These chapters cover galaxies and cosmology. Chapter 15 presents the Milky Way as a paradigm for galaxies in much the same way that Chapter 11 uses the Sun as a paradigm for stars. Chapter 16 presents the variety of galaxies, how we determine key parameters such as galactic distances and age, and current understanding of galaxy evolution. Chapter 17 then presents the Big Bang theory and the evidence supporting it, setting the stage for Chapter 18, which explores dark matter and its role in galaxy formation, as well as dark energy and its implications for the fate of the universe.

The Cosmic Context for Part V appears on pp. 494–495.

PART VI Life on Earth and Beyond (Chapter 19)

Guiding Philosophy The study of life on Earth helps us understand the search for life in the universe.

This part consists of a single chapter. It may be considered optional, to be used as time allows. Those who wish to teach a more detailed course on astrobiology may consider the text *Life in the Universe,* by Jeffrey Bennett and Seth Shostak.

The Cosmic Context for Part VI appears on pp. 532–533.

Pedagogical Features of *The Essential Cosmic Perspective*

Alongside the main narrative, *The Essential Cosmic Perspective* includes a number of pedagogical devices designed to enhance student learning:

- **Basic Chapter Structure** Each chapter is carefully structured to ensure that students understand the goals up front, learn the details, and pull together all the ideas at the end. In particular, note the following key structural elements:

  - **Chapter Learning Goals** Each chapter opens with a page offering an enticing image and a brief overview of the chapter, including a list of the section titles and associated learning goals. The learning goals are presented as key questions designed to help students both understand what they will be learning about and stay focused on these key goals as they work through the chapter.

  - **Introduction** The first page of the main chapter text begins with a two- to three-paragraph introduction to the chapter material.

  - **Section Structure** Chapters are divided into numbered sections, each addressing one key aspect of the chapter material. Each section begins with a short introduction that leads into a set of learning goals relevant to the section—the same learning goals listed at the beginning of the chapter.

  - **The Big Picture** Every chapter narrative ends with this feature, designed to help students put what they've learned in the chapter into the context of the overall goal of gaining a broader perspective on ourselves, our planet, and our place in the universe.

  - **Chapter Summary** The end-of-chapter summary offers a concise review of the learning goal questions, helping to reinforce student understanding of key concepts from the chapter. Thumbnail figures are included to remind students of key illustrations and photos in the chapter.

- **End-of-Chapter Exercises** Each chapter includes an extensive set of exercises that can be used for study, discussion, or assignment. All of the end-of-chapter exercises are organized into the following subsets:

  - **Visual Skills Check** A set of questions designed to help students build their skills at interpreting the many types of visual information used in astronomy.

  - **Review Questions** Questions that students should be able to answer from the reading alone.

  - **Does It Make Sense? (or similar title)** A set of short statements, each of which students are expected to evaluate critically so that they can explain why it does or does not make sense. These exercises are generally easy once students understand a particular concept, but very difficult otherwise; this makes them an excellent probe of comprehension.

- **Quick Quiz** A short multiple-choice quiz that allows students to check their basic understanding.

- **Process of Science Questions** Essay or discussion questions that help students focus on how science progresses over time.

- **Group Work Exercise** A suggested activity designed for collaborative learning in class.

- **Short-Answer/Essay Questions** Questions that go beyond the Review Questions in asking for conceptual interpretation.

- **Quantitative Problems** Problems that require some mathematics, usually based on topics covered in the Cosmic Calculations boxes.

- **Discussion Questions** Open-ended questions for class discussions.

- **Web Projects** A few suggestions for additional Web-based research.

- **Additional Features** You'll find a number of other features designed to increase student understanding, both within individual chapters and at the end of the book, including the following:

  - **Annotated Figures** Key figures in each chapter incorporate the research-proven technique of "annotation"—carefully crafted text placed on the figure (in blue) to guide students through interpreting graphs, following process figures, and translating between different representations.

  - **Cosmic Context Two-Page Figures** These two-page spreads provide visual summaries of key processes and concepts.

  - **Wavelength/Observatory Icons** For astronomical images, simple icons indicate whether the image is a photo, artist's impression, or computer simulation; whether a photo came from ground-based or space-based observations; and the wavelength band used to take the photo.

  - **Think About It** This feature, which appears throughout the book as short questions integrated into the narrative, gives students the opportunity to reflect on important new concepts. It also serves as an excellent starting point for classroom discussions.

  - **See It for Yourself** This feature also occurs throughout the book, integrated into the narrative, and gives students the opportunity to conduct simple observations or experiments that will help them understand key concepts.

  - **Common Misconceptions** These boxes address popularly held but incorrect ideas related to the chapter material.

  - **Special Topic Boxes** These boxes contain supplementary discussion topics related to the chapter material but not prerequisite to the continuing discussion.

  - **Extraordinary Claims Boxes** Carl Sagan made famous the statement "extraordinary claims require extraordinary evidence." These boxes provide students with examples of extraordinary claims about the universe and how they were either supported or debunked as scientists collected more evidence.

  - **Cosmic Calculations Boxes** These boxes contain most of the mathematics used in the book and can be covered or skipped depending on the level of mathematics that you wish to include in your course.

  - **Cross-References** When a concept is covered in greater detail elsewhere in the book, we include a cross-reference, printed in blue and surrounded by brackets, to the relevant section (e.g., [Section 5.2]).

  - **Glossary** A detailed glossary makes it easy for students to look up important terms.

  - **Appendixes** The appendixes include a number of useful references and tables, including key constants (Appendix A), key formulas (Appendix B), key mathematical skills (Appendix C), and numerous data tables and star charts (Appendixes D–I).

About MasteringAstronomy®

What is the single most important factor in student success in astronomy? Both research and common sense reveal the same answer: *study time*. No matter how good the teacher or how good the textbook, students learn only when they spend adequate time studying. Unfortunately, limitations on resources for grading have prevented most instructors from assigning much homework despite its obvious benefits to student learning. And limitations on help and office hours have made it difficult for students to make sure they use self-study time effectively. That, in a nutshell, is why we created MasteringAstronomy®. For students, it provides adaptive learning designed to coach them *individually*—responding to their errors with specific, targeted feedback and providing optional hints for those who need additional guidance. For professors, MasteringAstronomy® provides the unprecedented ability to automatically monitor and record students' step-by-step work and evaluate the effectiveness of assignments and exams. As a result, we believe that MasteringAstronomy® can change the way astronomy courses are taught: It is now possible, even in large classes, to ensure that each student spends his or her study time on optimal learning activities outside of class.

MasteringAstronomy® provides students with a wealth of self-study resources, including interactive tutorials targeting the most difficult concepts of the course, interactive or narrated versions of key figures and photos, and quizzes and other activities for self-assessment covering every chapter and every week. For professors, MasteringAstronomy® provides a library of tutoring activities that is periodically updated based on the performance of students nationwide. You can create assignments tailored to your specific class goals from among hundreds of activities and problems including pre- and post-lecture diagnostic quizzes, tutoring activities, end-of-chapter problems from this textbook, and test bank questions. MasteringAstronomy® now also includes Learning Catalytics, which provides additional capabilities for in-class learning. Visit MasteringAstronomy® to learn more.

Finally, in a world where everyone claims to have the best website, we'd like to point out three reasons why you'll discover that MasteringAstronomy® really does stand out from the crowd:

- MasteringAstronomy® has been built specifically to support the structure and pedagogy of *The Essential Cosmic Perspective*. You'll find the same concepts emphasized in the book and on the website, using the same terminology and the same pedagogical approaches. This type of consistency ensures that students focus on the concepts, without the risk of becoming confused by different presentations.

- Nearly all MasteringAstronomy® content has been developed either directly by *The Essential Cosmic Perspective* author team or in close collaboration with outstanding educators including Jim Dove, Jim Cooney, Jonathan Williams, Richard Gelderman, Ed Prather, Tim Slater, Daniel Lorenz, and Lauren Jones. The direct involvement of book authors ensures consistency from our website to the textbook, resulting in an effective, high-quality learning program.

- The MasteringAstronomy® platform uses the same unique student-driven engine as the highly successful MasteringPhysics® product (the most widely adopted physics tutorial and assessment system), developed by a group led by MIT physicist David Pritchard. This robust platform gives instructors unprecedented power not only to tailor content to their own courses, but also to evaluate the effectiveness of assignments and exams.

Additional Supplements for *The Essential Cosmic Perspective*

The Essential Cosmic Perspective is much more than just a textbook. It is a complete package of teaching, learning, and assessment resources designed to help both teachers and students. In addition to MasteringAstronomy®, the following supplements are available with this book:

- **SkyGazer v5.0**: Based on *Voyager V*, SkyGazer, one of the world's most popular planetarium programs now available for download, makes it easy for students to learn constellations and explore the wonders of the sky through interactive exercises and demonstrations. Accompanying activities are available in LoPresto's Astronomy Media Workbook, Seventh Edition, available both on the MasteringAstronomy® study area and on the SkyGazer site. Ask your Pearson sales representative for details.

- **Starry Night™ College** (ISBN 0-321-71295-1): Now available as an additional option with *The Essential Cosmic Perspective*, Starry Night has been acclaimed as the world's most realistic desktop planetarium software. This special version has an easy-to-use point-and-click interface and is available as an additional bundle. The Starry Night Activity Workbook, consisting of thirty-five worksheets for homework or lab, based on Starry Night planetarium software, is available for download in the MasteringAstronomy® study area or with a Starry Night College access code. Ask your Pearson sales representative for details.

- **Lecture Tutorials for Introductory Astronomy** (ISBN 0-321-82046-0) by Edward E. Prather, Timothy F. Slater, Jeffrey P. Adams, and Gina Brissenden: The forty-four lecture tutorials included are designed to engage students in critical reasoning and spark classroom discussion.

- **Sky and Telescope: Special Student Supplement** (ISBN 0-321-70620-X): The nine articles, each with an assessment following, provide a general review as well as covering such topics as the process of science, the scale of the universe, and our place in the universe. The supplement is available for bundling; ask your Pearson sales representative for details.

- **Observation Exercises in Astronomy** (ISBN 0-321-63812-3): This manual includes fifteen observation activities that can be used with a number of different planetarium software packages.

- **McCrady/Rice Astronomy Labs: A Concept Oriented Approach** (ISBN: 0-321-86177-9): This customizable lab is available in the Pearson Custom Library. It consists of 40 conceptually oriented introductory astronomy labs that focus on the mid to higher levels of Bloom's taxonomy: application, synthesis, and analysis. The labs are all written to minimize equipment requirements and are largely created to maximize the use of inexpensive everyday objects such as flashlights, construction paper, and theater gels.

Instructor-Only Supplements

Several additional supplements are available for instructors only. Contact your local Pearson sales representative to find out more about the following supplements:

- **The Instructor Resources tab** in MasteringAstronomy® provides a wealth of lecture and teaching resources, including high-resolution JPEGs of all images from the book for in-class projection, Narrated Figures, based on figures from the book, pre-built PowerPoint® Lecture Outlines, answers to SkyGazer and Starry Night workbooks, and PRS-enabled Clicker Quizzes based on the book and book-specific interactive media.

- **Instructor Guide** (ISBN 0-134-53247-3): This guide contains a detailed overview of the text, sample syllabi for courses of different emphasis and duration, suggestions for teaching strategies, answers or discussion points for all Think About It and See It for Yourself questions in the text, solutions to end-of-chapter problems, and a detailed reference guide summarizing media resources available for every chapter and section in the book. Word files can be downloaded from the instructor resource section of MasteringAstronomy®.

- **Test Bank** (ISBN 0-134-60203-X): The Test Bank includes hundreds of multiple-choice, true/false, and short-answer questions, plus Process of Science questions for each chapter. TestGen® and Word files can be downloaded from the instructor resource section of the study area in MasteringAstronomy®.

Acknowledgments

Our textbook carries only four author names, but in fact it is the result of hard work by a long list of committed individuals. We could not possibly list everyone who has helped, but we would like to call attention to a few people who have played particularly important roles. First, we thank our editors and friends at Pearson, who have stuck with us through thick and thin, including Adam Black, Nancy Whilton, Jim Smith, Michael Gillespie, Mary Ripley, Chandrika Madhavan, and Corinne Benson. Special thanks to our production teams, especially Sally Lifland, and our art and design team.

We've also been fortunate to have an outstanding group of reviewers, whose extensive comments and suggestions helped us shape the book. We thank all those who have reviewed drafts of the book in various stages, including

Marilyn Akins, *Broome Community College*
Christopher M. Anderson, *University of Wisconsin*
John Anderson, *University of North Florida*
Peter S. Anderson, *Oakland Community College*
Keith Ashman
Simon P. Balm, *Santa Monica College*
Reba Bandyopadhyay, *University of Florida*
Nadine Barlow, *Northern Arizona University*
John Beaver, *University of Wisconsin at Fox Valley*
Peter A. Becker, *George Mason University*
Timothy C. Beers, *National Optical Astronomy Observatory*
Jim Bell, *Arizona State University*
Priscilla J. Benson, *Wellesley College*
Philip Blanco, *Grossmont College*
Jeff R. Bodart, *Chipola College*
Bernard W. Bopp, *University of Toledo*
Sukanta Bose, *Washington State University*
David Brain, *University of Colorado*
David Branch, *University of Oklahoma*
John C. Brandt, *University of New Mexico*
James E. Brau, *University of Oregon*
Jean P. Brodie, *UCO/Lick Observatory, University of California, Santa Cruz*
Erik Brogt, *University of Canterbury*
James Brooks, *Florida State University*
Daniel Bruton, *Stephen F. Austin State University*
Debra Burris, *University of Central Arkansas*
Scott Calvin, *Sarah Lawrence College*
Amy Campbell, *Louisiana State University*
Eugene R. Capriotti, *Michigan State University*
Eric Carlson, *Wake Forest University*
David A. Cebula, *Pacific University*
Supriya Chakrabarti, *University of Massachusetts, Lowell*
Kwang-Ping Cheng, *California State University, Fullerton*
Dipak Chowdhury, *Indiana University—Purdue University Fort Wayne*
Chris Churchill, *New Mexico State University*
Josh Colwell, *University of Central Florida*
James Cooney, *University of Central Florida*
Anita B. Corn, *Colorado School of Mines*
Philip E. Corn, *Red Rocks Community College*
Kelli Corrado, *Montgomery County Community College*
Peter Cottrell, *University of Canterbury*
John Cowan, *University of Oklahoma*
Kevin Crosby, *Carthage College*
Christopher Crow, *Indiana University—Purdue University Fort Wayne*
Manfred Cuntz, *University of Texas at Arlington*
Christopher De Vries, *California State University, Stanislaus*
John M. Dickey, *University of Minnesota*

Matthias Dietrich, *Worcester State University*
Bryan Dunne, *University of Illinois, Urbana-Champaign*
Suzan Edwards, *Smith College*
Robert Egler, *North Carolina State University at Raleigh*
Paul Eskridge, *Minnesota State University*
David Falk, *Los Angeles Valley College*
Timothy Farris, *Vanderbilt University*
Robert A. Fesen, *Dartmouth College*
Tom Fleming, *University of Arizona*
Douglas Franklin, *Western Illinois University*
Sidney Freudenstein, *Metropolitan State College of Denver*
Martin Gaskell, *University of Nebraska*
Richard Gelderman, *Western Kentucky University*
Harold A. Geller, *George Mason University*
Donna Gifford, *Pima Community College*
Mitch Gillam, *Marion L. Steele High School*
Bernard Gilroy, *The Hun School of Princeton*
Owen Gingerich, *Harvard–Smithsonian* (Historical Accuracy Reviewer)
David Graff, *U.S. Merchant Marine Academy*
Richard Gray, *Appalachian State University*
Kevin Grazier, *Jet Propulsion Laboratory*
Robert Greeney, *Holyoke Community College*
Henry Greenside, *Duke University*
Alan Greer, *Gonzaga University*
John Griffith, *Lin-Benton Community College*
David Griffiths, *Oregon State University*
David Grinspoon, *Planetary Science Institute*
John Gris, *University of Delaware*
Bruce Gronich, *University of Texas at El Paso*
Thomasana Hail, *Parkland University*
Jim Hamm, *Big Bend Community College*
Charles Hartley, *Hartwick College*
J. Hasbun, *University of West Georgia*
Joe Heafner, *Catawba Valley Community College*
David Herrick, *Maysville Community College*
Scott Hildreth, *Chabot College*
Tracy Hodge, *Berea College*
Mark Hollabaugh, *Normandale Community College*
Richard Holland, *Southern Illinois University, Carbondale*
Joseph Howard, *Salisbury University*
James Christopher Hunt, *Prince George's Community College*
Richard Ignace, *University of Wisconsin*
James Imamura, *University of Oregon*
Douglas R. Ingram, *Texas Christian University*
Assad Istephan, *Madonna University*
Bruce Jakosky, *University of Colorado*
Adam G. Jensen, *University of Colorado*
Adam Johnston, *Weber State University*
Lauren Jones, *Gettysburg College*
Kishor T. Kapale, *Western Illinois University*
William Keel, *University of Alabama*
Julia Kennefick, *University of Arkansas*
Steve Kipp, *University of Minnesota, Mankato*
Kurtis Koll, *Cameron University*
Ichishiro Konno, *University of Texas at San Antonio*
John Kormendy, *University of Texas at Austin*
Eric Korpela, *University of California, Berkeley*
Arthur Kosowsky, *University of Pittsburgh*
Kevin Krisciunas, *Texas A&M*
David Lamp, *Texas Technical University*

Ted La Rosa, *Kennesaw State University*
Kristine Larsen, *Central Connecticut State University*
Ana Marie Larson, *University of Washington*
Stephen Lattanzio, *Orange Coast College*
Chris Laws, *University of Washington*
Larry Lebofsky, *University of Arizona*
Patrick Lestrade, *Mississippi State University*
Nancy Levenson, *University of Kentucky*
David M. Lind, *Florida State University*
Abraham Loeb, *Harvard University*
Michael LoPresto, *Henry Ford Community College*
William R. Luebke, *Modesto Junior College*
Ihor Luhach, *Valencia Community College*
Darrell Jack MacConnell, *Community College of Baltimore City*
Marie Machacek, *Massachusetts Institute of Technology*
Loris Magnani, *University of Georgia*
Steven Majewski, *University of Virginia*
Phil Matheson, *Salt Lake Community College*
John Mattox, *Fayetteville State University*
Marles McCurdy, *Tarrant County College*
Stacy McGaugh, *Case Western University*
Barry Metz, *Delaware County Community College*
William Millar, *Grand Rapids Community College*
Dinah Moche, *Queensborough Community College of City University, New York*
Stephen Murray, *University of California, Santa Cruz*
Zdzislaw E. Musielak, *University of Texas at Arlington*
Charles Nelson, *Drake University*
Gerald H. Newsom, *Ohio State University*
Lauren Novatne, *Reedley College*
Brian Oetiker, *Sam Houston State University*
Richard Olenick, *University of Dallas*
John P. Oliver, *University of Florida*
Stacy Palen, *Weber State University*
Russell L. Palma, *Sam Houston State University*
Mark Pecaut, *Rockhurst University*
Jon Pedicino, *College of the Redwoods*
Bryan Penprase, *Pomona College*
Eric S. Perlman, *Florida Institute of Technology*
Peggy Perozzo, *Mary Baldwin College*
Greg Perugini, *Burlington County College*
Charles Peterson, *University of Missouri, Columbia*
Cynthia W. Peterson, *University of Connecticut*
Jorge Piekarewicz, *Florida State University*
Lawrence Pinsky, *University of Houston*
Stephanie Plante, *Grossmont College*
Jascha Polet, *California State Polytechnic University, Pomona*
Matthew Price, *Oregon State University*
Harrison B. Prosper, *Florida State University*
Monica Ramirez, *Aims College, Colorado*
Christina Reeves-Shull, *Richland College*
Todd M. Rigg, *City College of San Francisco*
Elizabeth Roettger, *DePaul University*
Roy Rubins, *University of Texas at Arlington*
April Russell, *Siena College*
Carl Rutledge, *East Central University*
Bob Sackett, *Saddleback College*
Rex Saffer, *Villanova University*
John Safko, *University of South Carolina*
James A. Scarborough, *Delta State University*
Britt Scharringhausen, *Ithaca College*

Ann Schmiedekamp, *Pennsylvania State University, Abington*
Joslyn Schoemer, *Denver Museum of Nature and Science*
James Schombert, *University of Oregon*
Gregory Seab, *University of New Orleans*
Larry Sessions, *Metropolitan State College of Denver*
Anwar Shiekh, *Colorado Mesa University*
Ralph Siegel, *Montgomery College, Germantown Campus*
Philip I. Siemens, *Oregon State University*
Caroline Simpson, *Florida International University*
Paul Sipiera, *William Harper Rainey College*
Earl F. Skelton, *George Washington University*
Evan Skillman, *University of Minnesota*
Michael Skrutskie, *University of Virginia*
Mark H. Slovak, *Louisiana State University*
Norma Small-Warren, *Howard University*
Jessica Smay, *San Jose City College*
Dale Smith, *Bowling Green State University*
Brent Sorenson, *Southern Utah University*
James R. Sowell, *Georgia Technical University*
Kelli Spangler, *Montgomery County Community College*
John Spencer, *Southwest Research Institute*
Darryl Stanford, *City College of San Francisco*
George R. Stanley, *San Antonio College*
Peter Stein, *Bloomsburg University of Pennsylvania*
Adriane Steinacker, *University of California, Santa Cruz*
John Stolar, *West Chester University*
Irina Struganova, *Valencia Community College*
Jack Sulentic, *University of Alabama*
C. Sean Sutton, *Mount Holyoke College*
Beverley A. P. Taylor, *Miami University*
Brett Taylor, *Radford University*
Donald M. Terndrup, *Ohio State University*
Frank Timmes, *Arizona State University*
David Trott, *Metro State College*
David Vakil, *El Camino College*
Trina Van Ausdal, *Salt Lake Community College*
Licia Verde, *Institute of Cosmological Studies, Barcelona*
Nicole Vogt, *New Mexico State University*
Darryl Walke, *Rariton Valley Community College*
Fred Walter, *State University of New York, Stony Brook*
James Webb, *Florida International University*
Mark Whittle, *University of Virginia*
Paul J. Wiita, *The College of New Jersey*
Lisa M. Will, *Mesa Community College*
Jonathan Williams, *University of Hawaii*
Terry Willis, *Chesapeake College*
Grant Wilson, *University of Massachusetts, Amherst*
J. Wayne Wooten, *Pensacola Junior College*
Guy Worthey, *Washington State University, Pullman*
Scott Yager, *Brevard College*
Andrew Young, *Casper College*
Arthur Young, *San Diego State University*
Tim Young, *University of North Dakota*
Min S. Yun, *University of Massachusetts, Amherst*
Dennis Zaritsky, *University of Arizona*
Robert L. Zimmerman, *University of Oregon*

In addition, we thank the following colleagues who helped us clarify technical points or checked the accuracy of technical discussions in the book:

Caspar Amman, *NCAR*
Nahum Arav, *Virginia Technical University*
Phil Armitage, *University of Colorado*
Thomas Ayres, *University of Colorado*
Cecilia Barnbaum, *Valdosta State University*
Rick Binzel, *Massachusetts Institute of Technology*
Howard Bond, *Space Telescope Science Institute*
David Brain, *University of Colorado*
Humberto Campins, *University of Central Florida*
Robin Canup, *Southwest Research Institute*
Clark Chapman, *Southwest Research Institute*
Kelly Cline, *Carroll College*
Josh Colwell, *University of Central Florida*
James Cooney, *University of Central Florida*
Mark Dickinson, *National Optical Astronomy Observatory*
Jim Dove, *Metropolitan State College of Denver*
Doug Duncan, *University of Colorado*
Dan Fabrycky, *University of Chicago*
Harry Ferguson, *Space Telescope Science Institute*
Andrew Hamilton, *University of Colorado*
Todd Henry, *Georgia State University*
Dennis Hibbert, *Everett Community College*
Seth Hornstein, *University of Colorado*
Dave Jewitt, *University of California, Los Angeles*
Julia Kregenow, *Penn State University*
Emily Lakdawalla, *The Planetary Society*
Hal Levison, *Southwest Research Institute*
Mario Livio, *Space Telescope Science Institute*
J. McKim Malville, *University of Colorado*
Geoff Marcy
Mark Marley, *Ames Research Center*
Linda Martel, *University of Hawaii*
Kevin McLin, *University of Colorado*
Michael Mendillo, *Boston University*

Steve Mojzsis, *University of Colorado*
Francis Nimmo, *University of California, Santa Cruz*
Tyler Nordgren, *University of Redlands*
Rachel Osten, *Space Telescope Science Institute*
Bob Pappalardo, *Jet Propulsion Laboratory*
Bennett Seidenstein, *Arundel High School*
Michael Shara, *American Museum of Natural History*
Evan Skillman, *University of Minnesota*
Brad Snowder, *Western Washington University*
Bob Stein, *Michigan State University*
Glen Stewart, *University of Colorado*
John Stolar, *West Chester University*
Jeff Taylor, *University of Hawaii*
Dave Tholen, *University of Hawaii*
Nick Thomas, *University of Bern*
Dimitri Veras, *Cambridge University*
John Weiss, *Carleton College*
Francis Wilkin, *Union College*
Jeremy Wood, *Hazard Community College*
Jason Wright, *Penn State University*
Don Yeomans, *Jet Propulsion Laboratory*

Finally, we thank the many people who have greatly influenced our outlook on education and our perspective on the universe over the years, including Tom Ayres, Fran Bagenal, Forrest Boley, Robert A. Brown, George Dulk, Erica Ellingson, Katy Garmany, Jeff Goldstein, David Grinspoon, Robin Heyden, Don Hunten, Geoffrey Marcy, Joan Marsh, Catherine McCord, Dick McCray, Dee Mook, Cherilynn Morrow, Charlie Pellerin, Carl Sagan, Mike Shull, John Spencer, and John Stocke.

Jeff Bennett
Megan Donahue
Nick Schneider
Mark Voit

About the Authors

Jeffrey Bennett

Jeffrey Bennett, a recipient of the American Institute of Physics Science Communication Award, holds a B.A. in biophysics (UC San Diego), and an M.S. and Ph.D. in astrophysics (University of Colorado). He specializes in science and math education and has taught at every level from preschool through graduate school. Career highlights include serving 2 years as a visiting senior scientist at NASA headquarters, where he developed programs to build stronger links between research and education, and proposing and helping to develop the Voyage scale model solar system on the National Mall (Washington, DC). He is the lead author of textbooks in astronomy, astrobiology, mathematics, and statistics, and of critically acclaimed books for the public including *Beyond UFOs* (Princeton University Press, 2008/2011), *Math for Life* (Bid Kid Science, 2014), *What Is Relativity?* (Columbia University Press, 2014), *On Teaching Science* (Big Kid Science, 2014), and *A Global Warming Primer* (Big Kid Science, 2016). He is also the author of six science picture books for children, including *Max Goes to the Moon*, *The Wizard Who Saved the World*, and *I, Humanity*; all six have been launched to the International Space Station and read aloud by astronauts for NASA's Story Time From Space program. Jeff lives in Boulder, CO with his wife, children, and dog. His personal website is www.jeffreybennett.com.

Megan Donahue

Megan Donahue is a full professor in the Department of Physics and Astronomy at Michigan State University (MSU) and a Fellow of the American Association for the Advancement of Science. Her current research is mainly about using X-ray, UV, infrared, and visible light to study galaxies and clusters of galaxies: their contents—dark matter, hot gas, galaxies, active galactic nuclei—and what they reveal about the contents of the universe and how galaxies form and evolve. She grew up on a farm in Nebraska and received an S.B. in physics from MIT, where she began her research career as an X-ray astronomer. She has a Ph.D. in astrophysics from the University of Colorado. Her Ph.D. thesis on theory and optical observations of intergalactic and intracluster gas won the 1993 Trumpler Award from the Astronomical Society for the Pacific for an outstanding astrophysics doctoral dissertation in North America. She continued postdoctoral research as a Carnegie Fellow at Carnegie Observatories in Pasadena, California, and later as an STScI Institute Fellow at Space Telescope. Megan was a staff astronomer at the Space Telescope Science Institute until 2003, when she joined the MSU faculty. She is also actively involved in advising national and international astronomical facilities and NASA, including planning future NASA missions. Megan is married to Mark Voit, and they collaborate on many projects, including this textbook, over 50 peer-reviewed astrophysics papers, and the raising of their children, Michaela, Sebastian, and Angela. Megan has run three full marathons, including Boston. These days she does trail running, orienteers, and plays piano and bass guitar for fun and no profit.

Nicholas Schneider

Nicholas Schneider is an associate professor in the Department of Astrophysical and Planetary Sciences at the University of Colorado and a researcher in the Laboratory for Atmospheric and Space Physics. He received his B.A. in physics and astronomy from Dartmouth College in 1979 and his Ph.D. in planetary science from the University of Arizona in 1988. In 1991, he received the National Science Foundation's Presidential Young Investigator Award. His research interests include planetary atmospheres and planetary astronomy. One research focus is the odd case of Jupiter's moon Io. Another is the mystery of Mars's lost atmosphere, which he hopes to answer by leading the Imaging UV Spectrograph team on NASA's *MAVEN* mission now orbiting Mars. Nick enjoys teaching at all levels and is active in efforts to improve undergraduate astronomy education. In 2010 he received the Boulder Faculty Assembly's Teaching Excellence Award. Off the job, Nick enjoys exploring the outdoors with his family and figuring out how things work.

Mark Voit

Mark Voit is a professor in the Department of Physics and Astronomy and Associate Dean for Undergraduate Studies at Michigan State University. He earned his A.B. in astrophysical sciences at Princeton University and his Ph.D. in astrophysics at the University of Colorado in 1990. He continued his studies at the California Institute of Technology, where he was a research fellow in theoretical astrophysics, and then moved on to Johns Hopkins University as a Hubble Fellow. Before going to Michigan State, Mark worked in the Office of Public Outreach at the Space Telescope, where he developed museum exhibitions about the Hubble Space Telescope and helped design NASA's award-winning HubbleSite. His research interests range from interstellar processes in our own galaxy to the clustering of galaxies in the early universe, and he is a Fellow of the American Association for the Advancement of Science. He is married to coauthor Megan Donahue, and cooks terrific meals for her and their three children. Mark likes getting outdoors whenever possible and particularly enjoys running, mountain biking, canoeing, orienteering, and adventure racing. He is also author of the popular book *Hubble Space Telescope: New Views of the Universe*.

How to Succeed
in Your Astronomy Course

If Your Course Is	Times for Reading the Assigned Text (per week)	Times for Homework Assignments (per week)	Times for Review and Test Preparation (average per week)	Total Study Time (per week)
3 credits	2 to 4 hours	2 to 3 hours	2 hours	6 to 9 hours
4 credits	3 to 5 hours	2 to 4 hours	3 hours	8 to 12 hours
5 credits	3 to 5 hours	3 to 6 hours	4 hours	10 to 15 hours

The Key to Success: Study Time

The single most important key to success in any college course is to spend enough time studying. A general rule of thumb for college classes is that you should expect to study about 2 to 3 hours per week *outside* of class for each unit of credit. For example, based on this rule of thumb, a student taking 15 credit hours should expect to spend 30 to 45 hours each week studying outside of class. Combined with time in class, this works out to a total of 45 to 60 hours spent on academic work—not much more than the time a typical job requires, and you get to choose your own hours. Of course, if you are working or have family obligations while you attend school, you will need to budget your time carefully.

As a rough guideline, your study time might be divided as shown in the table above. If you find that you are spending fewer hours than these guidelines suggest, you can probably improve your grade by studying longer. If you are spending more hours than these guidelines suggest, you may be studying inefficiently; in that case, you should talk to your instructor about how to study more effectively.

Using This Book

Each chapter in this book is designed to help you to study effectively and efficiently. To get the most out of each chapter, you might wish to use the following study plan.

- A textbook is not a novel, and you'll learn best by reading the elements of this text in the following order:
  1. Start by reading the Learning Goals and the introductory paragraphs at the beginning of the chapter so that you'll know what you are trying to learn.
  2. Get an overview of key concepts by studying the illustrations and their captions and annotations. The illustrations highlight most major concepts, so this "illustrations first" strategy gives you an opportunity to survey the concepts before you read about them in depth. You will find the two-page Cosmic Context figures especially useful.
  3. Read the chapter narrative, trying the Think About It questions and the See It for Yourself activities as you go along, but save the boxed features (e.g., Common

Misconceptions, Special Topics) to read later. As you read, make notes on the pages to remind yourself of ideas you'll want to review later. Take notes as you read, but avoid using a highlight pen (or a highlighting tool if you are using an e-book), which makes it too easy to highlight mindlessly.
  4. After reading the chapter once, go back through and read the boxed features.
  5. Review the Chapter Summary, ideally by trying to answer the Learning Goal questions for yourself before reading the given answers.

- After completing the reading as outlined above, test your understanding with the end-of-chapter exercises. A good way to begin is to make sure you can answer all of the Review and Quick Quiz Questions; if you don't know an answer, look back through the chapter until you figure it out.

- Visit the MasteringAstronomy® site and make use of resources that will help you further build your understanding. These resources have been developed specifically to help you learn the most important ideas in your course, and they have been extensively tested to make sure they are effective. They really do work, and the only way you'll gain their benefits is by going to the website and using them.

General Strategies for Studying

- Budget your time effectively. Studying 1 or 2 hours each day is more effective, and far less painful, than studying all night before homework is due or before exams.
- Engage your brain. Learning is an active process, not a passive experience. Whether you are reading, listening to a lecture, or working on assignments, always make sure that your mind is actively engaged. If you find your mind drifting or find yourself falling asleep, make a conscious effort to revive yourself, or take a break if necessary.
- Don't miss class, and come prepared. Listening to lectures and participating in discussions is much more effective than reading someone else's notes or watching a video later. Active participation will help you retain what you are learning. Also, be sure to complete any assigned reading *before* the class in which it will be discussed. This

is crucial, since class lectures and discussions are designed to reinforce key ideas from the reading.

- Take advantage of resources offered by your professor, whether it be email, office hours, review sessions, online chats, or other opportunities to talk to and get to know your professor. Most professors will go out of their way to help you learn in any way that they can.
- Start your homework early. The more time you allow yourself, the easier it is to get help if you need it. If a concept gives you trouble, do additional reading or studying beyond what has been assigned. And if you still have trouble, ask for help: You surely can find friends, peers, or teachers who will be glad to help you learn.
- Working together with friends can be valuable in helping you understand difficult concepts, but be sure that you learn *with* your friends and do not become dependent on them.
- Don't try to multitask. Research shows that human beings simply are not good at multitasking: When we attempt it, we do more poorly at all of the individual tasks. And in case you think you are an exception, research has also found that those people who believe they are best at multitasking are often the worst! So when it is time to study, turn off your electronic devices, find a quiet spot, and concentrate on your work. (If you *must* use a device to study, as with an e-book or online homework, turn off email, text, and other alerts so that they will not interrupt your concentration; some apps will do this for you.)

Preparing for Exams

- Study the Review Questions, and rework problems and other assignments; try additional questions to be sure you understand the concepts. Study your performance on assignments, quizzes, or exams from earlier in the term.
- Work through the relevant chapter quizzes and other study resources available at the MasteringAstronomy® site.
- Study your notes from lectures and discussions. Pay attention to what your instructor expects you to know for an exam.
- Reread the relevant sections in the textbook, paying special attention to notes you have made on the pages.
- Study individually *before* joining a study group with friends. Study groups are effective only if every individual comes prepared to contribute.
- Don't stay up too late before an exam. Don't eat a big meal within an hour of the exam (thinking is more difficult when blood is being diverted to the digestive system).
- Try to relax before and during the exam. If you have studied effectively, you are capable of doing well. Staying relaxed will help you think clearly.

Presenting Homework and Writing Assignments

All work that you turn in should be of *collegiate quality:* neat and easy to read, well organized, and demonstrating mastery of the subject matter. Future employers and teachers will expect this quality of work. Moreover, although submitting homework of collegiate quality requires "extra" effort, it serves two important purposes directly related to learning:

1. The effort you expend in clearly explaining your work solidifies your learning. In particular, research has shown that writing (or typing) and speaking trigger different areas of your brain. Writing something down—even when you think you already understand it—reinforces your learning by involving other areas of your brain.
2. If you make your work clear and self-contained (that is, make it a document that you can read without referring to the questions in the text), you will have a much more useful study guide when you review for a quiz or exam.

The following guidelines will help ensure that your assignments meet the standards of collegiate quality:

- Always use proper grammar, proper sentence and paragraph structure, and proper spelling. Do not use texting shorthand.
- Make all answers and other writing fully self-contained. A good test is to imagine that a friend will be reading your work and to ask yourself whether the friend will understand exactly what you are trying to say. It is also helpful to read your work out loud to yourself, making sure that it sounds clear and coherent.
- In problems that require calculation:
  1. Be sure to *show your work* clearly so that both you and your instructor can follow the process you used to obtain an answer. Also, use standard mathematical symbols, rather than "calculator-ese." For example, show multiplication with the $\times$ symbol (not with an asterisk), and write 10^5, not 10^5 or 10E5.
  2. *Check that word problems have word answers.* That is, after you have completed any necessary calculations, make sure that any problem stated in words is answered with one or more *complete sentences* that describe the point of the problem and the meaning of your solution.
  3. Express your word answers in a way that would be *meaningful* to most people. For example, most people would find it more meaningful if you expressed a result of 720 hours as 1 month. Similarly, if a precise calculation yields an answer of 9,745,600 years, it may be more meaningfully expressed in words as "nearly 10 million years."

- Include illustrations whenever they help explain your answer, and make sure your illustrations are neat and clear. For example, if you graph by hand, use a ruler to make straight lines. If you use software to make illustrations, be careful not to make them overly cluttered with unnecessary features.
- If you study with friends, be sure that you turn in your own work stated in your own words—you should avoid anything that might give even the *appearance* of possible academic dishonesty.

Foreword

The Meaning of *The Cosmic Perspective*

© Neil deGrasse Tyson

by Neil deGrasse Tyson

Astrophysicist Neil deGrasse Tyson is the Frederick P. Rose Director of New York City's Hayden Planetarium at the American Museum of Natural History. He has written numerous books and articles, has hosted the PBS series NOVA scienceNOW *and the globally popular* Cosmos: A Spacetime Odyssey, *and was named one of the "Time 100"—*Time *magazine's list of the 100 most influential people in the world. He contributed this essay about the meaning of "The Cosmic Perspective," abridged from his 100th essay written for* Natural History *magazine.*

Of all the sciences cultivated by mankind, Astronomy is acknowledged to be, and undoubtedly is, the most sublime, the most interesting, and the most useful. For, by knowledge derived from this science, not only the bulk of the Earth is discovered ... ; but our very faculties are enlarged with the grandeur of the ideas it conveys, our minds exalted above [their] low contracted prejudices.

James Ferguson, *Astronomy Explained Upon Sir Isaac Newton's Principles, and Made Easy To Those Who Have Not Studied Mathematics* (1757)

LONG BEFORE ANYONE knew that the universe had a beginning, before we knew that the nearest large galaxy lies two and a half million light-years from Earth, before we knew how stars work or whether atoms exist, James Ferguson's enthusiastic introduction to his favorite science rang true.

But who gets to think that way? Who gets to celebrate this cosmic view of life? Not the migrant farm worker. Not the sweatshop worker. Certainly not the homeless person rummaging through the trash for food. You need the luxury of time not spent on mere survival. You need to live in a nation whose government values the search to understand humanity's place in the universe. You need a society in which intellectual pursuit can take you to the frontiers of discovery, and in which news of your discoveries can be routinely disseminated.

When I pause and reflect on our expanding universe, with its galaxies hurtling away from one another, embedded with the ever-stretching, four-dimensional fabric of space and time, sometimes I forget that uncounted people walk this Earth without food or shelter, and that children are disproportionately represented among them.

When I pore over the data that establish the mysterious presence of dark matter and dark energy throughout the universe, sometimes I forget that every day—every twenty-four-hour rotation of Earth—people are killing and being killed. In the name of someone's ideology.

When I track the orbits of asteroids, comets, and planets, each one a pirouetting dancer in a cosmic ballet choreographed by the forces of gravity, sometimes I forget that too many people act in wanton disregard for the delicate interplay of Earth's atmosphere, oceans, and land, with consequences that our children and our children's children will witness and pay for with their health and well-being.

And sometimes I forget that powerful people rarely do all they can to help those who cannot help themselves.

I occasionally forget those things because, however big the world is—in our hearts, our minds, and our outsize atlases—the universe is even bigger. A depressing thought to some, but a liberating thought to me.

Consider an adult who tends to the traumas of a child: a broken toy, a scraped knee, a schoolyard bully. Adults know that kids have no clue what constitutes a genuine problem, because inexperience greatly limits their childhood perspective.

As grown-ups, dare we admit to ourselves that we, too, have a collective immaturity of view? Dare we admit that our thoughts and behaviors spring from a belief that the world revolves around us? Part the curtains of society's racial, ethnic, religious, national, and cultural conflicts, and you find the human ego turning the knobs and pulling the levers.

Now imagine a world in which everyone, but especially people with power and influence, holds an expanded view of our place in the cosmos. With that perspective, our problems would shrink—or never arise at all—and we could celebrate our earthly differences while shunning the behavior of our predecessors who slaughtered each other because of them.

✳ ✳ ✳

Back in February 2000, the newly rebuilt Hayden Planetarium featured a space show called "Passport to the Universe," which took visitors on a virtual zoom from New York City to the edge of the cosmos. En route the audience saw Earth, then the solar system, then the 100 billion stars of the Milky Way galaxy shrink to barely visible dots on the planetarium dome.

I soon received a letter from an Ivy League professor of psychology who wanted to administer a questionnaire to visitors, assessing the depth of their depression after viewing the show. Our show, he wrote, elicited the most dramatic feelings of smallness he had ever experienced.

How could that be? Every time I see the show, I feel alive and spirited and connected. I also feel large, knowing that the goings-on within the three-pound human brain are what enabled us to figure out our place in the universe.

Allow me to suggest that it's the professor, not I, who has misread nature. His ego was too big to begin with, inflated by delusions of significance and fed by cultural assumptions that human beings are more important than everything else in the universe.

In all fairness to the fellow, powerful forces in society leave most of us susceptible. As was I . . . until the day I learned in biology class that more bacteria live and work in one centimeter of my colon than the number of people who have ever existed in the world. That kind of information makes you think twice about who—or what—is actually in charge.

From that day on, I began to think of people not as the masters of space and time but as participants in a great cosmic chain of being, with a direct genetic link across species both living and extinct, extending back nearly 4 billion years to the earliest single-celled organisms on Earth.

* * *

Need more ego softeners? Simple comparisons of quantity, size, and scale do the job well.

Take water. It's simple, common, and vital. There are more molecules of water in an eight-ounce cup of the stuff than there are cups of water in all the world's oceans. Every cup that passes through a single person and eventually rejoins the world's water supply holds enough molecules to mix 1,500 of them into every other cup of water in the world. No way around it: some of the water you just drank passed through the kidneys of Socrates, Genghis Khan, and Joan of Arc.

How about air? Also vital. A single breathful draws in more air molecules than there are breathfuls of air in Earth's entire atmosphere. That means some of the air you just breathed passed through the lungs of Napoleon, Beethoven, Lincoln, and Billy the Kid.

Time to get cosmic. There are more stars in the universe than grains of sand on any beach, more stars than seconds have passed since Earth formed, more stars than words and sounds ever uttered by all the humans who ever lived.

Want a sweeping view of the past? Our unfolding cosmic perspective takes you there. Light takes time to reach Earth's observatories from the depths of space, and so you see objects and phenomena not as they are but as they once were. That means the universe acts like a giant time machine: The farther away you look, the further back in time you see—back almost to the beginning of time itself. Within that horizon of reckoning, cosmic evolution unfolds continuously, in full view.

Want to know what we're made of? Again, the cosmic perspective offers a bigger answer than you might expect. The chemical elements of the universe are forged in the fires of high-mass stars that end their lives in stupendous explosions, enriching their host galaxies with the chemical arsenal of life as we know it. We are not simply in the universe. The universe is in us. Yes, we are stardust.

* * *

Again and again across the centuries, cosmic discoveries have demoted our self-image. Earth was once assumed to be astronomically unique, until astronomers learned that Earth is just another planet orbiting the Sun. Then we presumed the Sun was unique, until we learned that the countless stars of the night sky are suns themselves. Then we presumed our galaxy, the Milky Way, was the entire known universe, until we established that the countless fuzzy things in the sky are other galaxies, dotting the landscape of our known universe.

The cosmic perspective flows from fundamental knowledge. But it's more than just what you know. It's also about having the wisdom and insight to apply that knowledge to assessing our place in the universe. And its attributes are clear:

- The cosmic perspective comes from the frontiers of science, yet is not solely the provenance of the scientist. It belongs to everyone.
- The cosmic perspective is humble.
- The cosmic perspective is spiritual—even redemptive—but is not religious.
- The cosmic perspective enables us to grasp, in the same thought, the large and the small.
- The cosmic perspective opens our minds to extraordinary ideas but does not leave them so open that our brains spill out, making us susceptible to believing anything we're told.
- The cosmic perspective opens our eyes to the universe, not as a benevolent cradle designed to nurture life but as a cold, lonely, hazardous place.
- The cosmic perspective shows Earth to be a mote, but a precious mote and, for the moment, the only home we have.
- The cosmic perspective finds beauty in the images of planets, moons, stars, and nebulae but also celebrates the laws of physics that shape them.
- The cosmic perspective enables us to see beyond our circumstances, allowing us to transcend the primal search for food, shelter, and sex.
- The cosmic perspective reminds us that in space, where there is no air, a flag will not wave—an indication that perhaps flag waving and space exploration do not mix.
- The cosmic perspective not only embraces our genetic kinship with all life on Earth but also values our chemical kinship with any yet-to-be discovered life in the universe, as well as our atomic kinship with the universe itself.

* * *

At least once a week, if not once a day, we might each ponder what cosmic truths lie undiscovered before us, perhaps awaiting the arrival of a clever thinker, an ingenious experiment, or an innovative space mission to reveal them. We might further ponder how those discoveries may one day transform life on Earth.

Absent such curiosity, we are no different from the provincial farmer who expresses no need to venture beyond the county line, because his forty acres meet all his needs. Yet if all our predecessors had felt that way, the farmer would instead be a cave dweller, chasing down his dinner with a stick and a rock.

During our brief stay on planet Earth, we owe ourselves and our descendants the opportunity to explore—in part because it's fun to do. But there's a far nobler reason. The day our knowledge of the cosmos ceases to expand, we risk regressing to the childish view that the universe figuratively and literally revolves around us. In that bleak world, arms-bearing, resource-hungry people and nations would be prone to act on their "low contracted prejudices." And that would be the last gasp of human enlightenment—until the rise of a visionary new culture that could once again embrace the cosmic perspective.

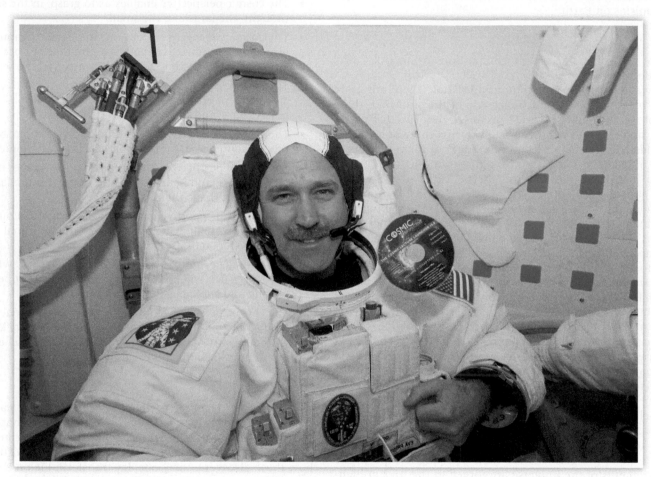

▲ Astronauts get a unique opportunity to experience a cosmic perspective. Here, astronaut John Grunsfeld has a CD of *The Cosmic Perspective* floating in front of him while orbiting Earth during the Space Shuttle's final servicing mission to the Hubble Space Telescope (May 2009).

1 A Modern View of the Universe

This Hubble Space Telescope photo shows thousands of galaxies in a region of the sky so small you could cover it with a grain of sand held at arm's length.

1

Far from city lights on a clear night, you can gaze upward at a sky filled with stars. Lie back and watch for a few hours, and you will observe the stars marching steadily across the sky. Confronted by the seemingly infinite heavens, you might wonder how Earth and the universe came to be. If you do, you will be sharing an experience common to humans around the world and in thousands of generations past.

Modern science offers answers to many of our fundamental questions about the universe and our place within it. We now know the basic content and scale of the universe. We know the ages of Earth and the universe. And, although much remains to be discovered, we are rapidly learning how the simple ingredients of the early universe developed into the incredible diversity of life on Earth—and, perhaps, of life on other worlds as well.

In this first chapter, we will survey the scale, history, and motion of the universe. This "big picture" perspective on our universe will provide a base on which you'll be able to build a deeper understanding in the rest of the book.

1.1 The Scale of the Universe

For most of human history, our ancestors imagined Earth to be stationary at the center of a relatively small universe. This idea made sense at a time when understanding was built upon everyday experience. After all, we cannot feel the constant motion of Earth as it rotates on its axis and orbits the Sun, and if you observe the sky you'll see that the Sun, Moon, planets, and stars all appear to revolve around us each day. Nevertheless, we now know that Earth is a planet orbiting a rather average star in a rather typical galaxy in a vast universe.

The historical path to this knowledge was long and complex. In later chapters, we'll see that the ancient belief in an Earth-centered (or *geocentric*) universe changed only when people were confronted by strong evidence to the contrary, and we'll explore how the method of learning that we call *science* enabled us to acquire this evidence. First, however, it's useful to have a general picture of the universe as we know it today.

◆ What is our place in the universe?

Take a look at the remarkable photo that opens this chapter (on page 1). This photo, taken by the Hubble Space Telescope, shows a piece of the sky so small that you could block your view of it with a grain of sand held at arm's length. Yet it covers an almost unimaginable expanse of both space and time: Nearly every object within it is a galaxy containing billions of stars, and some of the smaller smudges are galaxies so far away that their light has taken billions of years to reach us. Let's begin our study of astronomy by exploring what a photo like this one tells us about our own place in the universe.

Our Cosmic Address The galaxies that we see in the Hubble Space Telescope photo make up just one of several key levels of structure in our universe, all illustrated as our "cosmic address" in Figure 1.1.

Our Cosmic Address

Universe

approx. size: 10^{21} km ≈ 100 million ly

Local Supercluster

approx. size: 3×10^{19} km ≈ 3 million ly

Local Group

approx. size:
10^{18} km ≈ 100,000 ly

Milky Way Galaxy

Solar System
(not to scale)

Earth

approx. size: 10^{10} km ≈ 60 AU

approx. size: 10^4 km

Earth is a planet in our **solar system,** which consists of the Sun, the planets and their moons, and countless smaller objects that include rocky *asteroids* and icy *comets.* Keep in mind that our Sun is a *star*, just like the stars we see in our night sky.

Our solar system belongs to the huge, disk-shaped collection of stars called the **Milky Way Galaxy.** A **galaxy** is a great island of stars in space, all held together by gravity and orbiting a common center. The Milky Way is a relatively large galaxy, containing more than 100 billion stars, and many of these stars are orbited by planets. Our solar system is located a little over halfway from the galactic center to the edge of the galactic disk.

Billions of other galaxies are scattered throughout space. Some galaxies are fairly isolated, but most are found in groups. Our Milky Way, for example, is one of the two largest among more than 70 galaxies (most relatively small) in the **Local Group.** Groups of galaxies with many more large members are often called **galaxy clusters.**

We live on one planet orbiting one star among more than 100 billion stars in the Milky Way Galaxy, which in turn is one of billions of galaxies in the universe.

On a very large scale, galaxies and galaxy clusters appear to be arranged in giant chains and sheets with huge voids between them; the background of Figure 1.1 represents this large-scale structure. The regions in which galaxies and galaxy clusters are most tightly packed are called **superclusters,** which are essentially clusters of galaxy clusters. Our Local Group is located in the outskirts of the Local Supercluster (which was recently named *Laniakea*, Hawaiian for "immense heaven").

Together, all these structures make up our **universe.** In other words, the universe is the sum total of all matter and energy, encompassing the superclusters and voids and everything within them.

think about it Some people think that our tiny physical size in the vast universe makes us insignificant. Others think that our ability to learn about the wonders of the universe gives us significance despite our small size. What do *you* think?

Astronomical Distance Measurements The labels in Figure 1.1 give approximate sizes for the various structures in kilometers (recall that 1 kilometer $\approx$ 0.6 mile), but many distances in astronomy are so large that kilometers are not the most convenient unit. Instead, we often use two other units:

- One **astronomical unit (AU)** is Earth's average distance from the Sun, which is about 150 million kilometers (93 million miles). We commonly describe distances within our solar system in AU.

- One **light-year (ly)** is the distance that light can travel in 1 year, which is about 10 trillion kilometers (6 trillion miles). We generally use light-years to describe the distances of stars and galaxies.

Be sure to note that a light-year is a unit of *distance*, not of time. Light travels at the speed of light, which is about 300,000 kilometers per second. We therefore say that one *light-second* is about 300,000 kilometers, because that is the distance light travels in 1 second. Similarly, one light-minute is the distance that light travels in 1 minute, one light-hour is the distance that light travels in 1 hour, and so on. Cosmic Calculations 1.1 shows that light travels about 10 trillion kilometers in 1 year, so that distance represents a light-year.

Looking Back in Time The speed of light is extremely fast by earthly standards. It is so fast that if you could make light go in circles, it could circle Earth nearly eight times in a single second. Nevertheless, even light

cosmic calculations 1.1

How Far Is a Light-Year?

We can calculate the distance represented by a light-year by recalling that

$$\text{distance} = \text{speed} \times \text{time}$$

For example, at a speed of 50 km/hr, in 2 hours you travel 50 km/hr $\times$ 2 hr = 100 km. To find the distance represented by 1 light-year, we multiply the speed of light by 1 year. Because we are given the speed of light in kilometers per *second* but the time as 1 *year*, we must carry out the multiplication while converting 1 year into seconds. (See Appendix C for a review of unit conversions.) The result is

$$1 \text{ light-year} = (\text{speed of light}) \times (1 \text{ yr})$$

$$= \left(300{,}00\,\frac{\text{km}}{\text{s}}\right) \times (1\,\text{yr}) \times \frac{365\,\text{days}}{1\,\text{yr}}$$

$$\times \frac{24\,\text{hr}}{1\,\text{day}} \times \frac{60\,\text{min}}{1\,\text{hr}} \times \frac{60\,\text{s}}{1\,\text{min}}$$

$$= 9{,}460{,}000{,}000{,}000\,\text{km}$$

$$= 9.46\,\text{trillion km}$$

That is, 1 light-year is about 9.46 trillion kilometers, which we can approximate as 10 trillion kilometers. This can be easier to write with powers of 10 (see Appendix C.1 for a review); recall that 1 trillion is a 1 followed by 12 zeros, or 10^{12}, so 10 trillion can be written as 10^{13}.

takes time to travel the vast distances in space. Light takes a little more than 1 second to reach Earth from the Moon, and about 8 minutes to reach Earth from the Sun. Stars are so far away that their light takes years to reach us, which is why we measure their distances in light-years.

Because light takes time to travel through space, we are led to a remarkable fact: **The farther away we look in distance, the further back we look in time.** For example, the brightest star in the night sky, Sirius, is about 8 light-years away, which means its light takes about 8 years to reach us. When we look at Sirius, we are seeing it not as it is today but as it was about 8 years ago.

Light takes time to travel the vast distances in space. When we look deep into space, we also look far into the past.

The effect is more dramatic at greater distances. The Andromeda Galaxy (Figure 1.2) lies about 2.5 million light-years from Earth, which means we see it as it looked about 2.5 million years ago. We see more distant galaxies as they were even further in the past. Some of the galaxies in the Hubble Space Telescope photo that opens the chapter are more than 12 billion light-years away, meaning we see them as they were more than 12 billion years ago.

It's also amazing to realize that any "snapshot" of a distant galaxy is a picture of both space and time. For example, because the Andromeda Galaxy is about 100,000 light-years in diameter, the light we see from the far side of the galaxy must have left on its journey to us 100,000 years

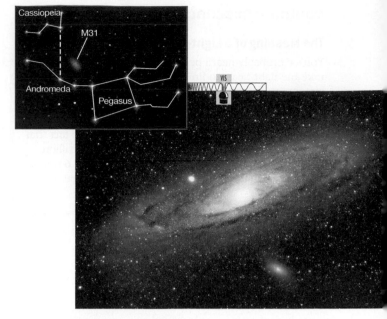

▲ **FIGURE 1.2**
The Andromeda Galaxy (M31). When we look at this galaxy, we see light that has been traveling through space for 2.5 million years. The inset shows the galaxy's location in the constellation Andromeda.

Basic Astronomical Definitions

Basic Astronomical Objects

star A large, glowing ball of gas that generates heat and light through nuclear fusion in its core. Our Sun is a star.

planet A moderately large object that orbits a star and shines primarily by reflecting light from its star. According to the current definition, an object can be considered a planet only if it (1) orbits a star, (2) is large enough for its own gravity to make it round, and (3) has cleared most other objects from its orbital path. An object that meets the first two criteria but has not cleared its orbital path, like Pluto, is designated a **dwarf planet.**

moon (or **satellite**) An object that orbits a planet. The term *satellite* is also used more generally to refer to any object orbiting another object.

asteroid A relatively small and rocky object that orbits a star.

comet A relatively small and ice-rich object that orbits a star.

small solar system body An asteroid, comet, or other object that orbits a star but is too small to qualify as a planet or dwarf planet.

Collections of Astronomical Objects

solar system The Sun and all the material that orbits it, including planets, dwarf planets, and small solar system bodies. Although the term *solar system* technically refers only to our own star system (*solar* means "of the Sun"), it is often applied to other star systems as well.

star system A star (sometimes more than one star) and any planets and other materials that orbit it.

galaxy A great island of stars in space, all held together by gravity and orbiting a common center, with a total mass equivalent to that of millions, billions, or even trillions of stars.

cluster (or **group**) **of galaxies** A collection of galaxies bound together by gravity. Small collections of galaxies are generally called *groups,* while larger collections are called *clusters.*

supercluster A gigantic region of space in which many groups and clusters of galaxies are packed more closely together than elsewhere in the universe.

universe (or **cosmos**) The sum total of all matter and energy—that is, all galaxies and everything between them.

observable universe The portion of the entire universe that can be seen from Earth, at least in principle. The observable universe is probably only a tiny portion of the entire universe.

Astronomical Distance Units

astronomical unit (AU) The average distance between Earth and the Sun, which is about 150 million kilometers. More technically, 1 AU is the length of the semimajor axis of Earth's orbit.

light-year The distance that light can travel in 1 year, which is about 10 trillion kilometers (more precisely, 9.46 trillion km).

Terms Relating to Motion

rotation The spinning of an object around its axis. For example, Earth rotates once each day around its axis, which is an imaginary line connecting the North and South Poles.

orbit (revolution) The orbital motion of one object around another due to gravity. For example, Earth orbits the Sun once each year.

expansion (of the universe) The increase in the average distance between galaxies as time progresses.

The Meaning of a Light-Year

You've probably heard people say things like "It will take me light-years to finish this homework!" But a statement like this one doesn't make sense, because a light-year is a unit of *distance*, not time. If you are unsure whether the term *light-year* is being used correctly, try testing the statement by using the fact that 1 light-year is about 10 trillion kilometers, or 6 trillion miles. The statement then reads "It will take me 6 trillion miles to finish this homework," which clearly does not make sense.

before the light from the near side. Figure 1.2 therefore shows different parts of the galaxy spread over a time period of 100,000 years. When we study the universe, it is impossible to separate space and time.

see it for yourself The central region of the Andromeda Galaxy is faintly visible to the naked eye and easy to see with binoculars. Use a star chart to find it in the night sky and remember that you are seeing light that spent 2.5 million years in space before reaching your eyes. If students on a planet in the Andromeda Galaxy were looking at the Milky Way, what would they see? Could they know that we exist here on Earth?

The Observable Universe As we'll discuss in Section 1.2, the measured the age of the universe is about 14 billion years. This fact, combined with the fact that looking deep into space means looking far back in time, places a limit on the portion of the universe that we can see, even in principle.

Figure 1.3 shows the idea. If we look at a galaxy that is 7 billion light-years away, we see it as it looked 7 billion years ago*—which means we see it as it was when the universe was half its current age. If

> Because the universe is about 14 billion years old, we cannot observe light coming from anything more than 14 billion light-years away.

we look at a galaxy that is 12 billion light-years away (like the most distant ones in the Hubble Space Telescope photo), we see it as it was 12 billion years ago, when the universe was only 2 billion years old.

If we tried to look beyond 14 billion light-years, we'd be looking to a time more than 14 billion years ago—which is before the universe existed and therefore means that there is nothing to see. This distance of 14 billion light-years therefore marks the boundary (or *horizon*) of our **observable universe**—the portion of the entire universe that we can potentially observe. Note that this fact does not put any limit on the size of the *entire* universe, which we assume to be far larger than our observable universe. We simply cannot see or study anything beyond the bounds of our observable universe, because the light from such distances has not yet had time to reach us in a 14-billion-year-old universe.

▼ **FIGURE 1.3**
The farther away we look in space, the further back we look in time. The age of the universe therefore puts a limit on the size of the observable universe—the portion of the entire universe that we could observe in principle.

*As we'll see in Chapter 16, distances to faraway galaxies must be defined carefully in an expanding universe; in this book, we use distances based on the light-travel time from a distant object (called the *lookback time*).

Far: We see a galaxy 7 billion light-years away as it was 7 billion years ago—when the universe was about half its current age of 14 billion years.

Farther: We see a galaxy 12 billion light-years away as it was 12 billion years ago—when the universe was only about 2 billion years old.

The limit of our observable universe: Light from nearly 14 billion light-years away shows the universe as it looked shortly after the Big Bang, before galaxies existed.

7 billion light-years

12 billion light-years

14 billion light-years

Beyond the observable universe: We cannot see anything farther than 14 billion light-years away, because its light has not had enough time to reach us.

◆ How big is the universe?

Figure 1.1 put numbers on the sizes of different structures in the universe, but these numbers have little meaning for most people—after all, they are literally astronomical. To help you develop a greater appreciation of our modern view of the universe, we'll discuss a few ways of putting these numbers into perspective.

The Scale of the Solar System   One of the best ways to develop perspective on cosmic sizes and distances is to imagine our solar system shrunk down to a scale that would allow you to walk through it. The Voyage scale model solar system (Figure 1.4) makes such a walk possible by showing the Sun, the planets, and the distances between them at *one ten-billionth* of their actual sizes and distances.

Figure 1.5a shows the Sun and planets at their correct sizes (but not distances) on the Voyage scale. The model Sun is about the size of a large

> On a scale in which the Sun is the size of a grapefruit, Earth is the size of a ballpoint from a pen, orbiting the Sun at a distance of 15 meters.

grapefruit, Jupiter is about the size of a marble, and Earth is about the size of the ballpoint in a pen. You can immediately see some key facts about our solar system. For example, the Sun is far larger than any of the planets; in mass, the Sun outweighs all the planets combined by a factor of nearly 1000. The planets also vary considerably in size: The storm on Jupiter known as the Great Red Spot (visible near Jupiter's lower left in the painting) could swallow up the entire Earth.

The scale of the solar system is even more remarkable when you combine the sizes shown in Figure 1.5a with the distances illustrated by the map of the Voyage model in Figure 1.5b. For example, the ballpoint-size Earth is located about 15 meters (16.5 yards) from the grapefruit-size Sun, which means you can picture Earth's orbit as a circle of radius 15 meters around a grapefruit.

Perhaps the most striking feature of our solar system when we view it to scale is its emptiness. The Voyage model shows the planets along a straight path, so we'd need to draw each planet's orbit around the model Sun to show the full extent of our planetary system. Fitting all these orbits would require an area measuring more than a kilometer on a side—an area equivalent to more than 300 football fields arranged in a grid. Spread over this large area, only the grapefruit-size Sun, the planets,

▲ FIGURE 1.4
This photo shows the pedestals housing the Sun (the gold sphere on the nearest pedestal) and the inner planets in the Voyage scale model solar system (Washington, D.C.). The model planets are encased in the sidewalk-facing disks visible at about eye level on the planet pedestals. To the left is the National Air and Space Museum.

---

special topic   How Many Planets Are in Our Solar System?

Until recently, children were taught that our solar system had nine planets. However, in 2006 astronomers voted to demote Pluto to a *dwarf planet*, leaving our solar system with only eight official planets. Why the change?

When Pluto was discovered in 1930, it was assumed to be similar to other planets. But as we'll discuss in Chapter 9, we now know that Pluto is much smaller than any of the first eight planets and that it shares the outer solar system with thousands of other icy objects. Still, as long as Pluto was the largest known of these objects, most astronomers were content to leave the planetary status quo. Change was forced by the 2005 discovery of an object called Eris. Because Eris is slightly larger in mass than Pluto, astronomers could no longer avoid the question of what objects should count as planets.

Official decisions on astronomical names and definitions rest with the International Astronomical Union (IAU), an organization made up of professional astronomers from around the world. In 2006, an IAU vote defined "planet" in a way that left out Pluto and Eris (see Basic Astronomical Definitions on page 5) but added the "dwarf planet" category to accommodate them. Three smaller solar system objects are also now considered dwarf planets (the asteroid Ceres and the Kuiper belt objects Makemake and Haumea). More than a half dozen other objects are still being studied to determine if they meet the dwarf planet definition.

Some astronomers object to these definitions, which may yet be revisited. Pluto and other objects will remain the same either way. Indeed, much as there are no well-defined distinctions between the flowing waterways that we call creeks, streams, or rivers, this case offers a good example of the difference between the fuzzy boundaries of nature and the human preference for categories.

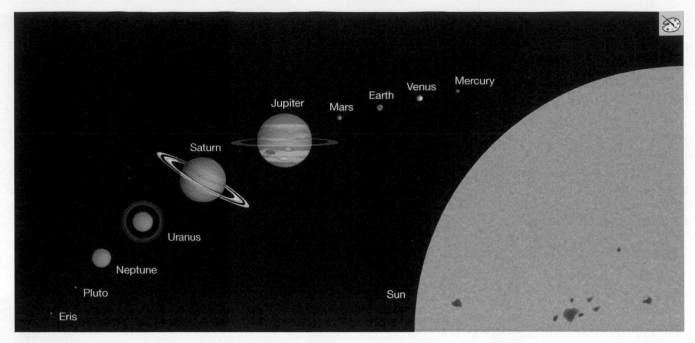

a The scaled sizes (but not distances) of the Sun, the planets, and the two largest known dwarf planets.

b Locations of the major objects in the Voyage model (Washington, D.C.); the distance from the Sun to Pluto is about 600 meters (1/3 mile). Planets are lined up in the model, but in reality each planet orbits the Sun independently and a perfect alignment never occurs.

▲ **FIGURE 1.5**
The Voyage scale model represents the solar system at one *ten-billionth* of its actual size. Pluto is included in the Voyage model for context.

common misconceptions

Confusing Very Different Things

Most people are familiar with the terms *solar system* and *galaxy*, but few realize how incredibly different they are. Our solar system is a single star system, while our galaxy is a collection of more than 100 billion star systems—so many that it would take thousands of years just to count them. Moreover, if you look at the sizes in Figure 1.1, you'll see that our galaxy is about 100 million times larger in diameter than our solar system. So be careful; numerically speaking, mixing up *solar system* and *galaxy* is a gigantic mistake!

and a few moons would be big enough to see. The rest of it would look virtually empty (that's why we call it *space!*).

Seeing our solar system to scale also helps put space exploration into perspective. The Moon, the only other world on which humans have ever stepped (Figure 1.6), lies only about 4 centimeters (1½ inches) from Earth in the Voyage model. On this scale, the palm of your hand can cover the entire region of the universe in which humans have so far traveled. The trip to Mars is more than 150 times as far as the trip to the Moon, even when Mars is on the same side of its orbit as Earth. And while you can walk from Earth to Pluto in a few minutes on the Voyage scale, the *New Horizons* spacecraft, which flew past Pluto in 2015, took more than 9 years to make the real journey, despite traveling at a speed nearly 100 times as fast as that of a commercial jet.

Distances to the Stars　If you visit the Voyage model in Washington, D.C., you can walk the roughly 600-meter distance from the Sun to Pluto in just a few minutes. How much farther would you have to walk to reach the next star on this scale?

Amazingly, you would need to walk to California. If this answer seems hard to believe, you can check it for yourself. A light-year is about 10 trillion kilometers, which becomes 1000 kilometers on the 1-to-10-billion scale (because 10 trillion ÷ 10 billion = 1000). The nearest star

On the same scale on which Pluto is a few minutes' walk from Earth, you'd have to walk across the United States to reach the nearest stars.

system to our own, a three-star system called Alpha Centauri (Figure 1.7), is about 4.4 light-years away. That distance is about 4400 kilometers (2700 miles) on the 1-to-10-billion scale, or roughly equivalent to the distance across the United States.

The tremendous distances to the stars give us some perspective on the technological challenge of astronomy. For example, because the largest star of the Alpha Centauri system is roughly the same size and brightness as our Sun, viewing it in the night sky is somewhat like being in Washington, D.C., and seeing a very bright grapefruit in San Francisco (neglecting the problems introduced by the curvature of Earth). It may seem remarkable that we can see the star at all, but the blackness of the night sky allows the naked eye to see it as a faint dot of light. It looks much brighter through powerful telescopes, but we still cannot see features of the star's surface.

Now, consider the difficulty of detecting *planets* orbiting nearby stars, which is equivalent to looking from Washington, D.C., and trying to find ballpoints or marbles orbiting grapefruits in California or beyond. When you consider this challenge, it is all the more remarkable to realize that we now have technology capable of finding such planets [Section 10.1].

The vast distances to the stars also offer a sobering lesson about interstellar travel. Although science fiction shows like *Star Trek* and *Star Wars* make such travel look easy, the reality is far different. Consider the *Voyager 2* spacecraft. Launched in 1977, *Voyager 2* flew by Jupiter in 1979, Saturn in 1981, Uranus in 1986, and Neptune in 1989. It is now bound for the stars at a speed of close to 50,000 kilometers per hour—about 100 times as fast as a speeding bullet. But even at this speed, *Voyager 2* would take about 100,000 years to reach Alpha Centauri if it were headed in that direction (which it's not). Convenient interstellar travel remains well beyond our present technology.

The Size of the Milky Way Galaxy The vast separation between our solar system and Alpha Centauri is typical of the separations between star systems in our region of the Milky Way Galaxy. We therefore cannot use the 1-to-10-billion scale for thinking about distances beyond the nearest stars, because more distant stars would not fit on Earth with this scale. To visualize the galaxy, let's reduce our scale by another factor of 1 billion (making it a scale of 1 to 10^{19}).

On this new scale, each light-year becomes 1 millimeter, and the 100,000-light-year diameter of the Milky Way Galaxy becomes 100 meters, or about the length of a football field. Visualize a football field with a scale model of our galaxy centered over midfield. Our entire solar system is a microscopic dot located around the 20-yard line. The 4.4-light-year separation between our solar system and Alpha Centauri becomes just 4.4 millimeters on this scale—smaller than the width of your little finger. If you stood at the position of our solar system in this model, millions of star systems would lie within reach of your arms.

Another way to put the galaxy into perspective is to consider its number of stars—more than 100 billion. Imagine that tonight you are having difficulty falling asleep (perhaps because you are contemplating the scale of the universe). Instead of counting sheep, you decide to count stars. If you are able to count about one star each second, how long would it take you to count 100 billion stars in the Milky Way? Clearly, the answer is 100 billion (10^{11}) seconds, but how long is that?

Amazingly, 100 billion seconds is more than 3000 years. (You can confirm this by dividing 100 billion by the number of seconds in 1 year.) You

▲ **FIGURE 1.6**

This famous photograph from the first Moon landing (*Apollo 11* in July 1969) shows astronaut Buzz Aldrin, with Neil Armstrong reflected in his visor. Armstrong was the first to step onto the Moon's surface, saying, "That's one small step for a man, one giant leap for mankind."

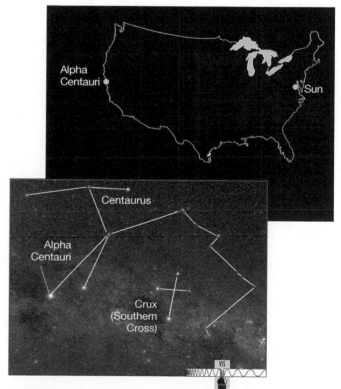

▲ **FIGURE 1.7**

On the same 1-to-10-billion scale on which you can walk from the Sun to Pluto in just a few minutes, you'd need to cross the United States to reach Alpha Centauri, the nearest other star system. The inset shows the location and appearance of Alpha Centauri in the night sky.

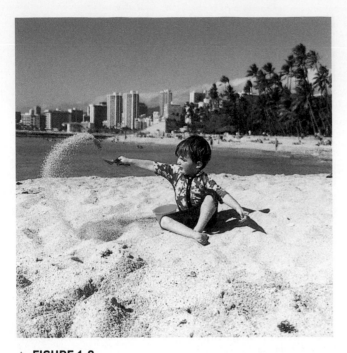

▲ FIGURE 1.8

The number of stars in the observable universe is comparable to the number of grains of dry sand on all the beaches on Earth.

It would take thousands of years just to count out loud the number of stars in the Milky Way Galaxy.

would need thousands of years just to *count* the stars in the Milky Way Galaxy, and this assumes you never take a break—no sleeping, no eating, and absolutely no dying!

The Observable Universe   As incredible as the scale of our galaxy may seem, the Milky Way is only one of roughly 100 billion galaxies in the observable universe. Just as it would take thousands of years to count the stars in the Milky Way, it would take thousands of years to count all the galaxies.

Think for a moment about the total number of stars in all these galaxies. If we assume 100 billion stars per galaxy, the total number of stars in the observable universe is roughly 100 billion × 100 billion, or 10,000,000,000,000,000,000,000 (10^{22}).

How big is this number? Visit a beach. Run your hands through the fine-grained sand. Imagine counting each tiny grain of sand as it slips through your fingers. Then imagine counting every grain of sand on the beach and continuing to count *every* grain of dry sand on *every* beach on Earth. If you could actually complete this task, you would find that the number of grains of sand is comparable to the number of stars in the observable universe (Figure 1.8).

Roughly speaking, there are as many stars in the observable universe as there are grains of sand on all the beaches on Earth.

think about it   Contemplate the incredible numbers of stars in our galaxy and in the universe, and the fact that each star is a potential sun for a system of planets. How does this perspective affect your thoughts about the possibilities for finding life—or intelligent life—beyond Earth? Explain.

1.2 The History of the Universe

Our universe is vast not only in space, but also in time. In this section, we will briefly discuss the history of the universe as we understand it today.

Before we begin, you may wonder how we can claim to know anything about what the universe was like in the distant past. We'll devote much of this textbook to understanding how science enables us to do this, but you already know part of the answer: Because looking farther into space means looking further back in time, we can actually *see* parts of the universe as they were long ago, simply by looking far enough away. In other words, telescopes are somewhat like time machines, enabling us to observe the history of the universe.

◆ How did we come to be?

Figure 1.9 (pp. 12–13) summarizes the history of the universe according to modern science. Let's start at the upper left of the figure, and discuss the key events and what they mean.

The Big Bang, Expansion, and the Age of the Universe   Telescopic observations of distant galaxies show that the entire universe is *expanding,* meaning that average distances between galaxies are increasing with time. This fact implies that galaxies must have been closer together in the past, and if we go back far enough, we must reach the point at which the expansion began. We call this beginning the **Big Bang,** and

The rate at which galaxies are moving apart suggests that the universe was born about 14 billion years ago, in the event we call the Big Bang. scientists use the observed rate of expansion to calculate that it occurred about 14 billion years ago. The three cubes in the upper left portion of Figure 1.9 represent the expansion of a small piece of the universe through time.

The universe as a whole has continued to expand ever since the Big Bang, but on smaller size scales, the force of gravity has drawn matter together. Structures such as galaxies and galaxy clusters occupy regions where gravity has won out against the overall expansion. That is, while the universe as a whole continues to expand, individual galaxies and galaxy clusters (and objects within them such as stars and planets) do *not* expand. This idea is also illustrated by the three cubes in Figure 1.9. Notice that as the cube as a whole grew larger, the matter within it clumped into galaxies and galaxy clusters. Most galaxies, including our own Milky Way, formed within a few billion years after the Big Bang.

Stellar Lives and Galactic Recycling   Within galaxies like the Milky Way, gravity drives the collapse of clouds of gas and dust to form stars and planets. Stars are not living organisms, but they nonetheless go through "life cycles." A star is born when gravity compresses the material in a cloud to the point at which the center becomes dense enough and hot enough to generate energy by **nuclear fusion,** the process in which lightweight atomic nuclei smash together and stick (or fuse) to make heavier nuclei. The star "lives" as long as it can generate energy from fusion and "dies" when it exhausts its usable fuel.

Stars are born in interstellar clouds, produce energy and new elements through nuclear fusion, and release those new elements in interstellar space when they die.

In its final death throes, a star blows much of its content back out into space. The most massive stars die in titanic explosions called *supernovae*. The returned matter mixes with other matter floating between the stars in the galaxy, eventually becoming part of new clouds of gas and dust from which future generations of stars can be born. Galaxies therefore function as cosmic recycling plants, recycling material expelled from dying stars into new generations of stars and planets. This cycle is illustrated in the lower right of Figure 1.9. Our own solar system is a product of many generations of such recycling.

Star Stuff   The recycling of stellar material is connected to our existence in an even deeper way. By studying stars of different ages, we have learned that the early universe contained only the simplest chemical elements: hydrogen and helium (and a trace of lithium). We and Earth are made primarily of other elements, such as carbon, nitrogen, oxygen, and iron. Where did these other elements come from? Evidence shows that they were manufactured by stars, some through the nuclear fusion that makes stars shine, and others through nuclear reactions accompanying the explosions that end stellar lives.

We are "star stuff"—made of material that was manufactured in stars from the simple elements born in the Big Bang.

By the time our solar system formed, about 4½ billion years ago, earlier generations of stars had already converted up to 2% of our galaxy's original hydrogen and helium into heavier elements. Therefore, the cloud that gave birth to our solar system was made of roughly 98% hydrogen and helium and 2% other elements. This 2% may sound small, but it was more than enough to make the small rocky planets of

Throughout this book we will see that human life is intimately connected with the development of the universe as a whole. This illustration presents an overview of our cosmic origins, showing some of the crucial steps that made our existence possible.

(1) Birth of the Universe: The expansion of the universe began with the hot and dense Big Bang. The cubes show how one region of the universe has expanded with time. The universe continues to expand, but on smaller scales gravity has pulled matter together to make galaxies.

(4) Earth and Life: By the time our solar system was born, 4½ billion years ago, about 2% of the original hydrogen and helium had been converted into heavier elements. We are therefore "star stuff," because we and our planet are made from elements manufactured

② **Galaxies as Cosmic Recycling Plants:** The early universe contained only two chemical elements: hydrogen and helium. All other elements were made by stars and recycled from one stellar generation to the next within galaxies like our Milky Way.

Stars are born in clouds of gas and dust; planets may form in surrounding disks.

Massive stars explode when they die, scattering the elements they've produced into space.

Stars shine with energy released by nuclear fusion, which ultimately manufactures all elements heavier than hydrogen and helium.

③ **Life Cycles of Stars:** Many generations of stars have lived and died in the Milky Way.

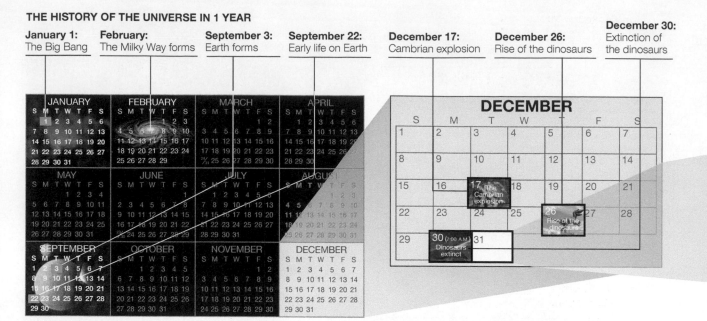

THE HISTORY OF THE UNIVERSE IN 1 YEAR

January 1: The Big Bang

February: The Milky Way forms

September 3: Earth forms

September 22: Early life on Earth

December 17: Cambrian explosion

December 26: Rise of the dinosaurs

December 30: Extinction of the dinosaurs

▲ **FIGURE 1.10**

The cosmic calendar compresses the 14-billion-year history of the universe into 1 year, so that each month represents a little more than 1 billion years. *Adapted from the cosmic calendar created by Carl Sagan.* (For a more detailed version, see the "You Are Here in Time" foldout diagram in the front of the book.)

our solar system, including Earth. On Earth, some of these elements became the raw ingredients of life, which ultimately blossomed into the great diversity of life on Earth today.

In summary, most of the material from which we and our planet are made was created inside stars that lived and died before the birth of our Sun. As astronomer Carl Sagan (1934–1996) said, we are "star stuff."

◆ How do our lifetimes compare to the age of the universe?

We can put the 14-billion-year age of the universe into perspective by imagining this time compressed into a single year, so each month represents a little more than 1 billion years. On this *cosmic calendar*, the Big Bang occurred at the first instant of January 1 and the present is the stroke of midnight on December 31 (Figure 1.10).

On this time scale, the Milky Way Galaxy probably formed in February. Many generations of stars lived and died in the subsequent cosmic months, enriching the galaxy with the "star stuff" from which we and our planet are made.

Our solar system and our planet did not form until early September on this scale, or 4½ billion years ago in real time. By late September, life on Earth was flourishing. However, for most of Earth's history, living organisms remained relatively primitive and microscopic. On the scale of the cosmic calendar, recognizable animals became prominent only in mid-December. Early dinosaurs appeared on the day after Christmas. Then, in a cosmic instant, the dinosaurs disappeared forever—probably because of the impact of an asteroid or a comet [Section 9.5]. In real time, the death of the dinosaurs occurred some 65 million years ago, but on the cosmic calendar it was only yesterday. With the dinosaurs gone, small furry mammals inherited Earth. Some 60 million years later, or around 9 p.m. on December 31 of the cosmic calendar, early hominids (human ancestors) began to walk upright.

> If we imagine the 14-billion-year history of the universe compressed into 1 year, a human lifetime lasts only a fraction of a second.

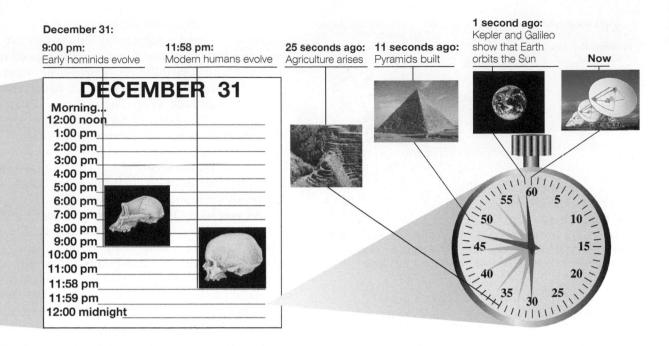

December 31:

9:00 pm: Early hominids evolve

11:58 pm: Modern humans evolve

25 seconds ago: Agriculture arises

11 seconds ago: Pyramids built

1 second ago: Kepler and Galileo show that Earth orbits the Sun

Now

DECEMBER 31

Morning...
12:00 noon
1:00 pm
2:00 pm
3:00 pm
4:00 pm
5:00 pm
6:00 pm
7:00 pm
8:00 pm
9:00 pm
10:00 pm
11:00 pm
11:58 pm
11:59 pm
12:00 midnight

Perhaps the most astonishing fact about the cosmic calendar is that the entire history of human civilization falls into just the last half-minute. The ancient Egyptians built the pyramids only about 11 seconds ago on this scale. About 1 second ago, Kepler and Galileo provided the key evidence that led us to understand that Earth orbits the Sun rather than vice versa. The average college student was born about 0.05 second ago, around 11:59:59.95 p.m. on the cosmic calendar. On the scale of cosmic time, the human species is the youngest of infants, and a human lifetime is a mere blink of an eye.

think about it Study the more detailed cosmic calendar found on the foldout in the front of this book. How does an understanding of the scale of time affect your view of human civilization? Explain.

1.3 Spaceship Earth

Wherever you are as you read this book, you probably have the feeling that you're "just sitting here." Nothing could be further from the truth. As we'll discuss in this section, all of us are moving through space in so many ways that noted inventor and philosopher R. Buckminster Fuller (1895–1983) described us as travelers on *spaceship Earth*.

◆ How is Earth moving through space?

Rotation and Orbit The most basic motions of Earth are its daily **rotation** (spin) and its yearly **orbit** (or *revolution*) around the Sun.

Earth rotates once each day around its axis (Figure 1.11), which is the imaginary line connecting the North Pole to the South Pole. Earth rotates

Earth rotates once each day and orbits the Sun once each year. Its average orbital distance, called an astronomical unit (AU), is about 150 million kilometers.

from west to east—counterclockwise as viewed from above the North Pole—which is why the Sun and stars appear to rise in the east and set in the west each day. Although the physical effects of rotation

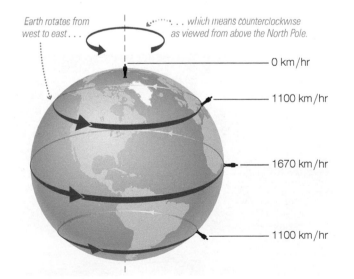

Earth rotates from west to east... ······ ...which means counterclockwise as viewed from above the North Pole.

0 km/hr

1100 km/hr

1670 km/hr

1100 km/hr

▲ **FIGURE 1.11**

As Earth rotates, your speed around Earth's axis depends on your location: The closer you are to the equator, the faster you travel with rotation.

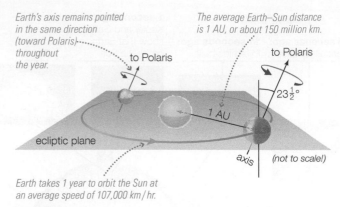

Earth's axis remains pointed in the same direction (toward Polaris) throughout the year.

to Polaris

The average Earth–Sun distance is 1 AU, or about 150 million km.

to Polaris

23½°

1 AU

ecliptic plane

axis   (not to scale!)

Earth takes 1 year to orbit the Sun at an average speed of 107,000 km/hr.

▲ **FIGURE 1.12**
Earth takes a year to complete an orbit of the Sun, but its orbital speed is still surprisingly fast. Notice that Earth both rotates and orbits counterclockwise as viewed from above the North Pole.

are so subtle that our ancestors assumed the heavens revolved around us, the rotation speed is substantial: Unless you live quite far north or south, you are whirling around Earth's axis at a speed of more than 1000 kilometers per hour (600 miles per hour)—faster than most airplanes travel.

At the same time as it is rotating, Earth also orbits the Sun, completing one orbit each year (Figure 1.12). Earth's orbital distance varies slightly over the course of each year, but as we discussed earlier, the average distance is one astronomical unit (AU), which is about 150 million kilometers. Again, even though we don't feel this motion, the speed is impressive: We are racing around the Sun at a speed in excess of 100,000 kilometers per hour (60,000 miles per hour), which is faster than any spacecraft yet launched.

As you study Figure 1.12, notice that Earth's orbital path defines a flat plane that we call the **ecliptic plane.** Earth's axis is tilted by 23½° from a line *perpendicular* to the ecliptic plane. This **axis tilt** happens to be oriented so that the axis points almost directly at a star called *Polaris,* or the *North Star*. Keep in mind that the idea of axis tilt makes sense only in relation to the ecliptic plane. That is, the idea of "tilt" by itself has no meaning in space, where there is no absolute up or down. In space, "up" and "down" mean only "away from the center of Earth (or another planet)" and "toward the center of Earth," respectively.

think about it If there is no up or down in space, why do you think most globes have the North Pole on top? Would it be equally correct to have the South Pole on top or to turn the globe sideways? Explain.

Notice also that Earth orbits the Sun in the same direction that it rotates on its axis: counterclockwise as viewed from above the North Pole. This is not a coincidence but a consequence of the way our planet was born. As we'll discuss in Chapter 6, strong evidence indicates that Earth and the other planets were born in a spinning disk of gas that surrounded our Sun as it formed, and Earth rotates and orbits in the same direction as the disk was spinning.

Motion Within the Milky Way Galaxy Rotation and orbit are only a small part of the travels of spaceship Earth. Our entire solar system is on a great journey within the Milky Way Galaxy. There are two major components to this motion, both shown in Figure 1.13.

First, our solar system is moving relative to nearby stars in our *local solar neighborhood*, the region of the Sun and nearby stars. The small box in Figure 1.13 shows that stars within the local solar neighborhood (like the stars of any other small region of the galaxy) move essentially at random relative to one another. The speeds are quite fast: On average, our Sun is moving relative to nearby stars at a speed of about 70,000 kilometers per hour (40,000 miles per hour), almost three times as fast as the international Space Station orbits Earth. Given these high speeds, you may wonder why we don't see stars racing around the sky. The answer lies in their vast distances from us. You've probably noticed that a distant airplane appears to move through the sky more slowly than one flying close overhead. Stars are so far away that even at speeds of 70,000 kilometers per hour, their motions would be noticeable to the naked eye only if we watched them for thousands of years. That is why the patterns in the constellations seem to remain fixed. Nevertheless, in 10,000 years the constellations will be noticeably different from those we see today. In 500,000 years they will be unrecognizable. If you could watch a time-lapse movie made over millions of years, you *would* see stars racing across the sky.

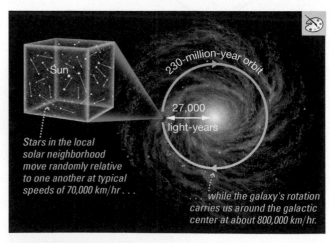

Sun

230-million-year orbit

27,000 light-years

Stars in the local solar neighborhood move randomly relative to one another at typical speeds of 70,000 km/hr . . .

. . . while the galaxy's rotation carries us around the galactic center at about 800,000 km/hr.

▲ **FIGURE 1.13**
This painting illustrates the motion of our solar system within our local solar neighborhood and around the center of the Milky Way Galaxy.

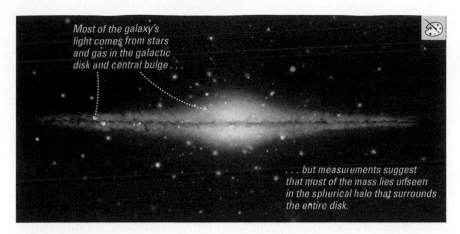

Most of the galaxy's light comes from stars and gas in the galactic disk and central bulge . . .

. . . but measurements suggest that most of the mass lies unseen in the spherical halo that surrounds the entire disk.

◀ **FIGURE 1.14**
This painting shows an edge-on view of the Milky Way Galaxy. Study of galactic rotation shows that although most visible stars lie in the disk and central bulge, most of the mass lies in the halo that surrounds and encompasses the disk. Because this mass emits no light that we have detected, we call it *dark matter*.

think about it Despite the chaos of motion in the local solar neighborhood over millions and billions of years, collisions between star systems are extremely rare. Explain why. (*Hint:* Consider the sizes of star systems, such as the solar system, relative to the distances between them.)

The second motion shown in Figure 1.13 is much more organized. If you look closely at leaves floating in a stream, their motions relative to one another might appear random, just like the motions of stars in the local solar neighborhood. As you widen your view, you see that all the leaves are being carried in the same general direction by the downstream current. In the same way, as we widen our view beyond the local solar neighborhood, the seemingly random motions of its stars give way to a simpler and even faster motion: rotation of the Milky Way Galaxy. Our solar system, located about 27,000 light-years from the galactic center, completes one orbit of the galaxy in about 230 million years. Even if you could watch from outside our galaxy, this motion would be unnoticeable to your naked eye. However, if you calculate the speed of our solar system as we orbit the center of the galaxy, you will find that it is close to 800,000 kilometers (500,000 miles) per hour.

Galactic rotation carries us around the center of the galaxy once every 230 million years.

Careful study of the galaxy's rotation reveals one of the greatest mysteries in science. Stars at different distances from the galactic center orbit at different speeds, and we can learn how mass is distributed in the galaxy by measuring these speeds. Such studies indicate that the stars in the disk of the galaxy represent only the "tip of the iceberg" compared to the mass of the entire galaxy (Figure 1.14). Most of the mass of the galaxy seems to be located outside the visible disk (occupying the galactic *halo* that surrounds and encompasses the disk), but the matter that makes up this mass is completely invisible to our telescopes. We therefore know very little about the nature of this matter, which we refer to as *dark matter* (because of the lack of light from it). Studies of other galaxies indicate that they also are made mostly of dark matter. These and other observations imply that dark matter significantly outweighs the ordinary matter that makes up planets and stars, making it the dominant source of gravity that has led to the formation of galaxies, clusters, and superclusters. We know even less about the mysterious **dark energy** that astronomers first recognized when they discovered that the expansion of the universe is actually getting faster with time, and that scientists have since found to make up the majority of the total energy content of the universe. We'll discuss the mysteries of dark matter and dark energy in Chapter 18.

◆ How do galaxies move within the universe?

The billions of galaxies in the universe also move relative to one another. Within the Local Group (see Figure 1.1), some of the galaxies move toward us, some move away from us, and numerous small galaxies (including the Large and Small Magellanic Clouds) apparently orbit our Milky Way Galaxy. Again, the speeds are enormous by earthly standards. For example, the Milky Way and Andromeda galaxies are moving toward each other at about 300,000 kilometers (180,000 miles) per hour. Despite this high speed, we needn't worry about a collision anytime soon. Even if the Milky Way and Andromeda galaxies are approaching each other head-on, it will be billions of years before any collision begins.

When we look outside the Local Group, however, we find two astonishing facts recognized in the 1920s by Edwin Hubble, for whom the Hubble Space Telescope was named:

1. Virtually every galaxy outside the Local Group is moving *away* from us.
2. The more distant the galaxy, the faster it appears to be racing away.

These facts might make it sound as if we suffer from a cosmic case of chicken pox, but there is a much more natural explanation: *The entire universe is expanding.* We'll save the details for later in the book, but you can understand the basic idea by thinking about a raisin cake baking in an oven.

The Raisin Cake Analogy Imagine that you make a raisin cake in which the distance between adjacent raisins is 1 centimeter. You place the cake in the oven, where it expands as it bakes. After 1 hour, you remove the cake, which has expanded so that the distance between adjacent raisins has increased to 3 centimeters (Figure 1.15). The expansion of the cake seems fairly obvious. But what would you see if you lived *in* the cake, as we live in the universe?

Pick any raisin (it doesn't matter which one) and call it the Local Raisin. Figure 1.15 shows one possible choice, with three nearby raisins also labeled. The accompanying table summarizes what you would see if you lived within the Local Raisin. Notice, for example, that Raisin 1 starts out at a distance of 1 centimeter before baking and ends up at a distance of 3 centimeters after baking, which means it moves a distance of 2 centimeters farther away from the Local Raisin during the hour of baking. Hence, its speed as seen from the Local Raisin is 2 centimeters per hour. Raisin 2 moves from a distance of 2 centimeters before baking to a distance of 6 centimeters after baking, which means it moves a distance of 4 centimeters farther away from the Local Raisin during the hour. Hence, its speed is 4 centimeters per hour, or twice the speed of Raisin 1. Generalizing, the fact that the cake is expanding means that all the raisins are moving away from the Local Raisin, with more distant raisins moving away faster.

> Distant galaxies are all moving away from us, with more distant ones moving faster, indicating that we live in an expanding universe.

Hubble's discovery that galaxies are moving in much the same way as the raisins in the cake, with most moving away from us and more distant ones moving away faster, implies that the universe is expanding much like the raisin cake. If you now imagine the Local Raisin as representing our Local Group of galaxies and the other raisins as representing more distant galaxies or clusters of galaxies, you have a

From an outside perspective, the cake expands uniformly as it bakes . . .

Before baking: raisins are all 1 cm apart.

Local Raisin

1 hr

After baking: raisins are all 3 cm apart.

Local Raisin

. . . but from the point of view of the Local Raisin, all other raisins move farther away during baking, with more distant raisins moving faster.

Distances and Speeds as Seen from the Local Raisin

Raisin Number	Distance Before Baking	Distance After Baking (1 hour later)	Speed
1	1 cm	3 cm	2 cm/hr
2	2 cm	6 cm	4 cm/hr
3	3 cm	9 cm	6 cm/hr
⋮	⋮	⋮	⋮

▲ **FIGURE 1.15**

An expanding raisin cake offers an analogy to the expanding universe. Someone living in one of the raisins inside the cake could figure out that the cake is expanding by noticing that all other raisins are moving away, with more distant raisins moving away faster. In the same way, we know that we live in an expanding universe because all galaxies outside our Local Group are moving away from us, with more distant ones moving faster.

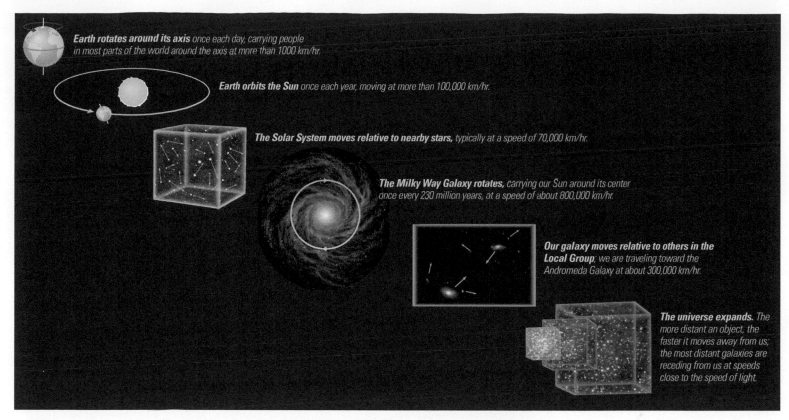

Earth rotates around its axis once each day, carrying people in most parts of the world around the axis at more than 1000 km/hr.

Earth orbits the Sun once each year, moving at more than 100,000 km/hr.

The Solar System moves relative to nearby stars, typically at a speed of 70,000 km/hr.

The Milky Way Galaxy rotates, carrying our Sun around its center once every 230 million years, at a speed of about 800,000 km/hr.

Our galaxy moves relative to others in the Local Group; we are traveling toward the Andromeda Galaxy at about 300,000 km/hr.

The universe expands. The more distant an object, the faster it moves away from us; the most distant galaxies are receding from us at speeds close to the speed of light.

▲ **FIGURE 1.16**
This figure summarizes the basic motions of Earth in the universe, along with their associated speeds.

basic picture of the expansion of the universe. Like the expanding dough between the raisins in the cake, *space* itself is growing between galaxies. More distant galaxies move away from us faster because they are carried along with this expansion like the raisins in the expanding cake. You can also now see how observations of expansion allow us to measure the age of the universe: The faster the rate of expansion, the more quickly the galaxies reached their current positions, and therefore the younger the universe must be. It is by precisely measuring the expansion rate that astronomers have learned that the universe is approximately 14 billion years old.

The Real Universe There's at least one important distinction between the raisin cake and the universe: A cake has a center and edges, but we do not think the same is true of the entire universe. Anyone living in any galaxy in an expanding universe sees just what we see—other galaxies moving away, with more distant ones moving away faster. Because the view from each point in the universe is about the same, no place can claim to be more "central" than any other place.

It's also important to realize that, unlike the case with a raisin cake, we can't actually *see* galaxies moving apart with time—the distances are too vast for any motion to be noticeable on the time scale of a human life. Instead, we measure the speeds of galaxies by spreading their light into spectra and observing what we call *Doppler shifts* [Section 5.2]. This illustrates how modern astronomy depends both on careful observations and on using current understanding of the laws of nature to explain what we see.

Motion Summary Figure 1.16 summarizes the motions we have discussed. As we have seen, we are never truly sitting still. We spin around Earth's axis at more than 1000 kilometers per hour, while our planet orbits the Sun at more than 100,000 kilometers per hour. Our solar system moves among the stars of the local solar neighborhood at typical speeds of 70,000 kilometers per hour, while also orbiting the center of the Milky Way Galaxy at a speed of about 800,000 kilometers per hour. Our galaxy moves among the other galaxies of the Local Group, while all other galaxies move away from us at speeds that grow greater with distance in our expanding universe. Spaceship Earth is carrying us on a remarkable journey.

the big picture · Putting Chapter 1 into Perspective

In this first chapter, we developed a broad overview of our place in the universe. As we consider the universe in more depth in the rest of the book, remember the following "big picture" ideas:

- Earth is not the center of the universe but instead is a planet orbiting a rather ordinary star in the Milky Way Galaxy. The Milky Way Galaxy, in turn, is one of billions of galaxies in our observable universe.

- Cosmic distances are literally astronomical, but we can put them in perspective with the aid of scale models and other scaling techniques. When you think about these enormous scales, don't forget that every star is a sun and every planet is a unique world.

- We are "star stuff." The atoms from which we are made began as hydrogen and helium in the Big Bang and

were later fused into heavier elements by massive stars. Stellar deaths released these atoms into space, where our galaxy recycled them into new stars and planets. Our solar system formed from such recycled matter some 4½ billion years ago.

- We are latecomers on the scale of cosmic time. The universe was already more than half its current age when our solar system formed, and it took billions of years more before humans arrived on the scene.

- All of us are being carried through the cosmos on spaceship Earth. Although we cannot feel this motion, the associated speeds are surprisingly high. Learning about the motions of spaceship Earth gives us a new perspective on the cosmos and helps us understand its nature and history.

my cosmic perspective The science of astronomy affects all of us on many levels. In particular, it helps us understand how we as humans fit into the universe as a whole, and the history of astronomy has been deeply intertwined with the development of civilization.

summary of key concepts

1.1 The Scale of the Universe

◆ **What is our place in the universe?**

Earth is a planet orbiting the Sun. Our Sun is one of more than 100 billion stars in the **Milky Way Galaxy.** Our galaxy is one of more than 70 galaxies in the **Local Group.** The Local Group is one small part of the **Local Supercluster,** which is one small part of the **universe.**

◆ **How big is the universe?**

If we imagine our Sun as a large grapefruit, Earth is a ballpoint that orbits 15 meters away; the nearest stars are thousands of kilometers away on the same scale. Our galaxy contains more than 100 billion stars—so many that it would take thousands of years just to count them out loud. The **observable universe** contains roughly 100 billion galaxies, and the total number of stars is comparable to the number of grains of dry sand on all the beaches on Earth.

1.2 The History of the Universe

◆ **How did we come to be?**

The universe began in the **Big Bang** and has been expanding ever since, except in localized regions where gravity has caused matter to collapse into galaxies and stars. The Big Bang essentially produced only two chemical elements: hydrogen and helium. The rest have been produced by stars and recycled within galaxies from one generation of stars to the next, which is why we are "star stuff."

◆ **How do our lifetimes compare to the age of the universe?**

On a cosmic calendar that compresses the history of the universe into 1 year, human civilization is just a few seconds old, and a human lifetime lasts only a fraction of a second.

1.3 Spaceship Earth

◆ How is Earth moving through space?

Earth **rotates** on its axis once each day and **orbits** the Sun once each year. At the same time, we move with our Sun in random directions relative to other stars in our local solar neighborhood, while the galaxy's rotation carries us around the center of the galaxy every 230 million years.

◆ How do galaxies move within the universe?

Galaxies move essentially at random within the Local Group, but all galaxies beyond the Local Group are moving away from us. More distant galaxies are moving faster, which tells us that we live in an expanding universe.

---

visual skills check   Check your understanding of some of the many types of visual information used in astronomy. For additional practice, try the Chapter 1 Visual Quiz at MasteringAstronomy®.

The figure at right shows the sizes of Earth and the Moon to scale; the scale used is 1 cm = 4000 km. Using what you've learned about astronomical scale in this chapter, answer the following questions. *Hint:* If you are unsure of the answers, you can calculate them using the given data.

Earth–Sun distance = 150,000,000 km

Diameter of Sun = 1,400,000 km

Earth–Moon distance = 384,000 km

Diameter of Earth = 12,800 km

1. If you wanted to show the distance between Earth and the Moon on the same scale, about how far apart would you need to place the two photos above?
   a. 10 centimeters (about the width of your hand)
   b. 1 meter (about the length of your arm)
   c. 100 meters (about the length of a football field)
   d. 1 kilometer (a little more than a half mile)

2. Suppose you wanted to show the Sun on the same scale. About how big would it need to be?
   a. 3.5 centimeters in diameter (the size of a golf ball)
   b. 35 centimeters in diameter (a little bigger than a basketball)
   c. 3.5 meters in diameter (about 11½ feet across)
   d. 3.5 kilometers in diameter (the size of a small town)

3. About how far away from Earth would the Sun be located on this scale?
   a. 3.75 meters (about 12 feet)
   b. 37.5 meters (about the height of a 12-story building)
   c. 375 meters (about the length of four football fields)
   d. 37.5 kilometers (the size of a large city)

4. Could you use the same scale to represent the distances to nearby stars? Why or why not?

---

exercises and problems

MasteringAstronomy®   For instructor-assigned homework and other learning materials, go to MasteringAstronomy®.

Review Questions

1. Briefly describe the major levels of structure (such as planet, star, galaxy) in the universe.
2. Define *astronomical unit* and *light-year*.
3. Explain the statement *The farther away we look in distance, the further back we look in time.*
4. What do we mean by the *observable universe*? Is it the same thing as the entire universe?
5. Using techniques described in the chapter, put the following into perspective: the size of our solar system; the distance to nearby stars; the size and number of stars in the Milky Way Galaxy; the number of stars in the observable universe.

6. What do we mean when we say that the universe is *expanding,* and how does expansion lead to the idea of the *Big Bang* and our current estimate of the age of the universe?
7. In what sense are we "star stuff"?
8. Use the cosmic calendar to describe how the human race fits into the scale of time.
9. Briefly explain Earth's daily rotation and annual orbit, defining the terms *ecliptic plane* and *axis tilt*.
10. Briefly describe our solar system's location and motion within the Milky Way Galaxy.
11. What is *dark matter*? Where does it reside in our galaxy? What makes dark matter and *dark energy* so mysterious and so important?

12. What key observations lead us to conclude that the universe is expanding? Use the raisin cake model to explain how these observations imply expansion.

13. How does the expansion rate of the universe allow us to determine the age of the universe? Would a faster expansion rate imply an older or a younger age for the universe? Explain.

Test Your Understanding

Does It Make Sense?

Decide whether the statement makes sense (or is clearly true) or does not make sense (or is clearly false). Explain clearly; not all of these have definitive answers, so your explanation is more important than your chosen answer.

Example: I walked east from our base camp at the North Pole.

Solution: The statement does not make sense because east has no meaning at the North Pole—all directions are south from the North Pole.

14. Our solar system is bigger than some galaxies.

15. The universe is billions of light-years in age.

16. It will take me light-years to complete this homework assignment!

17. Someday we may build spaceships capable of traveling a light-year in only a decade.

18. Astronomers discovered a moon that does not orbit a planet.

19. NASA will soon launch a spaceship that will photograph our Milky Way Galaxy from beyond its halo.

20. The observable universe is the same size today as it was a few billion years ago.

21. Photographs of distant galaxies show them as they were when they were much younger than they are today.

22. At a nearby park, I built a scale model of our solar system in which I used a basketball to represent Earth.

23. Because nearly all galaxies are moving away from us, we must be located at the center of the universe.

Quick Quiz

Choose the best answer to each of the following. Explain your reasoning with one or more complete sentences.

24. Which of the following correctly lists our "cosmic address" from small to large? (a) Earth, solar system, Milky Way Galaxy, Local Group, Local Supercluster, universe (b) Earth, solar system, Local Group, Local Supercluster, Milky Way Galaxy, universe (c) Earth, Milky Way Galaxy, solar system, Local Group, Local Supercluster, universe

25. An *astronomical unit* is (a) any planet's average distance from the Sun. (b) Earth's average distance from the Sun. (c) any large astronomical distance.

26. The star Betelgeuse is about 600 light-years away. If it explodes tonight, (a) we'll know because it will be brighter than the full Moon in the sky. (b) we'll know because debris from the explosion will rain down on us from space. (c) we won't know about it until about 600 years from now.

27. If we represent the solar system on a scale that allows us to walk from the Sun to Pluto in a few minutes, then (a) the planets are the size of basketballs and the nearest stars are a few miles away. (b) the planets are marble-size or smaller and the nearest stars are thousands of miles away. (c) the planets are microscopic and the stars are light-years away.

28. The total number of stars in the observable universe is roughly equivalent to (a) the number of grains of sand on all the beaches on Earth. (b) the number of grains of sand on Miami Beach. (c) infinity.

29. When we say the universe is *expanding*, we mean that (a) everything in the universe is growing in size. (b) the average distance between galaxies is growing with time. (c) the universe is getting older.

30. If stars existed but galaxies did not, (a) we would probably still exist anyway. (b) we would not exist because life on Earth depends on the light of galaxies. (c) we would not exist because we are made of material that was recycled in galaxies.

31. Could we see a galaxy that is 50 billion light-years away? (a) Yes, if we had a big enough telescope. (b) No, because it would be beyond the bounds of our observable universe. (c) No, because a galaxy could not possibly be that far away.

32. The age of our solar system is about (a) one-third of the age of the universe. (b) three-fourths of the age of the universe. (c) two billion years less than the age of the universe.

33. The fact that nearly all galaxies are moving away from us, with more distant ones moving faster, helped us to conclude that (a) the universe is expanding. (b) galaxies repel each other like magnets. (c) our galaxy lies near the center of the universe.

Process of Science

34. *Earth as a Planet.* For most of human history, scholars assumed Earth was the center of the universe. Today, we know that Earth is just one planet orbiting the Sun, and the Sun is just one star in a vast universe. How did science make it possible for us to learn these facts about Earth?

35. *Thinking About Scale.* One key to success in science is finding a simple way to evaluate new ideas, and making a simple scale model is often helpful. Suppose someone tells you that the reason it is warmer during the day than at night is that the day side of Earth is closer to the Sun than the night side. Evaluate this idea by thinking about the size of Earth and its distance from the Sun in a scale model of the solar system.

36. *Looking for Evidence.* In this first chapter, we have discussed the scientific story of the universe but have not yet discussed most of the evidence that backs it up. Choose one idea presented in this chapter—such as the idea that there are billions of galaxies in the universe, or that the universe was born in the Big Bang, or that the galaxy contains more dark matter than ordinary matter—and briefly discuss the type of evidence you would want to see before accepting the idea. (*Hint:* It's okay to look ahead in the book to see the evidence presented in later chapters.)

Group Work Exercise

37. *Counting the Milky Way's Stars.* **Roles:** *Scribe* (takes notes on the group's activities), *Proposer* (proposes explanations to the group), *Skeptic* (points out weaknesses in proposed explanations), *Moderator* (leads group discussion and makes sure everyone contributes). **Activity:** Work as a group to answer each part.
    a. Estimate the number of stars in the Milky Way from two facts: (1) the number of stars within 12 light-years of the Sun, which you can count in Appendix F; (2) the total volume of the Milky Way's disk (100,000 light-years in diameter and 1000 light-years thick) is about 1 billion times the volume of the region of your star count.
    b. Compare your value from part (a) to the value given in this chapter. Write down a list of possible reasons why your technique may have given you an underestimate or overestimate of the actual number.

Investigate Further

Short-Answer/Essay Questions

38. *Alien Technology.* Some people believe that Earth is regularly visited by aliens who travel here from other star systems. For this to be true, how much more advanced than our own technology would the aliens' technology have to be? Write one to two paragraphs to give a sense of the technological difference. (*Hint:* The ideas of scale in this chapter can help you contrast the distance the aliens would have to travel with the distances we currently are capable of traveling.)

39. *Stellar Collisions.* Is there any danger that another star will come crashing through our solar system in the near future? Explain.

40. *Raisin Cake Universe.* Suppose that all the raisins in a cake are 1 centimeter apart before baking and 4 centimeters apart after baking.
    a. Draw diagrams to represent the cake before and after baking.
    b. Identify one raisin as the Local Raisin on your diagrams. Construct a table showing the distances and speeds of other raisins as seen from the Local Raisin.
    c. Briefly explain how your expanding cake is similar to the expansion of the universe.

41. *The Cosmic Perspective.* Write a short essay describing how the ideas presented in this chapter affect your perspectives on your own life and on human civilization.

Quantitative Problems

Be sure to show all calculations clearly and state your final answers in complete sentences.

42. *Distances by Light.* Just as a light-year is the distance that light can travel in 1 year, we define a light-second as the distance that light can travel in 1 second, a light-minute as the distance that light can travel in 1 minute, and so on. Calculate the distance in both kilometers and miles represented by each of the following:
    a. 1 light-second
    b. 1 light-minute
    c. 1 light-hour
    d. 1 light-day

43. *Moonlight and Sunlight.* How long does it take light to travel from
    a. the Moon to Earth?
    b. the Sun to Earth?

44. *Saturn vs. the Milky Way.* Photos of Saturn and photos of galaxies can look so similar that children often think the photos show similar objects. In reality, a galaxy is far larger than any planet. About how many times larger is the diameter of the Milky Way Galaxy than the diameter of Saturn's rings? (*Data:* Saturn's rings are about 270,000 km in diameter; the Milky Way is 100,000 light-years in diameter.)

45. *Driving Trips.* Imagine that you could drive your car at a constant speed of 100 km/hr (62 mi/hr), even across oceans and in space. How long would it take to drive
    a. around Earth's equator? (Earth's circumference ≈ 40,000 km)
    b. from the Sun to Earth?
    c. from the Sun to Pluto? (Pluto distance ≈ 5.9×10^9 km)
    d. to Alpha Centauri (4.4 light-years)?

46. *Faster Trip.* Suppose you wanted to reach Alpha Centauri in 100 years.
    a. How fast would you have to go, in km/hr?
    b. How many times faster is the speed you found in (a) than the speeds of our fastest current spacecraft (around 50,000 km/hr)?

47. *Age of the Universe.* Suppose we did not yet know the expansion rate of the universe, and two astronomers came up with two different measurements: Allen measured an expansion rate for the universe that was 50% faster than the expansion rate Wendy measured. Is the age of the universe that Allen inferred older or younger than the age that Wendy inferred? By how much? Explain.

Discussion Questions

48. *Vast Orbs.* Dutch astronomer Christiaan Huygens may have been the first person to truly understand both the large sizes of other planets and the great distances to other stars. In 1690, he wrote, "How vast those Orbs must be, and how inconsiderable this Earth, the Theatre upon which all our mighty Designs, all our Navigations, and all our Wars are transacted, is when compared to them. A very fit consideration, and matter of Reflection, for those Kings and Princes who sacrifice the Lives of so many People, only to flatter their Ambition in being Masters of some pitiful corner of this small Spot." What do you think he meant? Explain.

49. *Infant Species.* In the last few tenths of a second before midnight on December 31 of the cosmic calendar, we have developed an incredible civilization and learned a great deal about the universe, but we also have developed technology through which we could destroy ourselves. The midnight bell is striking, and the choice for the future is ours. How far into the next cosmic year do you think our civilization will survive? Defend your opinion.

50. *A Human Adventure.* Astronomical discoveries clearly are important to science, but are they also important to our personal lives? Defend your opinion.

Web Projects

51. *NASA Missions.* Visit the NASA website to learn about upcoming astronomy missions. Write a one-page summary of the mission you feel is most likely to provide new astronomical information during the time you are enrolled in this astronomy course.

52. *The Hubble Extreme Deep Field.* The photo that opens this chapter is called the Hubble *Extreme* Deep Field. Find the photo on the Hubble Space Telescope website. Learn how it was taken, what it shows, and what we've learned from it. Write a short summary of your findings.

53. *Dwarf Planets.* The 2006 decision to call Pluto a "dwarf planet" still generates controversy. Gather and summarize information about the results from the *New Horizons* mission to Pluto and the *Dawn* mission to the dwarf planet (and large asteroid) Ceres. Where did you get your information? How do you know it is reliable? Has this information shed any light on the classification of Pluto, Ceres, and other solar system bodies? Overall, what is your opinion about the appropriate classification of these bodies?

2 Discovering the Universe for Yourself

This time-exposure photograph shows star paths at Arches National Park, Utah.

We live in an exciting time in the history of astronomy. New and powerful telescopes are scanning the depths of the universe. Sophisticated space probes are exploring our solar system. Rapid advances in computing technology are allowing scientists to analyze the vast amount of new data and to model the processes that occur in planets, stars, galaxies, and the universe.

One goal of this book is to help *you* share in the ongoing adventure of astronomical discovery. One of the best ways to become a part of this adventure is to do what other humans have done for thousands of generations: Go outside, observe the sky around you, and contemplate the awe-inspiring universe of which you are a part. In this chapter, we'll discuss a few key ideas that will help you understand what you see in the sky.

ESSENTIAL PREPARATION

1. What is our place in the universe? [Section 1.1]
2. How big is the universe? [Section 1.1]
3. How is Earth moving through space? [Section 1.3]

2.1 Patterns in the Night Sky

Today we take for granted that we live on a small planet orbiting an ordinary star in one of many galaxies in the universe. But this fact is not obvious from a casual glance at the night sky, and we've learned about our place in the cosmos only through a long history of careful observations. In this section, we'll discuss major features of the night sky and how we understand them in light of our current knowledge of the universe.

◆ What does the universe look like from Earth?

Shortly after sunset, as daylight fades to darkness, the sky appears to fill slowly with stars. On clear, moonless nights far from city lights, more than 2000 stars may be visible to your naked eye, along with the whitish band of light that we call the *Milky Way* (Figure 2.1). As you look at the stars, your mind may group them into patterns that look like familiar shapes or objects. If you observe the sky night after night or year after year, you will recognize the same patterns of stars. These patterns have not changed noticeably in the past few thousand years.

Constellations People of nearly every culture gave names to patterns they saw in the sky. We usually refer to such patterns as constellations, but to astronomers the term has a more precise meaning: A **constellation** is a *region* of the sky with well-defined borders; the familiar patterns of stars merely help us locate these constellations.

The names and borders of the 88 official constellations [Appendix H] were chosen in 1928 by members of the International Astronomical Union. Note that, just as every spot of land in the continental United States is part of some state, every point in the sky belongs to some constellation. For example, Figure 2.2 shows the borders of the constellation Orion and several of its neighbors.

Bright stars help us identify constellations, which officially are regions of the sky.

Recognizing the patterns of just 20 or so constellations is enough to make the sky seem as familiar as your own neighborhood. The best way to learn the constellations is to go out and view them, guided by a few visits to a planetarium, star charts [Appendix I], or sky-viewing apps.

▲ **FIGURE 2.1**
This photo shows the Milky Way over Haleakala crater on the island of Maui, Hawaii. The bright spot just below (and slightly left of) the center of the band is the planet Jupiter.

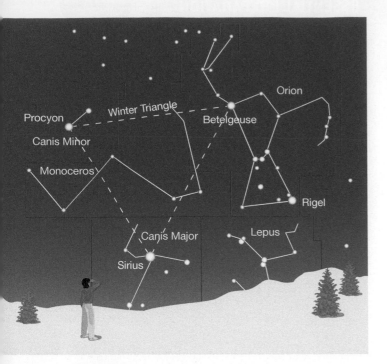

▲ FIGURE 2.2

Red lines mark official borders of several constellations near Orion. Yellow lines connect recognizable patterns of stars. Sirius, Procyon, and Betelgeuse form the *Winter Triangle*, which spans several constellations. This view shows how it appears (looking south) on winter evenings from the Northern Hemisphere.

The Celestial Sphere The stars in a particular constellation appear to lie close to one another but may be quite far apart in reality, because they may lie at very different distances from Earth. This illusion occurs because we lack depth perception when we look into space, a consequence of the fact that the stars are so far away [Section 1.1]. The ancient Greeks mistook this illusion for reality, imagining the stars and constellations as lying on a great **celestial sphere** that surrounds Earth (Figure 2.3).

> All stars appear to lie on the *celestial sphere*, but in reality they lie at different distances from Earth.

We now know that Earth seems to be in the center of the celestial sphere only because it is where we are located as we look into space. Nevertheless, the celestial sphere is a useful illusion, because it allows us to map the sky as seen from Earth. For reference, we identify two special points and two special circles on the celestial sphere (Figure 2.4).

- The **north celestial pole** is the point directly over Earth's North Pole.
- The **south celestial pole** is the point directly over Earth's South Pole.
- The **celestial equator,** which is a projection of Earth's equator into space, makes a complete circle around the celestial sphere.
- The **ecliptic** is the path the Sun follows as it appears to circle around the celestial sphere once each year. It crosses the celestial equator at a 23½° angle, because that is the tilt of Earth's axis.

The Milky Way The band of light that we call the *Milky Way* circles all the way around the celestial sphere, passing through more than a dozen constellations, and bears an important relationship to the Milky Way Galaxy: *It traces our galaxy's disk of stars—the galactic plane—as it appears from our location within the galaxy.*

▲ FIGURE 2.3

The stars appear to lie on a great celestial sphere that surrounds Earth. This is an illusion created by our lack of depth perception in space, but it is useful for mapping the sky.

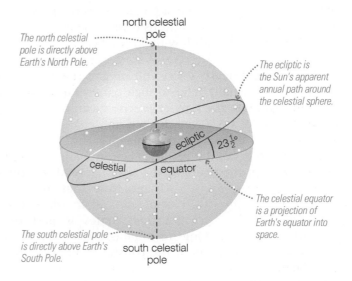

▲ FIGURE 2.4

This schematic diagram shows key features of the celestial sphere.

Figure 2.5 shows the idea. Our galaxy is shaped like a thin pancake with a bulge in the middle. We view the universe from our location a little more than halfway out from the center of this "pancake." In all directions that we look within the pancake, we see the countless stars and

The Milky Way in the night sky is our view in all directions into the disk of our galaxy.

vast interstellar clouds that make up the Milky Way in the night sky; that is why the band of light makes a full circle around our sky. The Milky Way appears somewhat wider in the direction of the constellation Sagittarius, because that is the direction in which we are looking toward the galaxy's central bulge. We have a clear view to the distant universe only when we look *away* from the galactic plane, along directions that have relatively few stars and clouds to block our view.

The dark lanes that run down the center of the Milky Way contain the densest clouds, obscuring our view of stars behind them. In most directions, these clouds prevent us from seeing more than a few thousand light-years into our galaxy's disk. As a result, much of our own galaxy remained hidden from view until just a few decades ago, when new technologies allowed us to peer through the clouds by observing forms of light that are invisible to our eyes (such as radio waves, infrared light, and X rays [Section 5.1]).

The Local Sky   The celestial sphere provides a useful way of thinking about the appearance of the universe from Earth. But it is not what we actually see when we go outside. Instead, your **local sky**—the sky as seen from wherever you happen to be standing—appears to take the shape of a hemisphere or dome. The dome shape arises from the fact that we see only half of the celestial sphere at any particular moment from any particular location, while the ground blocks the other half from view.

Figure 2.6 shows key reference features of the local sky. The boundary between Earth and sky defines the **horizon.** The point directly overhead is the **zenith.** The **meridian** is an imaginary half-circle stretching from the horizon due south, through the zenith, to the horizon due north.

We pinpoint an object in the local sky by stating its altitude above the horizon and direction along the horizon.

We can pinpoint the position of any object in the local sky by stating its **direction** along the horizon (sometimes stated as *azimuth,* which is degrees clockwise from due north) and its **altitude** above the horizon. For example, Figure 2.6 shows a person pointing to a star located in the southeast direction at an altitude of 60°. Note that the zenith has altitude 90° but no direction, because it is straight overhead.

Angular Sizes and Distances   Our lack of depth perception on the celestial sphere makes it difficult to judge the true sizes or separations of the objects we see in the sky. However, we can describe the *angular* sizes or separations of objects without knowing how far away they are.

The farther away an object is, the smaller its angular size.

The **angular size** of an object is the angle it appears to span in your field of view. For example, the angular sizes of the Sun and the Moon are each about ½° (Figure 2.7a). Note that angular size does not by itself tell us an object's true size, because angular size also depends on distance. The Sun is about 400 times as large in diameter as the Moon, but it has the same angular size in our sky because it is also about 400 times as far away.

▲ **FIGURE 2.5**

This painting shows how our galaxy's structure affects our view from Earth.

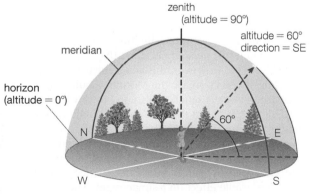

▲ **FIGURE 2.6**

From any place on Earth, the local sky looks like a dome (hemisphere). This diagram shows key reference points in the local sky. It also shows how we can describe any position in the local sky by its altitude and direction.

a The angular sizes of the Sun and the Moon are about 1/2°.

b The angular distance between the "pointer stars" of the Big Dipper is about 5°, and the angular length of the Southern Cross is about 6°.

c You can estimate angular sizes or distances with your outstretched hand.

Stretch out your arm as shown here.

▲ **FIGURE 2.7**
We measure *angular sizes* or *angular distances*, rather than actual sizes or distances, when we look at objects in the sky.

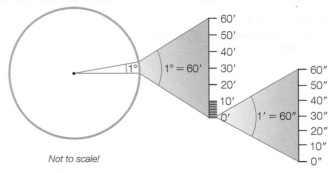

Not to scale!

▲ **FIGURE 2.8**
We subdivide each degree into 60 arcminutes and each arcminute into 60 arcseconds.

common **misconceptions**

The Moon Illusion

You've probably noticed that the full moon appears to be larger when it is near the horizon than when it is high in your sky. However, this apparent size change is an illusion: If you compare the Moon's angular size to that of a small object (such as a small button) held at arm's length, you'll see that it remains essentially the same throughout the night. The reason is that the Moon's angular size depends on its true size and distance, and while the latter varies over the course of the Moon's monthly orbit, it does not change enough to cause a noticeable effect on a single night. The Moon illusion clearly occurs within the human brain, though its precise cause is still hotly debated. Interestingly, you may be able to make the illusion go away by viewing the Moon upside down between your legs.

think about it Children often try to describe the sizes of objects in the sky (such as the Moon or an airplane) in inches or miles, or by holding their fingers apart and saying, "It was THIS big." Can we really describe objects in the sky in this way? Why or why not?

The **angular distance** between a pair of objects in the sky is the angle that appears to separate them. For example, the angular distance between the "pointer stars" at the end of the Big Dipper's bowl is about 5° and the angular length of the Southern Cross is about 6° (Figure 2.7b). You can use your outstretched hand to make rough estimates of angles in the sky (Figure 2.7c).

For greater precision, we subdivide each degree into 60 **arcminutes** (symbolized by ') and each arcminute into 60 arcseconds (symbolized by "), as shown in Figure 2.8. For example, we read 35°27'15" as *35 degrees, 27 arcminutes, 15 arcseconds*.

◆ Why do stars rise and set?

If you spend a few hours out under a starry sky, you'll notice that the universe seems to be circling around us, with stars moving gradually across the sky from east to west. Many ancient people took this appearance at face value, concluding that we lie in the center of a universe that rotates around us each day. Today we know that the ancients had it backward: It is Earth that rotates daily, not the rest of the universe.

We can picture the movement of the sky by imagining the celestial sphere rotating around Earth (Figure 2.9). From this perspective you can see how the universe seems to turn around us: Every object on the celestial sphere appears to make a simple daily circle around Earth. However, the motion can look a little more complex in the local sky, because the horizon cuts the celestial sphere in half. Figure 2.10 shows the idea for a typical Northern Hemisphere location (latitude 40°N). If you study the figure carefully, you'll notice the following key facts about the paths of various stars through the local sky:

- Stars near the north celestial pole are **circumpolar,** meaning that they remain perpetually above the horizon, circling (counterclockwise) around the north celestial pole each day.

- Stars near the south celestial pole never rise above the horizon at all.

- All other stars have daily circles that are partly above the horizon and partly below, which means they appear to rise in the east and set in the west.

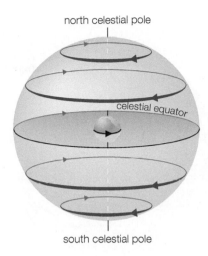

▲ **FIGURE 2.9**
Earth rotates from west to east (black arrow), making the celestial sphere *appear* to rotate around us from east to west (red arrows).

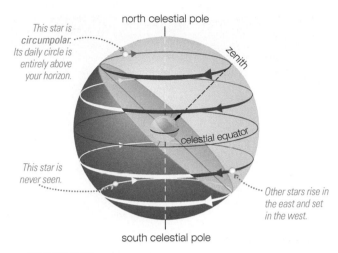

▲ **FIGURE 2.10**
The local sky for a location at latitude 40°N. The horizon slices through the celestial sphere at an angle to the celestial equator, causing the daily circles of stars to appear tilted in the local sky. Note: It is easier to follow the star paths if you rotate the page so that the zenith points up.

The time-exposure photograph that opens this chapter (p. 24) shows a part of the daily paths of stars. Paths of circumpolar stars are visible within the arch; notice that the complete daily circles for these stars are above the horizon, although the photo shows only a portion of each circle. The north celestial pole lies at the center of these circles. The circles grow larger for stars farther from the north celestial pole.

Earth's west-to-east rotation makes stars appear to move from east to west through the sky as they circle around the celestial poles.

If they are large enough, the circles cross the horizon, so that the stars rise in the east and set in the west. The same ideas apply in the Southern Hemisphere, except that circumpolar stars are those near the south celestial pole and they circle clockwise rather than counterclockwise.

think about it Do distant galaxies also rise and set like the stars in our sky? Why or why not?

◆ Why do the constellations we see depend on latitude and time of year?

If you stay in one place, the basic patterns of motion in the sky will stay the same from one night to the next. However, if you travel far north or south, you'll see a different set of constellations than you see at home. And even if you stay in one place, you'll see different constellations at different times of year. Let's explore why.

Variation with Latitude **Latitude** measures north-south position on Earth and **longitude** measures east-west position (Figure 2.11). Latitude is defined to be 0° at the equator, increasing to 90°N at the North Pole and 90°S at the South Pole. By international treaty, longitude is defined to be 0° along the **prime meridian,** which passes through Greenwich, England. Stating a latitude and a longitude pinpoints a location on Earth. For example, Miami lies at about 26°N latitude and 80°W longitude.

cosmic **calculations 2.1**

Angular Size, Physical Size, and Distance

If you hold a coin in front of your eye, it can block your entire field of view. But as you move it farther away, it appears to get smaller and it blocks less of your view. As long as a coin or any other object is far enough away so that its angular size is relatively small (less than a few degrees), the following formula relates the object's angular size (in degrees), physical size, and distance:

$$\frac{\text{angular size}}{360°} = \frac{\text{physical size}}{2\pi \times \text{distance}}$$

Example: The Moon's angular diameter is about 0.5° and its distance is about 380,000 km. What is the Moon's physical diameter?

Solution: To solve the formula for physical size, we multiply both sides by $2\pi \times$ distance and rearrange:

$$\text{physical size} = \text{angular size} \times \frac{2\pi \times \text{distance}}{360°}$$

We now plug in the given values of the Moon's angular size and distance:

$$\text{physical size} = 0.5° \times \frac{2\pi \times 380,000 \text{ km}}{360°}$$
$$\approx 3300 \text{ km}$$

The Moon's diameter is about 3300 km. We could find a more exact value (3476 km) by using more precise values for the angular diameter and distance.

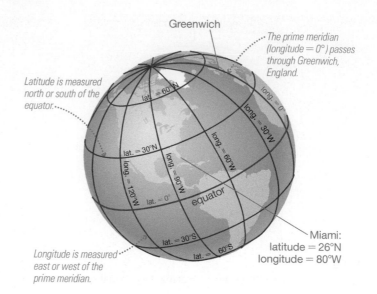

► FIGURE 2.11

We can locate any place on Earth's surface by its latitude and longitude.

Labels on figure:
- Greenwich
- The prime meridian (longitude = 0°) passes through Greenwich, England.
- Latitude is measured north or south of the equator.
- long. = 0°
- long. = 30°W
- long. = 60°W
- long. = 90°W
- long. = 120°W
- lat. = 60°N
- lat. = 30°N
- lat. = 0°
- equator
- lat. = 30°S
- lat. = 60°S
- Miami: latitude = 26°N longitude = 80°W
- Longitude is measured east or west of the prime meridian.

common **misconceptions**

Stars in the Daytime

Stars may appear to vanish in the daytime and "come out" at night, but in reality the stars are always present. The reason you don't see stars in the daytime is that their dim light is overwhelmed by the bright daytime sky. You *can* see bright stars in the daytime with the aid of a telescope, or if you are fortunate enough to observe a total solar eclipse. Astronauts can also see stars in the daytime. Above Earth's atmosphere, where there is no air to scatter sunlight, the Sun is a bright disk against a dark sky filled with stars. (However, the Sun is so bright that astronauts must block its light if they wish to see the stars.)

Latitude affects the constellations we see because it affects the locations of the horizon and zenith relative to the celestial sphere. Figure 2.12 shows how this works for the latitudes of the North Pole (90°N) and Sydney, Australia (34°S). Note that although the sky varies with latitude, it does *not* vary with longitude. For example, Charleston (South Carolina) and San Diego (California) are at about the same latitude, so people in both cities see the same set of constellations at night.

The constellations you see depend on your latitude, but not on your longitude.

You can learn more about how the sky varies with latitude by studying diagrams like those in Figures 2.10 and 2.12. For example, at the North Pole, you can see only objects that lie on the northern half of the celestial sphere, and they are all circumpolar. That is why the Sun remains above the horizon for 6 months at the North Pole: The Sun lies north of the celestial equator for half of each year (see Figure 2.4), so during these 6 months it circles the sky at the North Pole just like a circumpolar star.

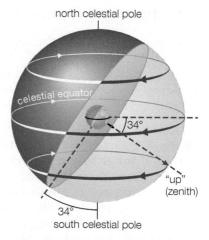

► FIGURE 2.12

The sky varies with latitude. Notice that the altitude of the celestial pole that is visible in your sky is always equal to your latitude.

a The local sky at the North Pole (latitude 90°N).

b The local sky at latitude 34°S.

Labels on figure a:
- "up" (zenith) north celestial pole
- 90°
- celestial equator
- 90°
- south celestial pole

Labels on figure b:
- north celestial pole
- celestial equator
- 34°
- 34°
- "up" (zenith)
- 34°
- south celestial pole

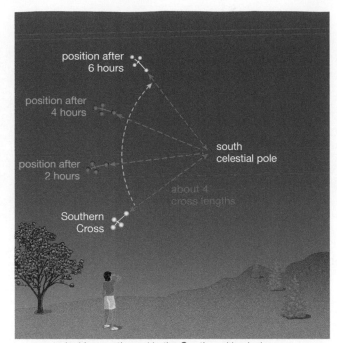

a The pointer stars of the Big Dipper point to the North Star, Polaris, which lies within 1° of the north celestial pole. The sky appears to turn *counterclockwise* around the north celestial pole.

b The Southern Cross points to the south celestial pole, which is not marked by any bright star. The sky appears to turn *clockwise* around the south celestial pole.

▲ **FIGURE 2.13**
You can determine your latitude by measuring the altitude of the celestial pole in your sky.

The diagrams also show a fact that is very important to navigation: *The altitude of the celestial pole in your sky is equal to your latitude.* For example, if you see the north celestial pole at an altitude of 40° above your north horizon, your latitude is 40°N. Similarly, if you see the south celestial pole at an altitude of 34° above your south horizon, your latitude is 34°S. Finding the north celestial pole is fairly easy, because it lies very close to the star Polaris, also known as the North Star (Figure 2.13a). In the Southern Hemisphere, you can find the south celestial pole with the aid of the Southern Cross (Figure 2.13b).

> The altitude of the celestial pole in your sky is equal to your latitude.

see it for yourself What is *your* latitude? Use Figure 2.13 to find the celestial pole in your sky, and estimate its altitude with your hand as shown in Figure 2.7c. Is its altitude what you expect?

Variation with Time of Year The night sky changes throughout the year because of Earth's changing position in its orbit around the Sun. Figure 2.14 shows the idea. From our vantage point on Earth, the annual orbit of Earth around the Sun makes the Sun *appear* to move steadily eastward along the ecliptic, with the stars of different constellations in the background at different times of year. The constellations along the ecliptic make up what we call the **zodiac;** tradition places 12 constellations along the zodiac, but the official borders include a thirteenth constellation, Ophiuchus.

> The constellations visible at a particular time of night change as we orbit the Sun.

The Sun's apparent location along the ecliptic determines which constellations we see at night. For example, Figure 2.14 shows that the Sun appears to be in Leo

common **misconceptions**

What Makes the North Star Special?

Most people are aware that the North Star, Polaris, is a special star. Contrary to a relatively common belief, however, it is *not* the brightest star in the sky. More than 50 other stars are just as bright or brighter. Polaris is special not because of its brightness, but because it is so close to the north celestial pole and therefore very useful in navigation.

Follow the "Night" arrow for Aug. 21: Notice that Aquarius is opposite the Sun in the sky, and hence visible all night long.

Follow the "Day" arrow for Aug. 21: Notice that the Sun appears to be in Leo.

▲ FIGURE 2.14

The Sun appears to move steadily eastward along the ecliptic as Earth orbits the Sun, so we see the Sun against the background of different zodiac constellations at different times of year. For example, on August 21 the Sun appears to be in Leo, because it is between us and the much more distant stars that make up Leo.

in late August. We therefore cannot see Leo at this time (because it is in our daytime sky), but we can see Aquarius all night long because of its location opposite Leo on the celestial sphere. Six months later, in February, we see Leo at night while Aquarius is above the horizon only in the daytime.

see it for yourself Based on Figure 2.14 and today's date, in what constellation does the Sun currently appear? What constellation of the zodiac will be on your meridian at midnight? What constellation of the zodiac will you see in the west shortly after sunset? Go outside at night to confirm your answers.

2.2 The Reason for Seasons

We have seen how Earth's rotation makes the sky appear to circle us daily and how the night sky changes as Earth orbits the Sun each year. The combination of Earth's rotation and orbit also leads to the progression of the seasons.

◆ What causes the seasons?

You know that we have seasonal changes, such as longer and warmer days in summer and shorter and cooler days in winter. But why do the seasons occur? The answer is that the tilt of Earth's axis causes sunlight to fall differently on Earth at different times of year.

Figure 2.15 illustrates the key ideas. Step 1 illustrates the tilt of Earth's axis, which remains pointed in the same direction in space (toward Polaris) throughout the year. As a result, the orientation of the axis *relative to the Sun* changes over the course of each orbit: The Northern Hemisphere is tipped toward the Sun in June and away from the

Sun in December, while the reverse is true for the Southern Hemisphere. That is why the two hemispheres experience opposite seasons. The rest of the figure shows how the changing angle of sunlight on the two hemispheres leads directly to seasons.

Step 2 shows Earth in June, when the axis tilt causes sunlight to strike the Northern Hemisphere at a steeper angle and the Southern Hemisphere at a shallower angle. The steeper sunlight angle makes it

Earth's axis points in the same direction all year round, which means its orientation relative to the Sun changes as Earth orbits the Sun.

summer in the Northern Hemisphere for two reasons. First, as shown in the zoom-out, the steeper angle means more concentrated sunlight, which tends to make it warmer. Second, if you visualize what happens as Earth rotates each day, you'll see that the steeper angle also means the Sun follows a longer and higher path through the sky, giving the Northern Hemisphere more hours of daylight during which it is warmed by the Sun. The opposite is true for the Southern Hemisphere at this time: The shallower sunlight angle makes it winter there because sunlight is less concentrated and the Sun follows a shorter, lower path through the sky.

The sunlight angle gradually changes as Earth orbits the Sun. At the opposite side of Earth's orbit, Step 4 shows that it has become winter for the Northern Hemisphere and summer for the Southern Hemisphere. In between these two extremes, Step 3 shows that both hemispheres are illuminated equally in March and September. It is therefore spring for the hemisphere that is on the way from winter to summer, and fall for the hemisphere on the way from summer to winter.

Notice that the seasons on Earth are caused only by the axis tilt and *not* by any change in Earth's distance from the Sun. Although Earth's orbital

common **misconceptions**

The Cause of Seasons

Many people guess that seasons are caused by variations in Earth's distance from the Sun. But if this were true, the whole Earth would have summer or winter at the same time, and it doesn't: The seasons are opposite in the Northern and Southern Hemispheres. In fact, Earth's slightly varying orbital distance has virtually no effect on the weather. The real cause of seasons is Earth's axis tilt, which causes the two hemispheres to take turns being tipped toward the Sun over the course of each year.

special **topic**   How Long Is a Day?

We usually associate our 24-hour day with Earth's rotation, but if you measure the rotation period, you'll find that it is about 23 hours and 56 minutes (more precisely $23^h56^m4.09^s$)—or about 4 minutes short of 24 hours. What's going on?

Astronomically, we define two different types of day. Earth's 23 hour and 56 minute rotation period, which we measure by timing how long it takes any star to make one full circuit through our sky, is called a **sidereal day;** *sidereal* (pronounced *sy-dear-ee-al*) means "related to the stars." Our 24-hour day, which we call a **solar day,** is the average time it takes *the Sun* to make one circuit through the sky.

A simple demonstration shows why the solar day is about 4 minutes longer than the sidereal day. Set an object representing the Sun on a table, and stand a few steps away to represent Earth. Point at the Sun and imagine that you also happen to be pointing toward a distant star that lies in the same direction. If you rotate (counterclockwise) while standing in place, you'll again be pointing at both the Sun and the star after one full rotation. However, to show that Earth also orbits the Sun, you should take a couple of steps around the Sun (counterclockwise) as you rotate (see figure). After one full rotation, you will again be pointing in the direction of the distant star, so this rotation represents a sidereal day. But notice that you need to rotate a little extra to point back at the Sun. This "extra" bit of rotation makes a solar day longer than a sidereal day. To figure out how long this extra rotation takes, note

that Earth completes a full 360° orbit around the Sun in about 365 days (1 year), which is a rate of about 1° per day. This extra rotation therefore takes about $\frac{1}{360}$ of Earth's rotation period—which is about 4 minutes.

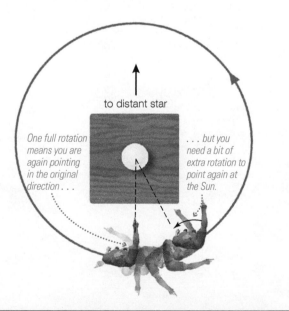

to distant star

One full rotation means you are again pointing in the original direction . . .

. . . but you need a bit of extra rotation to point again at the Sun.

cosmic context

FIGURE 2.15 The Seasons

Earth's seasons are caused by the tilt of its rotation axis, which is why the seasons are opposite in the two hemispheres. The seasons do *not* depend on Earth's distance from the Sun, which varies only slightly throughout the year.

① **Axis Tilt:** Earth's axis points in the same direction throughout the year, which causes changes in Earth's orientation *relative to the Sun*.

② **Northern Summer/Southern Winter:** In June, sunlight falls more directly on the Northern Hemisphere, which makes it summer there because solar energy is more concentrated and the Sun follows a longer and higher path through the sky. The Southern Hemisphere receives less direct sunlight, making it winter.

perpendicular to ecliptic plane

23½°

N

S

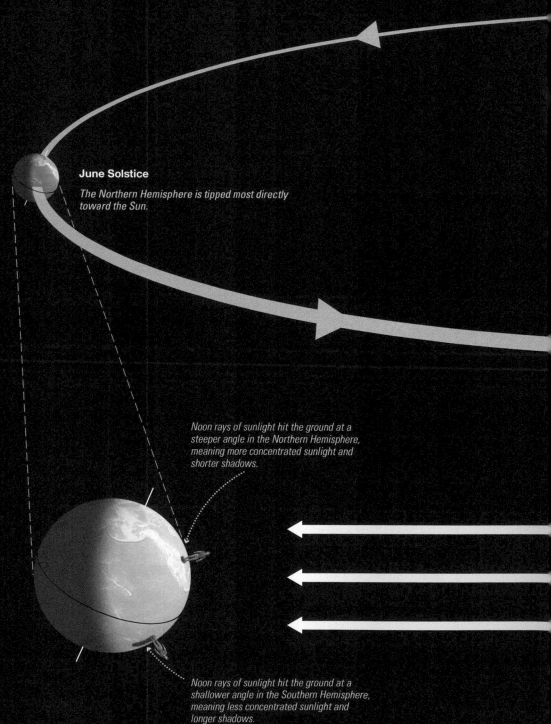

June Solstice

The Northern Hemisphere is tipped most directly toward the Sun.

Noon rays of sunlight hit the ground at a steeper angle in the Northern Hemisphere, meaning more concentrated sunlight and shorter shadows.

Noon rays of sunlight hit the ground at a shallower angle in the Southern Hemisphere, meaning less concentrated sunlight and longer shadows.

Interpreting the Diagram

To interpret the seasons diagram properly, keep in mind:

1. Earth's size relative to its orbit would be microscopic on this scale, meaning that both hemispheres are at essentially the same distance from the Sun.

2. The diagram is a side view of Earth's orbit. A top-down view (below) shows that Earth orbits in a nearly perfect circle and comes closest to the Sun in January.

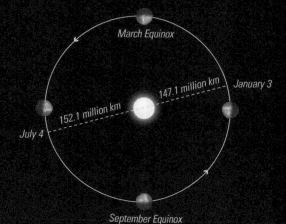

March Equinox

147.1 million km

January 3

152.1 million km

July 4

September Equinox

(3) **Spring/Fall:** Spring and fall begin when sunlight falls equally on both hemispheres, which happens twice a year: In March, when spring begins in the Northern Hemisphere and fall in the Southern Hemisphere; and in September, when fall begins in the Northern Hemisphere and spring in the Southern Hemisphere.

(4) **Northern Winter/Southern Summer:** In December, sunlight falls less directly on the Northern Hemisphere, which makes it winter because solar energy is less concentrated and the Sun follows a shorter and lower path through the sky. The Southern Hemisphere receives more direct sunlight, making it summer.

March Equinox

The Sun shines equally on both hemispheres.

The variation in Earth's orientation relative to the Sun means that the seasons are linked to four special points in Earth's orbit:

Solstices *are the two points at which sunlight becomes most extreme for the two hemispheres.*

Equinoxes *are the two points at which the hemispheres are equally illuminated.*

December Solstice

The Southern Hemisphere is tipped most directly toward the Sun.

September Equinox

The Sun shines equally on both hemispheres.

Noon rays of sunlight hit the ground at a shallower angle in the Northern Hemisphere, meaning less concentrated sunlight and longer shadows.

Noon rays of sunlight hit the ground at a steeper angle in the Southern Hemisphere, meaning more concentrated sunlight and shorter shadows.

distance varies over the course of each year, the variation is fairly small: Earth is only about 3% farther from the Sun at its farthest point (which is in July) than at its nearest (in January). The difference in the strength of sunlight due to this small change in distance is overwhelmed by the effects caused by the axis tilt. If Earth did not have an axis tilt, we would not have seasons.

think about it Jupiter has an axis tilt of about 3°, while Saturn has an axis tilt of about 27°. Both planets have nearly circular orbits around the Sun. Do you expect Jupiter to have seasons? Do you expect Saturn to have seasons? Explain.

Solstices and Equinoxes To help us mark the changing seasons, we define four special moments in the year, each of which corresponds to one of the four special positions in Earth's orbit shown in Figure 2.15.

- The **June solstice,** called the *summer solstice* by people in the Northern Hemisphere, occurs around June 21 and is the moment when the Northern Hemisphere is tipped most directly toward the Sun and receives the most direct sunlight.

- The **December solstice,** called the *winter solstice* by people in the Northern Hemisphere, occurs around December 21 and is the moment when the Northern Hemisphere receives the least direct sunlight.

- The **March equinox,** called the *spring equinox* (or *vernal equinox*) by people in the Northern Hemisphere, occurs around March 21 and is the moment when the Northern Hemisphere goes from being tipped slightly away from the Sun to being tipped slightly toward the Sun.

- The **September equinox,** called the *fall equinox* (or *autumnal equinox*) by people in the Northern Hemisphere, occurs around September 22 and is the moment when the Northern Hemisphere first starts to be tipped away from the Sun.

The exact dates and times of the solstices and equinoxes can vary by up to a couple days from the dates given above, depending on where we are in the leap year cycle. In fact, our modern calendar includes leap years (usually adding one day—February 29—every fourth year) specifically to keep the solstices and equinoxes around the same dates; the leap year pattern is based on the fact that the true length of the year* is very close to 365¼ days.

We use the equinoxes and solstices to mark the progression of the seasons.

We can mark the dates of the equinoxes and solstices by observing changes in the Sun's path through our sky (Figure 2.16). The equinoxes occur on the only two days of the year on which the Sun rises precisely due east and sets precisely due west; these are also the two days when the Sun is above and below the horizon for equal times of 12 hours (*equinox* means "equal night"). The June solstice occurs on the day on which the Sun follows its longest and highest path through the Northern Hemisphere sky (and its shortest and lowest path

The Sun rises precisely due east and sets precisely due west only on the days of the March and September equinoxes.

▲ **FIGURE 2.16**
This diagram shows the Sun's path on the solstices and equinoxes for a Northern Hemisphere sky (latitude 40°N). The precise paths are different for other latitudes; for example, at latitude 40°S, the paths look similar except tilted to the north rather than to the south. Notice that the Sun rises exactly due east and sets exactly due west only on the equinoxes.

---

*Technically, we are referring here to the *tropical year*—the time from one March equinox to the next. Axis precession (discussed later in this section) causes the tropical year to be slightly shorter (by about 20 minutes) than Earth's orbital period, called the *sidereal year*.

◄ **FIGURE 2.17**

This composite photograph shows images of the Sun taken at the same time of morning (technically, at the same "mean solar time") and from the same spot (over a large sundial in Carefree, Arizona) at 7- to 11-day intervals over the course of a year; the photo looks eastward, so north is to the left and south is to the right. Because this location is in the Northern Hemisphere, the Sun images that are high and to the north represent times near the June solstice and the images that are low and south represent times near the December solstice. The "figure 8" shape (called an *analemma*) arises from a combination of Earth's axis tilt and Earth's varying speed as it orbits the Sun.

through the Southern Hemisphere sky). It is therefore the day on which the Sun rises and sets farthest to the north of due east and due west; it is also the day on which the Northern Hemisphere has its longest hours of daylight and the Sun rises highest in the midday sky. The opposite is true on the day of the December solstice, when the Sun rises and sets farthest to the south and the Northern Hemisphere has its shortest hours of daylight and lowest midday Sun. Figure 2.17 shows how the Sun's position in the sky varies over the course of the year.

First Days of Seasons We usually say that each equinox and solstice marks the first day of a season. For example, the day of the June solstice is usually called the "first day of summer" in the Northern Hemisphere. Notice, however, that the Northern Hemisphere has its *maximum* tilt toward the Sun at this time. You might then wonder why we consider the solstice to be the beginning rather than the midpoint of summer.

The choice is somewhat arbitrary, but it makes sense in at least two ways. First, it was much easier for ancient people to identify the days on which the Sun reached extreme positions in the sky—such as when it reached its highest point on the summer solstice—than other days in between. Second, we usually think of the seasons in terms of weather, and the warmest summer weather tends to come 1 to 2 months after the solstice. To understand why, think about what happens when you heat a pot of cold soup. Even though you may have the stove turned on high from the start, it takes a while for the soup to warm up. In the same way, it takes some time for sunlight to heat the ground and oceans from the cold of winter to the warmth of summer. "Midsummer" in terms of weather therefore comes in late July or early August, which makes the June solstice a pretty good choice for the "first day of summer." Similar logic applies to the starting times for spring, fall, and winter.

Seasons Around the World The seasons have different characteristics in different parts of the world. High latitudes have more extreme seasons. For example, Vermont has much longer summer days and much longer winter nights than Florida. At the Arctic Circle (latitude 66½°), the Sun remains above the horizon all day long on the June solstice (Figure 2.18), and never rises on the December solstice (although

common **misconceptions**

High Noon

When is the Sun directly overhead in your sky? Many people answer "at noon." It's true that the Sun reaches its *highest* point each day when it crosses the meridian, giving us the term "high noon" (though the meridian crossing is rarely at precisely 12:00). However, unless you live in the tropics (between latitudes 23.5°S and 23.5°N), the Sun is *never* directly overhead. In fact, any time you can see the Sun as you walk around, you can be sure it is *not* at your zenith. Unless you are lying down, seeing an object at the zenith requires tilting your head back into a very uncomfortable position.

| Approximate time: | Midnight | 6:00 A.M. | Noon | 6:00 P.M. |
| Direction: | due north | due east | due south | due west |

▲ **FIGURE 2.18**

This sequence of photos shows the progression of the Sun around the horizon on the June solstice at the Arctic Circle. Notice that the Sun skims the northern horizon at midnight, then gradually rises higher, reaching its highest point when it is due south at noon.

bending of light by the atmosphere makes the Sun *appear* to be about a half-degree higher than it really is). The most extreme cases occur at the North and South Poles, where the Sun remains above the horizon for 6 months in summer and below the horizon for 6 months in winter.

Seasons also differ in equatorial regions, because the equator gets its most direct sunlight on the two equinoxes and its least direct sunlight on the solstices. As a result, instead of the four seasons experienced at higher latitudes, equatorial regions tend to have rainy and dry seasons, with the rainy seasons coming when the Sun is higher in the sky.

> At very high latitudes, the summer Sun remains above the horizon all day long.

◆ How does the orientation of Earth's axis change with time?

Our calendar keeps the solstices and equinoxes around the same dates each year, but the constellations associated with them change gradually over time. The reason is **precession,** a gradual wobble that alters the orientation of Earth's axis in space.

Precession occurs with many rotating objects. You can see it easily by spinning a top (Figure 2.19a). As the top spins rapidly, you'll notice that its axis also sweeps out a circle at a slower rate. We say that the top's axis *precesses.* Earth's axis precesses in much the same way, but far more slowly (Figure 2.19b). Each cycle of Earth's precession takes about 26,000 years. This gradually changes the direction in which the axis points in space.

think about it   Was Polaris the North Star in ancient times? Explain.

Note that precession does not change the *amount* of the axis tilt (which stays close to 23½°) and therefore does not affect the pattern of the seasons. However, it changes the points in Earth's orbit at which the solstices and equinoxes occur, and therefore changes the constellations that

> The tilt of Earth's axis remains close to 23½°, but the direction the axis points in space changes slowly with the 26,000-year cycle of precession.

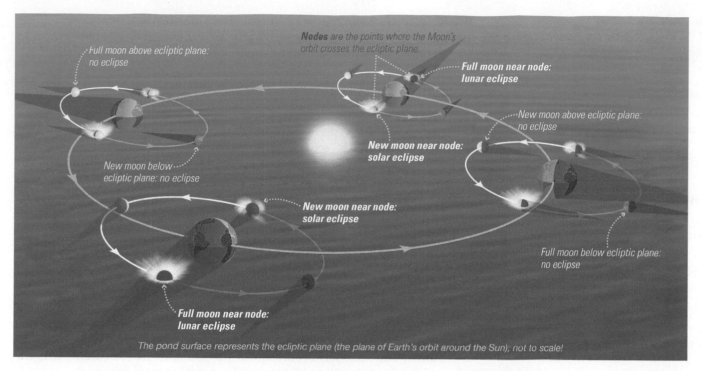

Nodes are the points where the Moon's orbit crosses the ecliptic plane.

Full moon above ecliptic plane: no eclipse

Full moon near node: lunar eclipse

New moon above ecliptic plane: no eclipse

New moon below ecliptic plane: no eclipse

New moon near node: solar eclipse

New moon near node: solar eclipse

Full moon below ecliptic plane: no eclipse

Full moon near node: lunar eclipse

The pond surface represents the ecliptic plane (the plane of Earth's orbit around the Sun); not to scale!

▲ **FIGURE 2.23**

This illustration represents the ecliptic plane as the surface of a pond. The Moon's orbit is tilted by about 5° to the ecliptic plane, so the Moon spends half of each orbit above the plane (the pond surface) and half below it. Eclipses occur only when the Moon is near a node (passing through the pond surface) *and* in a phase of either new moon (for a solar eclipse) or full moon (for a lunar eclipse)—as is the case with the lower left and top right orbits shown.

Conditions for Eclipses   Look again at Figure 2.21. The figure makes it look as if the Sun, Earth, and Moon line up with every new and full moon. If this figure told the whole story of the Moon's orbit, we would have both a lunar and a solar eclipse every month—but we don't.

The missing piece of the story in Figure 2.21 is that the Moon's orbit is slightly inclined (by about 5°) to the ecliptic plane (the plane of Earth's orbit around the Sun). To visualize this inclination, imagine the ecliptic plane as the surface of a pond, as shown in Figure 2.23. Because of the inclination of its orbit, the Moon spends most of its time either above or below this surface. It crosses *through* this surface only twice during each orbit: once coming out and once going back in. The two points in each orbit at which the Moon crosses the surface are called the **nodes** of the Moon's orbit.

We see a lunar eclipse when Earth's shadow falls on the Moon, and a solar eclipse when the Moon blocks our view of the Sun.

Notice that the nodes are aligned approximately the same way throughout the year (diagonally in Figure 2.23), which means they lie along a nearly straight line with the Sun and Earth about twice each year. Eclipses can occur only during these periods, because these are the only times when the Moon can be directly in line with the Sun and Earth. In other words, eclipses can occur only when

1. the phase of the Moon is full (for a lunar eclipse) or new (for a solar eclipse) *and*

2. the new or full moon occurs at a time when the Moon is very close to a node.

Note also that while Figure 2.23 shows the Moon and Earth casting only simple "shadow cones" (extending away from the Sun), a closer look at the geometry shows that each shadow consists of two distinct regions (Figure 2.24): a central **umbra,** where sunlight is

We see an eclipse only when a full or new moon occurs near one of the points where the Moon's orbit crosses the ecliptic plane.

penumbra
umbra

▲ **FIGURE 2.24**

The shadow cast by an object in sunlight. Sunlight is fully blocked in the umbra and partially blocked in the penumbra.

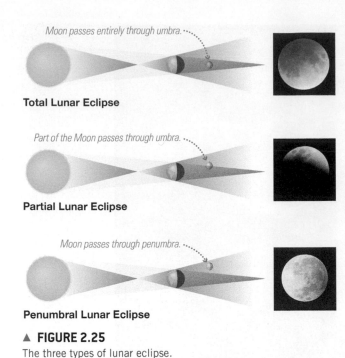

Moon passes entirely through umbra. ········

Total Lunar Eclipse

Part of the Moon passes through umbra. ········

Partial Lunar Eclipse

Moon passes through penumbra. ········

Penumbral Lunar Eclipse

▲ **FIGURE 2.25**
The three types of lunar eclipse.

A total solar eclipse occurs in the small central region. ········

Moon

path of total eclipse

Total Solar Eclipse

A partial solar eclipse occurs in the lighter area surrounding the area of totality. ········

Moon

path of annular eclipse

If the Moon's umbral shadow does not reach Earth, an annular eclipse occurs in the small central region.

Partial Solar Eclipse

Annular Solar Eclipse

▲ **FIGURE 2.26**
The three types of solar eclipse. The diagrams show the Moon's shadow falling on Earth; note the dark central umbra surrounded by the much lighter penumbra.

completely blocked, and a surrounding **penumbra,** where sunlight is only partially blocked. Lunar and solar eclipses vary in appearance depending on which part of the shadow is involved.

Lunar Eclipses   A lunar eclipse begins at the moment when the Moon's orbit first carries it into Earth's penumbra. After that, we will see one of three types of lunar eclipse (Figure 2.25). If the Sun, Earth, and Moon are nearly perfectly aligned, the Moon will pass through Earth's umbra and we see a **total lunar eclipse.** If the alignment is somewhat less perfect, only part of the full moon will pass through the umbra (with the rest in the penumbra) and we see a **partial lunar eclipse.** If the Moon passes *only* through Earth's penumbra, we see a **penumbral lunar eclipse.** Penumbral eclipses are the most common, but they are the least visually impressive because the full moon darkens only slightly.

Total lunar eclipses are the most spectacular. The Moon becomes dark and eerily red during **totality,** when the Moon is entirely engulfed in the umbra. Totality usually lasts about an hour, with partial phases both before and after. The curvature of Earth's shadow during partial phases shows that Earth is round. To understand the redness during totality, consider the view of an observer on the eclipsed Moon, who would see Earth's night side surrounded by the reddish glow of all the sunrises and sunsets occurring on the Earth at that moment. It is this reddish light that illuminates the Moon during total eclipse.

Solar Eclipses   We can also see three types of solar eclipse (Figure 2.26). If a solar eclipse occurs when the Moon is in a part of its orbit where it is relatively close to Earth (see Figure 2.20), the Moon's umbra can cover a small area of Earth's surface (up to about 270 kilometers in diameter). Within this area you will see a **total solar eclipse.** If the eclipse occurs when the Moon is in a part of its orbit that puts it farther from Earth, the umbra may not reach Earth's surface, leading to an **annular eclipse**—a ring of sunlight surrounding the Moon—in the small region of Earth directly behind the umbra. In either case, the region of totality or annularity will be surrounded by a much larger region (typically about 7000 kilometers in diameter) that falls within the Moon's penumbral shadow. Here you will see a **partial solar eclipse,** in which only part of the Sun is blocked from view. (Some solar eclipses are partial only, meaning that no locations on Earth see a total or annular eclipse.) The combination of Earth's rotation and the Moon's orbital motion causes the Moon's shadow to race across the face of Earth at a typical speed of about 1700 kilometers per hour. As a result, the umbral shadow traces a narrow path across Earth, and totality never lasts more than a few minutes in any particular place.

A total solar eclipse is a spectacular sight. It begins when the disk of the Moon first appears to touch the Sun. Over the next couple of hours, the Moon appears to take a larger and larger "bite" out of the Sun. As

A total solar eclipse is visible only within the narrow path that the Moon's umbral shadow makes across Earth's surface.

totality approaches, the sky darkens and temperatures fall. Birds head back to their nests, and crickets begin their nighttime chirping. During the few minutes of totality, the Moon completely blocks the normally visible disk of the Sun, allowing the faint *corona* to be seen (Figure 2.27). The surrounding sky takes on a twilight glow, and planets and bright stars become visible in the daytime. As totality ends, the Sun slowly emerges from behind the Moon over the next couple of hours. However, because your eyes have adapted to the darkness, totality appears to end far more abruptly than it began.

Predicting Eclipses Few phenomena have so inspired and humbled humans throughout the ages as eclipses. For many cultures, eclipses were mystical events associated with fate or the gods, and countless stories and legends surround them.

Much of the mystery of eclipses probably stems from the relative difficulty of predicting them. Look once more at Figure 2.23, focusing on the two periods—called *eclipse seasons*—in which the nodes of the Moon's orbit are closely aligned with the Sun. If the figure showed the whole story, these periods would always occur 6 months apart and predicting eclipses would be easy. For example, if the eclipse seasons occurred in January and July, eclipses would always occur on the dates of new and full moons in those months. Actual eclipse prediction is more difficult because of something the figure does not show: The nodes slowly move around the Moon's orbit, so the eclipse seasons occur slightly *less* than 6 months apart (about 173 days apart).

The combination of the changing dates of eclipse seasons and the 29½-day cycle of lunar phases makes eclipses recur in a cycle of about 18 years, 11⅓ days, called the **saros cycle**. Astronomers in many ancient cultures identified the saros cycle and used it to predict *when* eclipses would occur. However, they still could not predict eclipses in every detail (such as exactly where an eclipse would be visible and whether it would be total or partial).

Today, we can predict eclipses because we know the precise details of the orbits of Earth and the Moon.

> The general pattern of eclipses repeats with the roughly 18-year saros cycle.

Table 2.1 lists upcoming lunar eclipses; notice that, as we expect, eclipses come a little less than 6 months apart. (On rare occasions, two lunar eclipses may occur in the same eclipse season and therefore come just a month apart.) Figure 2.28 shows paths of totality for upcoming

▲ **FIGURE 2.27**

This multiple-exposure photograph shows the progression of a total solar eclipse above a thorny acacia tree near Chisamba, Zambia. Totality (central image) lasts only a few minutes, during which time we can see the faint corona around the outline of the Sun.

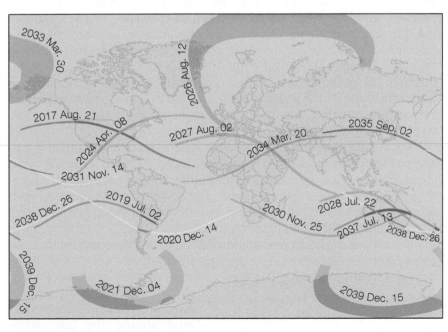

▲ **FIGURE 2.28**

This map shows the paths of totality for solar eclipses from 2017 through 2040. Paths of the same color represent eclipses occurring in successive saros cycles, separated by 18 years 11 days. For example, the 2039 eclipse occurs 18 years 11 days after the 2021 eclipse, both shown in green. Eclipse predictions by Fred Espenak, NASA GSFC. **Note:** Students in the United States should pay special attention to the eclipses of 2017 and 2024, the first total eclipses in the continental United States since 1979. It is worth traveling to make sure you are *in* the path of totality when the eclipse occurs.

TABLE 2.1 Lunar Eclipses 2017–2020*

Date	Type	Where You Can See It
Feb. 11, 2017	penumbral	Americas, Europe, Africa, Asia
Aug. 7, 2017	partial	Europe, Africa, Asia, Australia
Jan. 31, 2018	total	Asia, Australia, Pacific, western N. America
July 27, 2018	total	S. America, Europe, Africa, Asia, Australia
Jan. 21, 2019	total	Pacific, Americas, Europe, Africa
Jul. 16, 2019	partial	S. America, Europe, Africa, Asia, Australia
Jan. 10, 2020	penumbral	Americas, Europe, Africa
Jun. 5, 2020	penumbral	Asia, Australia, Pacific, Americas

*Dates are based on Universal Time and hence are those in Greenwich, England, at the time of the eclipse; check a news source for the local time and date. Eclipse predictions by Fred Espenak, NASA GSFC.

total solar eclipses (but not for partial or annular eclipses), using color coding to show eclipses that repeat with the saros cycle.

2.4 The Ancient Mystery of the Planets

We've now covered the appearance and motion of the stars, Sun, and Moon in the sky. That leaves us with the planets to discuss. As you'll see, planetary motion posed an ancient mystery that played a critical role in the development of modern civilization.

Five planets are easy to find with the naked eye: Mercury, Venus, Mars, Jupiter, and Saturn. Mercury is visible infrequently, and only just after sunset or just before sunrise because it is so close to the Sun. Venus often shines brightly in the early evening in the west or before dawn in the east. If you see a very bright "star" in the early evening or early morning, it is probably Venus. Jupiter, when it is visible at night, is the brightest object in the sky besides the Moon and Venus. Mars is often recognizable by its reddish color, though you should check a star chart to make sure you aren't looking at a bright red star. Saturn is also easy to see with the naked eye, but because many stars are just as bright as Saturn, it helps to know where to look. (It also helps to know that planets tend not to twinkle as much as stars.)

◆ Why was planetary motion so hard to explain?

Over the course of a single night, planets behave like all other objects in the sky: Earth's rotation makes them appear to rise in the east and set in the west. But if you continue to watch the planets night after night, you will notice that their movements among the constellations are quite complex. Instead of moving steadily eastward relative to the stars, like the Sun and Moon, the planets vary substantially in both speed and brightness; in fact, the word *planet* comes from a Greek term meaning "wandering star." Moreover, while the planets *usually* move eastward through the constellations, they occasionally reverse course, moving westward through the zodiac (Figure 2.29). These periods of **apparent retrograde motion** (*retrograde* means "backward") last from a few weeks to a few months, depending on the planet.

For ancient people who believed in an Earth-centered universe, apparent retrograde motion was very difficult to explain. After all, what could make planets sometimes turn around and go backward if everything moves in circles around Earth? The ancient Greeks came up with some very clever ways to explain it, but their explanations (which we'll study in Chapter 3) were quite complex.

In contrast, apparent retrograde motion has a simple explanation in a Sun-centered solar system. You can demonstrate it for yourself with the help of a friend (Figure 2.30a). Pick a spot in an open area to represent the Sun. You can represent Earth by walking counterclockwise around the Sun, while your friend represents a more distant planet (such as Mars or Jupiter) by walking in the same direction around the Sun at a greater distance. Your friend should walk more slowly than you, because more distant planets orbit the Sun more slowly. As you walk, watch how your friend appears to move relative to buildings or trees in the distance. Although both of you always walk the same way around the Sun, your friend will appear to move backward against

Mars usually moves eastward relative to the stars . . .

. . . but it reverses course during its apparent retrograde motion.

11 Apr. 2012

4 Mar. 2012

3 Nov. 2011

23 Jan. 2012

6 Jul. 2012

← East   West →

▲ **FIGURE 2.29**

This composite of images (taken at 5- to 7-day intervals in 2011 and 2012) shows a retrograde loop of Mars. Note that Mars is biggest and brightest in the middle of the retrograde loop, because that is where it is closest to Earth in its orbit.

A planet appears to move backward relative to the stars during the period when Earth passes it in its orbit.

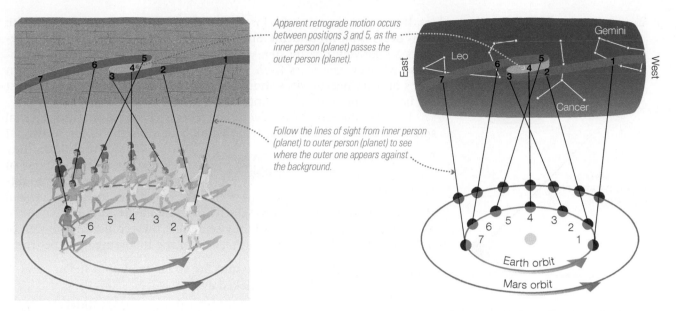

Apparent retrograde motion occurs between positions 3 and 5, as the inner person (planet) passes the outer person (planet).

Follow the lines of sight from inner person (planet) to outer person (planet) to see where the outer one appears against the background.

a The retrograde motion demonstration: Watch how your friend (in red) usually appears to move forward against the background of the building in the distance but appears to move backward as you (in blue) catch up to and pass her in your "orbit."

b This diagram shows the same idea applied to a planet. Follow the lines of sight from Earth to Mars in numerical order. Notice that Mars appears to move westward relative to the distant stars (from points 3 to 5) as Earth passes it by in its orbit.

▲ **FIGURE 2.30**

Apparent retrograde motion—the occasional "backward" motion of the planets relative to the stars—has a simple explanation in a Sun-centered solar system.

the background during the part of your "orbit" at which you catch up to and pass him or her. Figure 2.30b shows how the same idea applies to Mars. Note that Mars never actually changes direction; it only *appears* to go backward as Earth passes Mars in its orbit. (To understand the apparent retrograde motions of Mercury and Venus, which are closer to the Sun than is Earth, simply switch places with your friend and repeat the demonstration.)

◆ Why did the ancient Greeks reject the real explanation for planetary motion?

If the apparent retrograde motion of the planets is so readily explained by recognizing that Earth orbits the Sun, why wasn't this idea accepted in ancient times? In fact, the idea that Earth goes around the Sun was suggested as early as 260 B.C. by the Greek astronomer Aristarchus. No one knows why Aristarchus proposed a Sun-centered solar system, but the fact that it so naturally explains planetary motion probably played a role. Nevertheless, Aristarchus's contemporaries rejected his idea, and the Sun-centered solar system did not gain wide acceptance until almost 2000 years later.

Although there were many reasons why the Greeks were reluctant to abandon the idea of an Earth-centered universe, one of the most important was their inability to detect what we call **stellar parallax.** Extend your arm and hold up one finger. If you keep your finger still and alternately close your left eye and right eye, your finger will appear to jump back and forth against the background. This apparent shifting, called *parallax*, occurs because your two eyes view your finger from opposite sides of your nose. If you move your finger closer to your face, the parallax increases. If you look at a distant tree or flagpole instead of your finger, you may not notice any parallax at all. In other words, parallax depends on distance, with nearer objects exhibiting greater parallax than more distant objects.

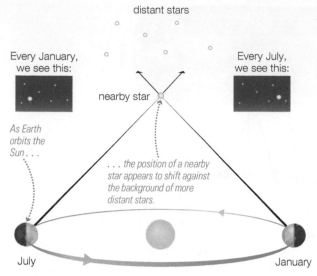

distant stars

Every January, we see this:

nearby star

Every July, we see this:

As Earth orbits the Sun...

...the position of a nearby star appears to shift against the background of more distant stars.

July

January

▲ **FIGURE 2.31**

Stellar parallax is an apparent shift in the position of a nearby star as we look at it from different places in Earth's orbit. This figure is greatly exaggerated; in reality, the amount of shift is far too small to detect with the naked eye.

If you now imagine that your two eyes represent Earth at opposite sides of its orbit around the Sun and that the tip of your finger represents a relatively nearby star, you have the idea of stellar parallax. Because we view the stars from different places in our orbit at different times of year, nearby stars should *appear* to shift back and forth against the background of more distant stars (Figure 2.31).

Because the Greeks believed that all stars lie on the same celestial sphere, they expected to see stellar parallax in a slightly different way. If

The Greeks knew that stellar parallax should occur if Earth orbits the Sun, but they could not detect it.

Earth orbited the Sun, they reasoned, at different times of year we would be closer to different parts of the celestial sphere and would notice changes in the angular separations of stars. However, no matter how hard they searched, they could find no sign of stellar parallax. They concluded that one of the following must be true:

1. Earth orbits the Sun, but the stars are so far away that stellar parallax is not detectable to the naked eye.

2. There is no stellar parallax because Earth remains stationary at the center of the universe.

Aside from notable exceptions, such as Aristarchus, the Greeks rejected the correct answer (the first one) because they could not imagine that the stars could be *that* far away. Today, we can detect stellar parallax with the aid of telescopes, providing direct proof that Earth really does orbit the Sun. Careful measurements of stellar parallax also provide the most reliable means of measuring distances to nearby stars [Section 12.1].

think about it How far apart are opposite sides of Earth's orbit? How far away are the nearest stars? Using the 1-to-10-billion scale from Chapter 1, describe the challenge of detecting stellar parallax.

The ancient mystery of the planets drove much of the historical debate over Earth's place in the universe. In many ways, the modern technological society we take for granted today can be traced directly to the scientific revolution that began in the quest to explain the strange wanderings of the planets among the stars in our sky. We will turn our attention to this revolution in the next chapter.

---

the big picture **Putting Chapter 2 into Perspective**

In this chapter, we surveyed the phenomena of our sky. Keep the following "big picture" ideas in mind as you continue your study of astronomy:

- You can enhance your enjoyment of astronomy by observing the sky. The more you learn about the appearance and apparent motions of objects in the sky, the more you will appreciate what you can see in the universe.

- From our vantage point on Earth, it is convenient to imagine that we are at the center of a great celestial sphere—even though we really are on a planet orbiting

a star in a vast universe. We can then understand what we see in the local sky by thinking about how the celestial sphere appears from our latitude.

- Most of the phenomena of the sky are relatively easy to observe and understand. The more complex phenomena—particularly eclipses and apparent retrograde motion of the planets—challenged our ancestors for thousands of years. The desire to understand these phenomena helped drive the development of science and technology.

my cosmic perspective Astronomy begins with an understanding of and appreciation for the motions of the Sun, Moon, planets, and stars in our sky. Studies of these patterns ultimately helped ignite the scientific and technological revolution upon which our modern civilization is based.

2.1 Patterns in the Night Sky

◆ What does the universe look like from Earth?

Stars and other celestial objects appear to lie on a great **celestial sphere** surrounding Earth. We divide the celestial sphere into **constellations** with well-defined borders. From any location on Earth, we see half the celestial sphere at any given time as the dome of our **local sky,** in which the **horizon** is the boundary between Earth and sky, the **zenith** is the point directly overhead, and the **meridian** runs from due south to due north through the zenith.

◆ Why do stars rise and set?

Earth's rotation makes stars appear to circle around Earth each day. A star whose complete circle lies above our horizon is said to be **circumpolar.** Other stars have circles that cross the horizon, so they rise in the east and set in the west each day.

◆ Why do the constellations we see depend on latitude and time of year?

The visible constellations vary with time of year because our night sky lies in different directions in space as we orbit the Sun. The constellations vary with **latitude** because your latitude determines the orientation of your horizon relative to the celestial sphere. The sky does not vary with **longitude.**

2.2 The Reason for Seasons

◆ What causes the seasons?

The tilt of Earth's axis causes the seasons. The axis points in the same direction throughout the year, so as Earth orbits the Sun, sunlight hits different parts of Earth more directly at different times of year.

◆ How does the orientation of Earth's axis change with time?

Earth's 26,000-year cycle of **precession** changes the orientation of its axis in space, although the tilt remains about 23½°. The changing orientation of the axis does not affect the pattern of seasons, but it changes the identity of the North Star and shifts the locations of the solstices and equinoxes in Earth's orbit.

2.3 The Moon, Our Constant Companion

◆ Why do we see phases of the Moon?

The phase of the Moon depends on its position relative to the Sun as it orbits Earth. The half of the Moon facing the Sun is always illuminated while the other half is dark, but from Earth we see varying combinations of the illuminated and dark halves.

◆ What causes eclipses?

We see a **lunar eclipse** when Earth's shadow falls on the Moon and a **solar eclipse** when the Moon blocks our view of the Sun. We do not see an eclipse at every new and full moon because the Moon's orbit is slightly inclined to the ecliptic plane.

2.4 The Ancient Mystery of the Planets

◆ Why was planetary motion so hard to explain?

Planets generally appear to move eastward relative to the stars over the course of the year, but for weeks or months they reverse course during periods of **apparent retrograde motion.** This motion occurs when Earth passes by (or is passed by) another planet in its orbit, but it posed a major mystery to ancient people who assumed Earth to be at the center of the universe.

◆ Why did the ancient Greeks reject the real explanation for planetary motion?

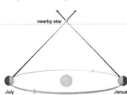

The Greeks rejected the idea that Earth goes around the Sun in part because they could not detect **stellar parallax**—slight apparent shifts in stellar positions over the course of the year. To most Greeks, it seemed unlikely that the stars could be so far away as to make parallax undetectable to the naked eye, even though that is, in fact, the case.

Use the diagram above to answer questions 1–5.

1. Which of the four labeled points (A through D) represents the day with the most hours of daylight for the Northern Hemisphere?

2. Which of the four labeled points represents the day with the most hours of daylight for the Southern Hemisphere?

3. Which of the four labeled points represents the beginning of spring for the Southern Hemisphere?

4. The diagram exaggerates the sizes of Earth and the Sun relative to the orbit. If Earth were correctly scaled relative to the orbit in the figure, how big would it be?
   a. about half the size shown
   b. about 2 millimeters across
   c. about 0.1 millimeter across
   d. microscopic

5. Given that Earth's actual distance from the Sun varies by less than 3% over the course of a year, why does the diagram look so elliptical?
   a. It correctly shows that Earth is closest to the Sun at points A and C and farthest at points B and D.
   b. The elliptical shape is an effect of perspective, since the diagram shows an almost edge-on view of a nearly circular orbit.
   c. The shape of the diagram is meaningless and is only for artistic effect.

Use the diagram above to answer questions 6–8.

6. As viewed from Earth, in which zodiac constellation does the Sun appear to be located on April 21?
   a. Leo   b. Aquarius
   c. Libra   d. Aries

7. If the date is April 21, what zodiac constellation will be visible on your meridian at midnight?
   a. Leo   b. Aquarius
   c. Libra   d. Aries

8. If the date is April 21, what zodiac constellation will you see setting in the west shortly after sunset?
   a. Scorpius   b. Pisces
   c. Taurus   d. Virgo

exercises and problems

MasteringAstronomy® For instructor-assigned homework and other learning materials, go to MasteringAstronomy®.

Review Questions

1. What are *constellations*? How did they get their names?
2. Suppose you were making a model of the celestial sphere with a ball. Briefly describe all the things you would need to mark on your celestial sphere.
3. On a clear, dark night, the sky may appear to be "full" of stars. Does this appearance accurately reflect the way stars are distributed in space? Explain.
4. Why does the *local sky* look like a dome? Define *horizon, zenith,* and *meridian*. How do we describe the location of an object in the local sky?

5. Explain why we can measure only *angular sizes* and *angular distances* for objects in the sky. What are *arcminutes* and *arcseconds*?
6. What are *circumpolar stars*? Are more stars circumpolar at the North Pole or in the United States? Explain.
7. What are *latitude* and *longitude*? Does the local sky vary with latitude? Does it vary with longitude? Explain.
8. What is the *zodiac*, and why do we see different parts of it at different times of year?
9. Suppose Earth's axis had no tilt. Would we still have seasons? Why or why not?
10. Briefly describe key facts about the solstices and equinoxes.

11. What is *precession*? How does it affect our view of the sky?
12. Briefly describe the Moon's cycle of *phases*. Can you ever see a full moon at noon? Explain.
13. Why do we always see the same face of the Moon?
14. Why don't we see an *eclipse* at every new and full moon? Describe the conditions needed for a *solar* or *lunar eclipse*.
15. What do we mean by the *apparent retrograde motion* of the planets? Why was it difficult for ancient astronomers to explain but easy for us to explain?
16. What is *stellar parallax*? How did an inability to detect it support the ancient belief in an Earth-centered universe?

Test Your Understanding

Does It Make Sense?

Decide whether the statement makes sense (or is clearly true) or does not make sense (or is clearly false). Explain clearly; not all of these have definitive answers, so your explanation is more important than your chosen answer.

17. The constellation Orion didn't exist when my grandfather was a child.
18. When I looked into the dark lanes of the Milky Way with my binoculars, I saw a cluster of distant galaxies.
19. Last night the Moon was so big that it stretched for a mile across the sky.
20. I live in the United States, and during a trip to Argentina I saw many constellations that I'd never seen before.
21. Last night I saw Jupiter in the middle of the Big Dipper. (*Hint*: Is the Big Dipper part of the zodiac?)
22. Last night I saw Mars move westward through the sky in its apparent retrograde motion.
23. Although all the known stars rise in the east and set in the west, we might someday discover a star that will rise in the west and set in the east.
24. If Earth's orbit were a perfect circle, we would not have seasons.
25. Because of precession, someday it will be summer everywhere on Earth at the same time.
26. This morning I saw the full moon setting at about the same time the Sun was rising.

Quick Quiz

Choose the best answer to each of the following. Explain your reasoning with one or more complete sentences.

27. Two stars that are in the same constellation (a) must both be part of the same cluster of stars in space. (b) must both have been discovered at about the same time. (c) may actually be very far away from each other.
28. The north celestial pole is 35° above your northern horizon. This tells you that you are at (a) latitude 35°N. (b) longitude 35°E. (c) latitude 35°S.
29. Beijing and Philadelphia have about the same latitude but different longitudes. Therefore, tonight's night sky in these two places will (a) look about the same. (b) have completely different sets of constellations. (c) have partially different sets of constellations.
30. In winter, Earth's axis points toward the star Polaris. In spring, the axis points toward (a) Polaris. (b) Vega. (c) the Sun.
31. When it is summer in Australia, the season in the United States is (a) winter. (b) summer. (c) spring.
32. If the Sun rises precisely due east, (a) you must be located at Earth's equator. (b) it must be the day of either the March or the September equinox. (c) it must be the day of the June solstice.
33. A week after full moon, the Moon's phase is (a) first quarter. (b) third quarter. (c) new.
34. The fact that we always see the same face of the Moon tells us that the Moon (a) does not rotate. (b) rotates with the same period that it orbits Earth. (c) looks the same on both sides.
35. If there is going to be a total lunar eclipse tonight, then you know that (a) the Moon's phase is full. (b) the Moon's phase is new. (c) the Moon is unusually close to Earth.
36. When we see Saturn going through a period of apparent retrograde motion, it means (a) Saturn is temporarily moving backward in its orbit of the Sun. (b) Earth is passing Saturn in its orbit, with both planets on the same side of the Sun. (c) Saturn and Earth must be on opposite sides of the Sun.

Process of Science

37. *Earth-Centered or Sun-Centered?* For each of the following, decide whether the phenomenon is consistent or inconsistent with a belief in an Earth-centered system. If consistent, describe how. If inconsistent, explain why, and also explain why the inconsistency did not immediately lead people to abandon the Earth-centered model.
    a. The daily paths of stars through the sky
    b. Seasons
    c. Phases of the Moon
    d. Eclipses
    e. Apparent retrograde motion of the planets
38. *Shadow Phases.* Many people incorrectly guess that the phases of the Moon are caused by Earth's shadow falling on the Moon. How would you convince a friend that the phases of the Moon have nothing to do with Earth's shadow? Describe the observations you would use to show that Earth's shadow isn't the cause of phases.

Group Work Exercise

39. *Lunar Phases and Time of Day.* **Roles:** *Scribe* (takes notes on the group's activities), *Proposer* (proposes explanations to the group), *Skeptic* (points out weaknesses in proposed explanations), *Moderator* (leads group discussion and makes sure everyone contributes). **Activity:** The diagram below represents the Moon's orbit as seen from above Earth's North Pole (not to scale). Each group member should draw a copy of the diagram and label it as you work together on the following questions.

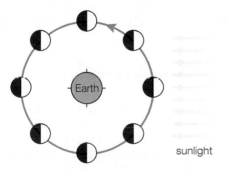

sunlight

    a. How would the Moon appear from Earth at each of the eight Moon positions? Label each one with the corresponding phase.

b. What time of day corresponds to each of the four tick marks on Earth? Label each tick mark accordingly.

c. Why doesn't the Moon's phase change during the course of one night? Explain your reasoning.

d. At what times of day would a full moon be visible to someone standing on Earth? Write down when a full moon rises and explain why it appears to rise at that time.

e. At what times of day would a third-quarter moon be visible to someone standing on Earth? Write down when a third-quarter moon sets and explain why it appears to set at that time.

f. At what times of day would a waxing crescent moon be visible to someone standing on Earth? Write down when a waxing crescent moon rises and explain why it appears to rise at that time.

Investigate Further

Short-Answer/Essay Questions

40. *New Planet.* A planet in another solar system has a circular orbit and an axis tilt of 35°. Would you expect this planet to have seasons? If so, would you expect them to be more extreme than the seasons on Earth? If not, why not?

41. *Your View of the Sky.*
    a. What are your latitude and longitude?
    b. Where does the north (or south) celestial pole appear in your sky?
    c. Is Polaris a circumpolar star in your sky? Explain.

42. *View from the Moon.* Suppose you lived on the Moon, in which case you would see Earth going through phases in your sky. Assume you live near the center of the face that looks toward Earth.
    a. Suppose you see a full Earth in your sky. What phase of the Moon would people on Earth see? Explain.
    b. Suppose people on Earth see a full moon. What phase would you see for Earth? Explain.
    c. Suppose people on Earth see a waxing gibbous moon. What phase would you see for Earth? Explain.
    d. Suppose people on Earth are viewing a total lunar eclipse. What would you see from your home on the Moon? Explain.

43. *View from the Sun.* Suppose you lived on the Sun (and could ignore the heat). Would you still see the Moon go through phases as it orbits Earth? Why or why not?

44. *Farther Moon.* Suppose the distance to the Moon were twice its actual value. Would it still be possible to have a total solar eclipse? Why or why not?

45. *Smaller Earth.* Suppose Earth were smaller. Would solar eclipses be any different? What about lunar eclipses? Explain.

46. *Observing Planetary Motion.* Find out what planets are currently visible in your evening sky. At least once a week, observe these planets and draw a diagram showing their positions relative to stars in a zodiac constellation. How long does it take to notice the "wandering" features of planetary motion? Explain.

Quantitative Problems

Be sure to show all calculations clearly and state your final answers in complete sentences.

47. *Arcminutes and Arcseconds.* There are 360° in a full circle.
    a. How many arcminutes are in a full circle?
    b. How many arcseconds are in a full circle?
    c. The Moon's angular size is about ½°. What is this in arcminutes? In arcseconds?

48. *Find the Sun's Diameter.* The Sun has an angular diameter of about 0.5° and an average distance from Earth of about 150 million km. What is the Sun's approximate physical diameter? Compare your answer to the actual value of 1,390,000 km.

49. *Find a Star's Diameter.* Estimate the diameter of the supergiant star Betelgeuse, using its measured angular diameter of about 0.5 arcsecond and distance of about 600 light-years. Compare your answer to the size of our Sun and the Earth–Sun distance.

50. *Eclipse Conditions.* The Moon's precise equatorial diameter is 3476 km, and its orbital distance from Earth varies between 356,400 km and 406,700 km. The Sun's diameter is 1,390,000 km, and its distance from Earth ranges between 147.5 and 152.6 million km.
    a. Find the Moon's angular size at its minimum and maximum distances from Earth.
    b. Find the Sun's angular size at its minimum and maximum distances from Earth.
    c. Based on your answers to (a) and (b), is it possible to have a total solar eclipse when the Moon and Sun are both at their maximum distances? Explain.

Discussion Questions

51. *Earth-Centered Language.* Many common phrases reflect the ancient Earth-centered view of our universe. For example, the phrase "the Sun rises each day" implies that the Sun is really moving over Earth. We know that the Sun only *appears* to rise as the rotation of Earth carries us to a place where we can see the Sun in our sky. Identify other common phrases that imply an Earth-centered viewpoint.

52. *Flat Earth Society.* Believe it or not, there is an organization called the Flat Earth Society. Its members hold that Earth is flat and that all indications to the contrary (such as pictures of Earth from space) are fabrications made as part of a conspiracy to hide the truth from the public. Discuss the evidence for a round Earth and how you can check it for yourself. In light of the evidence, is it possible that the Flat Earth Society is correct? Defend your opinion.

Web Projects

53. *Sky Information.* Search the Web for sources of daily information about sky phenomena (such as lunar phases, times of sunrise and sunset, or dates of equinoxes and solstices). Identify and briefly describe your favorite source.

54. *Constellations.* Search the Web for information about the constellations and their mythology. Write a one- to three-page report about one or more constellations.

55. *Eclipse Trip.* Find details about an upcoming total solar eclipse that you may be able to observe. Create a plan for a trip to see the eclipse, including details of where you will view it and how you will get there, and describe what you should expect to see. Bonus: Describe how you could photograph the eclipse.

3 The Science of Astronomy

Astronaut Bruce McCandless orbits Earth as if he were
a tiny moon during Space Shuttle mission STS-41-B.

Today we know that Earth is a planet orbiting a rather ordinary star, in a galaxy of more than a hundred billion stars, in an incredibly vast universe. We know that Earth, along with the entire cosmos, is in constant motion. We know that, on the scale of cosmic time, human civilization has existed for only the briefest moment. How did we manage to learn these things?

It wasn't easy. In this chapter, we will trace how modern astronomy grew from its roots in ancient observations, including those of the Greeks. We'll discuss the Copernican revolution, which overturned the ancient belief in an Earth-centered universe and laid the foundation for the rise of our technological civilization. Finally, we'll explore the nature of modern science and how science can be distinguished from nonscience.

3.1 The Ancient Roots of Science

The rigorous methods of modern science have proven to be one of the most valuable inventions in human history. These methods have enabled us to discover almost everything we now know about nature and the universe, and they also have made our modern technology possible. In this section, we will explore the ancient roots of science, which grew out of experiences common to nearly all people and all cultures.

◆ In what ways do all humans use scientific thinking?

Scientific thinking comes naturally to us. By about a year of age, a baby notices that objects fall to the ground when she drops them. She lets go of a ball—it falls. She pushes a plate of food from her high chair—it falls, too. She continues to drop all kinds of objects, and they all plummet to Earth. Through her powers of observation, the baby learns about the physical world, finding that things fall when they are unsupported. Eventually, she becomes so certain of this fact that, to her parents' delight, she no longer needs to test it continually.

One day someone gives the baby a helium balloon. She releases it, and to her surprise it rises to the ceiling! Her understanding of nature must be revised. She now knows that the principle "all things fall" does not represent the whole truth, although it still serves her quite well in most situations. It will be years before she learns enough about the atmosphere, the force of gravity, and the concept of density to understand *why* the balloon rises when most other objects fall. For now, she is delighted to observe something new and unexpected.

The baby's experience with falling objects and balloons exemplifies scientific thinking. In essence, science is a way of learning about nature through careful observation and trial-and-error experiments. Rather than thinking differently than other people, modern scientists simply are trained to organize everyday thinking in a way that makes it easier for them to share their discoveries and use their collective wisdom.

Scientific thinking is based on everyday observations and trial-and-error experiments.

think about it Describe a few cases where you have learned by trial and error—while cooking, participating in sports, fixing something, learning on the job, or in any other situation.

Just as learning to communicate through language, art, or music is a gradual process for a child, the development of science has been a gradual process for humanity. Science in its modern form requires painstaking attention to detail, relentless testing of each piece of information to ensure its reliability, and a willingness to give up old beliefs that are not consistent with observed facts about the physical world. For professional scientists, these demands are the "hard work" part of the job. At heart, professional scientists are like the baby with the balloon, delighted by the unexpected and motivated by those rare moments when they—and all of us—learn something new about the universe.

◆ How is modern science rooted in ancient astronomy?

Astronomy has been called the oldest of the sciences, because its roots stretch deepest into antiquity. Ancient civilizations did not always practice astronomy in the same ways or for the same reasons that we study it today, but they nonetheless had some amazing achievements. Understanding this ancient astronomy can give us a greater appreciation of how and why science developed through time.

Practical Benefits of Astronomy Humans have been making careful observations of the sky for many thousands of years. Part of the reason for this interest in astronomy probably comes from our inherent curiosity as humans, but ancient cultures also discovered that astronomy had practical benefits for timekeeping, keeping track of seasonal changes, and navigation.

One amazing example comes from people of central Africa. Although we do not know exactly when they developed the skill, people in some regions learned to predict rainfall patterns through observations

Ancient people used observations of the sky to keep track of the time and seasons and as an aid in navigation.

of the Moon. Figure 3.1 shows how the method works. The orientation of the "horns" of a waxing crescent moon (relative to the horizon) varies over the course of the year, primarily because the angle at which the ecliptic intersects the horizon changes during the

▼ **FIGURE 3.1**
In central Nigeria, the orientation of the "horns" of a waxing crescent moon (shown along the top) correlates with the average amount of rainfall at different times of year. Local people could use this fact to predict the weather with reasonable accuracy. (Adapted from *Ancient Astronomers* by Anthony F. Aveni.)

TABLE 3.1 The Seven Days of the Week and the Astronomical Objects They Honor

The seven days were originally linked directly to the seven objects. The correspondence is no longer perfect, but the pattern is clear in many languages; some English names come from Germanic gods.

Object	Germanic God	English	French	Spanish
Sun	—	Sunday	dimanche	domingo
Moon	—	Monday	lundi	lunes
Mars	Tiw	Tuesday	mardi	martes
Mercury	Woden	Wednesday	mercredi	miércoles
Jupiter	Thor	Thursday	jeudi	jueves
Venus	Fria	Friday	vendredi	viernes
Saturn	—	Saturday	samedi	sábado

▲ **FIGURE 3.2**

This ancient Egyptian obelisk resides in St. Peter's Square at the Vatican in Rome; it is one of 21 surviving Egyptian obelisks. Shadows cast by the obelisks may have been used to tell time.

▲ **FIGURE 3.3**

The remains of Stonehenge, which was built in stages from about 2750 B.C. to about 1550 B.C.

year. (The orientation also depends on latitude.) In tropical regions in which there are distinct rainy and dry seasons—rather than the four seasons familiar at temperate latitudes—the orientation of the crescent moon can be used to predict how much rainfall should be expected over coming days and weeks.

Astronomy and Measures of Time The impact of ancient astronomical observations is still with us in our modern measures of time. The length of our day is the time it takes the Sun to make one full circuit of the sky. The length of a month comes from the Moon's cycle of phases [Section 2.3], and our year is based on the cycle of the seasons [Section 2.2]. The seven days of the week were named after the seven "planets" of ancient times (Table 3.1), which were the Sun, the Moon, and the five planets that are easily visible to the naked eye: Mercury, Venus, Mars, Jupiter, Saturn. Note that the ancient definition of *planet* (which meant "wandering star") applied to any object that appeared to wander among the fixed stars. That is why the Sun and Moon were on the list while Earth was not, because we don't see our own planet moving in the sky.

think about it Uranus is faintly visible to the naked eye, but it was not recognized as a planet in ancient times. If Uranus had been brighter, would we now have eight days in a week? Defend your opinion.

Because timekeeping was so important and required precise observations, many ancient cultures built structures or created special devices to help with it. Let's briefly investigate a few of the ways that ancient cultures learned to keep track of time.

The seven days of the week are named for the seven "planets" known in ancient times.

Determining the Time of Day In the daytime, ancient peoples could tell time by observing the Sun's path through the sky. Many cultures probably used the shadows cast by sticks as simple sundials. The ancient Egyptians built huge obelisks, often decorated in homage to the Sun, which probably also served as simple clocks (Figure 3.2). At night, ancient people could estimate the time from the position and phase of the Moon (see Figure 2.21) or by observing the constellations visible at a particular time (see Figure 2.14).

We also trace the origins of our modern clock to ancient Egypt. Some 4000 years ago, the Egyptians divided daytime and nighttime into 12 equal parts each, which is how we got our 12 hours each of a.m. and p.m. The abbreviations a.m. and p.m. stand for the Latin terms *ante meridiem* and *post meridiem,* respectively, which mean "before the middle of the day" and "after the middle of the day."

Marking the Seasons Many ancient cultures built structures to help them mark the seasons. Stonehenge (Figure 3.3) is a well-known example that served both as an astronomical device and as a social and religious gathering place. In the Americas, one of the most spectacular structures was the Templo Mayor (Figure 3.4) in the Aztec city of Tenochtitlán (in modern-day Mexico City), which featured twin temples on a flat-topped pyramid. From the vantage point of a royal observer watching from the opposite side of the plaza, the Sun rose through the notch between the temples on the equinoxes.

Many cultures aligned buildings and streets with the cardinal directions (north, south, east, and west), which made it easier to keep track of the rise and set positions of the Sun over the course of the year. Other structures marked special dates. For example, the Ancestral Pueblo People carved a spiral—known as the *Sun Dagger*—on a cliff face in Chaco Canyon, New Mexico (Figure 3.5). The Sun's rays formed a dagger of sunlight that pierced the center of the carved spiral only at noon on the summer solstice.

Solar and Lunar Calendars The tracking of the seasons eventually led to the advent of written calendars. Today, we use a *solar calendar*, meaning a calendar that is synchronized with the seasons so that seasonal events such as the solstices and equinoxes occur on approximately the same dates each year. However, recall that the length of our month comes from the Moon's 29½-day cycle of phases. Some cultures therefore created *lunar calendars* that aimed to stay synchronized with the lunar cycle, so that the Moon's phase was always the same on the first day of each month.

A basic lunar calendar has 12 months, with some months lasting 29 days and others lasting 30 days; the lengths are chosen to make the average agree with the approximately 29½-day lunar cycle. A 12-month lunar calendar therefore has 354 or 355 days, or about 11 days fewer than a calendar based on the Sun. Such a calendar is still used in the Muslim religion. That is why the month-long fast of Ramadan (the ninth month) begins about 11 days earlier with each subsequent year.

A lunar calendar always has the same moon phase on the first day of each month.

It's possible to keep lunar calendars roughly synchronized with solar calendars by taking advantage of a timing coincidence: 19 years on a solar calendar is almost precisely 235 months on a lunar calendar. As a result, the lunar phases repeat on the same solar dates about every 19 years (a pattern known as the *Metonic cycle*). For example, there was a full moon on February 11, 2017, and there will be a full moon 19 years later, on February 11, 2036. Because an ordinary lunar calendar has only 19 × 12 = 228 months in a 19-year period, adding 7 extra months (to make 235) can keep the lunar calendar roughly synchronized to the seasons. The Jewish calendar does this by adding a thirteenth month in the third, sixth, eighth, eleventh, fourteenth, seventeenth, and nineteenth years of each 19-year cycle.

Learning About Ancient Achievements The study of ancient astronomical achievements is a rich field of research. Many ancient cultures made careful observations of planets and stars, and some left remarkably detailed records. The Chinese, for example, began recording astronomical observations at least 5000 years ago, allowing ancient Chinese astronomers to make many important discoveries.

Other cultures either did not leave clear written records or had records that were lost or destroyed, so we must piece together their astronomical achievements by studying the physical evidence they left behind. This type of study is usually called *archaeoastronomy*, a word that combines archaeology and astronomy.

Archaeoastronomy is the study of astronomical uses of ancient structures.

The cases we've discussed to this point have been fairly straightforward for archaeoastronomers to interpret, but many other cases are more ambiguous. For example, ancient people in what is now Peru etched hundreds of lines and patterns in the sand of the Nazca desert. Many of the lines point to places where the Sun or bright stars rise at particular times of year, but that doesn't prove anything: With hundreds of lines, random chance ensures that many will have astronomical alignments no matter how or why they were made. The patterns, many of which are large figures of animals (Figure 3.6), have evoked even more debate. Some people think they may be representations of constellations

▲ **FIGURE 3.4**
This scale model shows the Templo Mayor and the surrounding plaza as they are thought to have looked five centuries ago.

▲ **FIGURE 3.5**
The Sun Dagger. Three large slabs of rock are arranged so that a dagger of sunlight pierced the carved spiral only at noon on the summer solstice. (Unfortunately, within just 12 years of the site's 1977 discovery, erosion caused the rocks to shift so that the effect no longer occurs.)

▲ **FIGURE 3.6**
Hundreds of lines and patterns are etched in the sand of the Nazca desert in Peru. This aerial photo shows a large figure of a hummingbird.

▲ FIGURE 3.7
The World Heritage Site of Machu Picchu has structures aligned with sunrise at the winter and summer solstices.

▲ FIGURE 3.8
Polynesian Navigators used astronomy and ocean swell patterns to navigate among Pacific islands. Here, we see a Micronesian stick chart, an instrument used to represent swell patterns around islands.

recognized by the people who lived in the region, but we do not know for sure.

In some cases, scientists can use other clues to establish the intentions of ancient builders. For example, traditions of the Inca Empire of South America held that its rulers were descendants of the Sun and therefore demanded that movements of the Sun be watched closely. This fact supports the idea that astronomical alignments in Inca cities and ceremonial centers, such as the World Heritage Site of Machu Picchu (Figure 3.7), were deliberate rather than accidental.

A different type of evidence makes a convincing case for the astronomical sophistication of ancient Polynesians, who lived and traveled among the many islands of the mid- and South Pacific. Navigation was crucial to survival, because the next island in a journey usually was too distant to be seen. The most esteemed position in Polynesian culture was that of the Navigator, a person who had acquired the knowledge necessary to navigate great distances among the islands. Navigators used a detailed knowledge of astronomy for their broad navigational sense, and a deep understanding of wave and swell patterns to locate precise landing points (Figure 3.8).

3.2 Ancient Greek Science

Before a structure such as Stonehenge or the Templo Mayor could be built, careful observations had to be made and repeated over and over to ensure their accuracy. Careful, repeatable observations also underlie modern science. Elements of modern science were therefore present in many early human cultures. If the circumstances of history had been different, almost any culture might have been the first to develop what we consider to be modern science. In the end, however, history takes only one of countless possible paths. The path that led to modern science emerged from the ancient civilizations of the Mediterranean and the Middle East—especially from ancient Greece.

◆ Why does modern science trace its roots to the Greeks?

Greece gradually rose as a power in the Middle East beginning around 800 B.C. and was well established by about 500 B.C. Its geographical location placed it at a crossroads for travelers, merchants, and armies from northern Africa, Asia, and Europe. Building on the diverse ideas brought forth by the meeting of these many cultures, ancient Greek philosophers soon began their efforts to move human understanding of nature from the mythological to the rational.

Three Philosophical Innovations Greek philosophers developed at least three major innovations that helped pave the way for modern science. First, they developed a tradition of trying to understand nature without relying on supernatural explanations, and of working communally to debate and challenge each other's ideas. Second, the Greeks used mathematics to give precision to their ideas, which allowed them to explore the implications of new ideas in much greater depth than would have otherwise been possible. Third, while much of their philosophical activity consisted of subtle debates grounded only in thought and was not scientific in the modern sense, the Greeks also saw the power of reasoning from observations. They understood that an explanation could not be right if it disagreed with observed facts.

Models of Nature Perhaps the greatest Greek contribution to science came from the way they synthesized all three of the above innovations in creating models of nature, a practice that is central to modern science. Scientific models differ somewhat from the models you may be familiar with in everyday life. In our daily lives, we tend to think of models as miniature physical representations, such as model cars or airplanes. In contrast, a scientific **model** is a conceptual representation created to explain and predict observed phenomena.

For example, a scientific model of Earth's climate uses logic and mathematics to represent what we know about how the climate works.

The Greeks developed models of nature that aimed to explain and predict observed phenomena.

Its purpose is to explain and predict climate changes, such as the changes that may occur with global warming. Just as a model airplane does not faithfully represent every aspect of a real airplane, a scientific model may not fully explain our observations of nature. Nevertheless, even the failings of a scientific model can be useful, because they often point the way toward building a better model.

In astronomy, the Greeks constructed conceptual models of the universe in an attempt to explain what they observed in the sky, an effort that quickly led them past simplistic ideas of a flat Earth under a dome-shaped sky. We do not know precisely when other Greeks began to think that Earth is round, but this idea was being taught by about 500 B.C. by the famous mathematician Pythagoras (c. 560–480 B.C.). He and his followers envisioned Earth as a sphere floating at the center of the celestial sphere. More than a century later, Aristotle cited observations of Earth's curved shadow on the Moon during lunar eclipses as evidence for a spherical Earth. Greek philosophers therefore adopted a **geocentric model** of the universe with a spherical Earth at the center of a great celestial sphere.

From Greece to the Renaissance Before we discuss the Greek geocentric model, it's worth briefly discussing how ancient Greek philosophy was passed to Europe, where it ultimately grew into the principles of modern science. Greek philosophy began to spread widely with the conquests of Alexander the Great (356–323 B.C.). Alexander had a deep interest in science, perhaps in part because Aristotle had been his personal tutor. Alexander founded the city of Alexandria in Egypt, and his successors founded the renowned Library of Alexandria (Figure 3.9). Though it is sometimes difficult to distinguish fact from legend in stories of this great library, there is little doubt that it was once the world's preeminent center of research, housing up to a half million books written on papyrus scrolls. Most were ultimately burned, their contents lost forever.

> **think about it** Estimate the number of books you're likely to read in your lifetime and compare this number to the half million books once housed in the Library of Alexandria. Can you think of other ways to put into perspective the loss of ancient wisdom resulting from the destruction of the Library of Alexandria?

The relatively few books from the library that survive today were preserved primarily thanks to scholars of the new religion of Islam. Around A.D. 800, the Islamic leader Al-Mamun (A.D. 786–833) established a "House of Wisdom" in Baghdad (in present-day Iraq), where Islamic scholars—often working together with colleagues from other

cosmic calculations 3.1

Eratosthenes Measures Earth

The first accurate estimate of Earth's circumference was made by the Greek scientist Eratosthenes in about 240 B.C. Eratosthenes knew that the Sun passed directly overhead in the Egyptian city of Syene (modern-day Aswan) on the summer solstice and that on the same day the Sun came only within 7° of the zenith in Alexandria. He concluded that Alexandria must be 7° of latitude north of Syene (see figure), making the north-south distance between the two cities $\frac{7}{360}$ of Earth's circumference.

Eratosthenes estimated the north-south distance between Syene and Alexandria to be 5000 stadia (the *stadium* was a Greek unit of distance), which meant

$$\frac{7}{360} \times \text{Earth's circumference} = 5000 \text{ stadia}$$

Multiplying both sides by $\frac{360}{7}$ gives us

$$\text{Earth's circumference} = \frac{360}{7} \times 5000 \text{ stadia}$$
$$\approx 250,000 \text{ stadia}$$

Based on the actual sizes of Greek stadiums, we estimate that stadia must have been about $\frac{1}{6}$ km each, making Eratosthenes' estimate about $\frac{250,000}{6} = 42,000$ km—remarkably close to the actual value of just over 40,000 km.

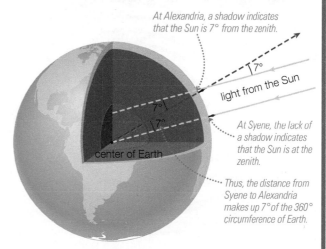

At Alexandria, a shadow indicates that the Sun is 7° from the zenith.

light from the Sun

At Syene, the lack of a shadow indicates that the Sun is at the zenith.

Thus, the distance from Syene to Alexandria makes up 7° of the 360° circumference of Earth.

center of Earth

This diagram shows how Eratosthenes concluded that the north-south distance from Syene to Alexandria is $\frac{7}{360}$ of Earth's circumference.

a This painting shows a courtyard of the ancient Library of Alexandria, as it may have looked shortly after its completion.

b The New Library of Alexandria in Egypt, which opened in 2003.

▲ FIGURE 3.9
The ancient Library of Alexandria thrived for centuries, starting some time after about 300 B.C.

▲ FIGURE 3.10
This model represents the Greek idea of the heavenly spheres (c. 400 B.C.). Earth is a sphere that rests in the center. The Moon, the Sun, and the planets each have their own spheres. The outermost sphere holds the stars.

religions—translated and thereby saved many ancient Greek works. They were also in frequent contact with Hindu scholars from India, who in turn brought knowledge of ideas and discoveries from China, which allowed the Islamic scholars to achieve a synthesis of the surviving work of the ancient Greeks along with that of the Indians and the Chinese. Using all these ideas as building blocks, scholars in the House of Wisdom developed the mathematics of algebra and many new instruments and techniques for astronomical observation. The latter explains why many official constellation and star names come from Arabic; for example, the names of many bright stars begin with *al* (e.g., Aldebaran, Algol), which simply means "the" in Arabic.

The accumulated knowledge of the Baghdad scholars spread throughout the Byzantine empire (part of the former Roman Empire).

> Islamic scholars preserved and extended ancient Greek scholarship, and their work helped ignite the European Renaissance.

When the Byzantine capital of Constantinople (modern-day Istanbul) fell to the Turks in 1453, many scholars headed west to Europe, carrying with them the knowledge that helped ignite the European Renaissance.

◆ How did the Greeks explain planetary motion?

Greek philosophers quickly realized that there had to be more to the heavens than just a single sphere surrounding Earth. To account for the fact that the Sun and Moon each move gradually eastward through the constellations, the Greeks added separate spheres for them, with these spheres turning at different rates from the sphere of the stars. The planets also move relative to the stars, so the Greeks added an additional sphere for each planet (Figure 3.10).

The difficulty with this model was that it made it hard to explain the apparent retrograde motion of the planets [Section 2.4]. You might guess that the Greeks would simply have allowed the planetary spheres to sometimes turn forward and sometimes turn backward relative to the sphere of the stars, but they did not because it would have violated their deeply held belief in "heavenly perfection." According to this idea, enunciated most clearly by Plato, heavenly objects could move only in perfect circles. But how could the planets sometimes go backward in our sky if they were moving in perfect circles?

One potential answer would have been to discard the geocentric model and replace it with a Sun-centered model, which gives a simple and natural explanation for apparent retrograde motion (see Figure 2.30). However, while such a model had been proposed by Aristarchus in about 260 B.C., it never gained much support in ancient times (in part because of the lack of detectable stellar parallax [Section 2.4]). Instead, the Greeks found ingenious ways to explain planetary motion while preserving Earth's central position and motion in perfect circles. The final synthesis of these ideas came with the work of Claudius Ptolemy (c. A.D. 100–170; pronounced *tol-e-mee*). We refer to Ptolemy's model as the **Ptolemaic model** to distinguish it from earlier geocentric models.

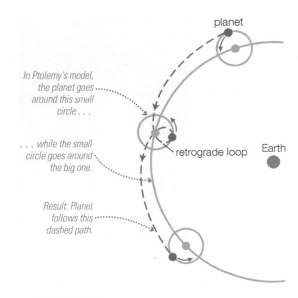

▲ FIGURE 3.11

This diagram shows how the Ptolemaic model accounted for apparent retrograde motion. Each planet is assumed to move around a small circle that turns upon a larger circle. The resulting path (dashed) includes a loop in which the planet goes backward as seen from Earth.

The essence of the Ptolemaic model was that each planet moves on a small circle whose center moves around Earth on a larger circle (Figure 3.11).

In the Ptolemaic model, each planet moved on a small circle whose center moved around Earth on a larger circle. (The small circle is called an *epicycle*, and the larger circle is called a *deferent*.) A planet following this circle-upon-circle motion traces a loop as seen from Earth, with the backward portion of the loop mimicking apparent retrograde motion. However, to make his model agree well with observations, Ptolemy had to include a number of other complexities, such as positioning some of the large circles slightly off-center from Earth. As a result, the full Ptolemaic model was mathematically complex and tedious. Many centuries later, while supervising computations based on the Ptolemaic model, the Spanish monarch Alphonso X (1221–1284) is said to have complained, "If I had been present at the creation, I would have recommended a simpler design for the universe."

Despite its complexity, the Ptolemaic model worked remarkably well: It could correctly forecast future planetary positions to within a few degrees of arc, which is about the angular size of your hand held at arm's length against the sky. This was sufficiently accurate to keep the model in use for the next 1500 years. When Ptolemy's book describing the model was translated by Arabic scholars around A.D. 800, they gave it the title *Almagest*, derived from words meaning "the greatest work."

3.3 The Copernican Revolution

The Greeks and other ancient peoples developed many important scientific ideas, but what we now think of as science arose during the European Renaissance. Within a half century of the fall of Constantinople, Polish scientist Nicholas Copernicus began the work that ultimately overturned the Earth-centered Ptolemaic model.

◆ How did Copernicus, Tycho, and Kepler challenge the Earth-centered model?

The ideas introduced by Copernicus fundamentally changed the way we perceive our place in the universe. The story of this dramatic change, known as the **Copernican revolution,** is in many ways the story of the origin of modern science. It is also the story of several key personalities, beginning with Copernicus himself.

Copernicus   Copernicus was born in Torún, Poland, on February 19, 1473. He began studying astronomy in his late teens, and soon learned

common misconceptions

Columbus and a Flat Earth

A widespread myth gives credit to Columbus for learning that Earth is round, but knowledge of Earth's shape predated Columbus by nearly 2000 years. Not only were scholars of Columbus's time well aware that Earth is round, they even knew its approximate size: Earth's circumference was first measured in about 240 B.C. by the Greek scientist Eratosthenes. In fact, a likely reason Columbus had so much difficulty finding a sponsor for his voyages was that he tried to argue a point on which he was wrong: He claimed the distance by sea from western Europe to eastern Asia to be much less than scholars knew it to be. When he finally found a patron in Spain and left on his journey, he was so woefully underprepared that the voyage would almost certainly have ended in disaster if the Americas hadn't stood in his way.

Copernicus (1473–1543)

that tables of planetary motion based on the Ptolemaic model had been growing increasingly inaccurate. He began a quest to find a better way to predict planetary positions.

Copernicus was aware of and adopted Aristarchus's ancient Sun-centered idea, perhaps because it offered such a simple explanation for the apparent retrograde motion of the planets. But he went beyond Aristarchus in working out mathematical details of the model. In the process, Copernicus discovered simple geometric relationships that strengthened his belief in the Sun-centered idea, because they allowed him to calculate each planet's orbital period and relative distance (compared to Earth's distance) from the Sun.

Copernicus was nonetheless hesitant to publish his work, fearing that the idea of a moving Earth would be considered absurd. However, he discussed his system with other scholars, including high-ranking officials of the Church, who urged him to publish a book. Copernicus saw the first printed copy of his book, *De Revolutionibus Orbium Coelestium* ("On the Revolutions of the Heavenly Spheres"), on the day he died—May 24, 1543.

Publication of the book spread the Sun-centered idea widely, and many scholars were drawn to its aesthetic advantages. However, the Copernican model gained relatively few converts over the next 50 years, for a good reason: It didn't work all that well. The primary problem was that while Copernicus had been willing to overturn Earth's central place in the cosmos, he held fast to the ancient belief that heavenly motion must occur in perfect circles. This incorrect assumption forced him to add numerous complexities to his system (including circles on circles much like those used by Ptolemy) to get it to make decent predictions. In the end, his complete model was no more accurate and no less complex than the Ptolemaic model, and few people were willing to throw out thousands of years of tradition for a new model that worked just as poorly as the old one.

> Copernicus's Sun-centered model was based on the right general ideas, but its predictions were not substantially better than those of Ptolemy's Earth-centered model.

Tycho Part of the difficulty faced by astronomers who sought to improve either the Ptolemaic or the Copernican models was a lack of quality data. The telescope had not yet been invented, and existing naked-eye observations were not very accurate. Better data were needed, and they were provided by the Danish nobleman Tycho Brahe (1546–1601), usually known simply as Tycho (pronounced "tie-koe").

Tycho was an eccentric genius who once lost part of his nose in a sword fight with another student over who was the better mathematician. In 1563, Tycho decided to observe a widely anticipated alignment of Jupiter and Saturn. To his surprise, the alignment occurred nearly 2 days later than the date Copernicus had predicted. Resolving to improve the state of astronomical prediction, he set about compiling careful observations of stellar and planetary positions in the sky.

Tycho's fame grew after he observed what he called a *nova*, meaning "new star," in 1572 and showed that it was much farther away than the Moon. (Today, we know that Tycho saw a *supernova*—the explosion of a distant star [Section 13.3].) In 1577, Tycho observed a comet and showed that it too lay in the realm of the heavens. Others, including Aristotle, had argued that comets were phenomena of Earth's atmosphere. King Frederick II of Denmark decided to sponsor Tycho's ongoing work, providing him with money to build an unparalleled observatory for

Tycho Brahe (1546–1601)

naked-eye observations (Figure 3.12). After Frederick II died in 1588, Tycho moved to Prague, where his work was supported by German emperor Rudolf II.

Over a period of three decades, Tycho and his assistants compiled naked-eye observations accurate to within less than 1 arcminute—less than the thickness of a finger-nail viewed at arm's length. Despite the quality of his observations, Tycho never succeeded in coming up with a satisfying explanation for planetary motion. He was convinced that the *planets* must orbit the Sun, but his inability to detect stellar parallax [Section 2.4] led him to conclude that Earth must remain stationary. He therefore advocated a model in which the Sun orbits Earth while all other planets orbit the Sun. Few people took this model seriously.

Tycho's accurate naked-eye observations provided the data needed to improve the Copernican system.

Kepler Tycho failed to explain the motions of the planets satisfactorily, but he succeeded in finding someone who could: In 1600, he hired the young German astronomer Johannes Kepler (1571–1630). Kepler and Tycho had a strained relationship, but Tycho recognized the talent of his young apprentice. In 1601, as he lay on his deathbed, Tycho begged Kepler to find a system that would make sense of his observations so "that it may not appear I have lived in vain."

Kepler was deeply religious and believed that understanding the geometry of the heavens would bring him closer to God. Like Copernicus, he believed that planetary orbits should be perfect circles, so he worked diligently to match circular motions to Tycho's data. After years of effort, he found a set of circular orbits that matched most of Tycho's observations quite well. Even in the worst cases, which were for the planet Mars, Kepler's predicted positions differed from Tycho's observations by only about 8 arcminutes.

Kepler surely was tempted to attribute these discrepancies to errors by Tycho. After all, 8 arcminutes is barely one-fourth the angular diameter of the full moon. But Kepler trusted Tycho's work. The small discrepancies finally led Kepler to abandon the idea of circular orbits—and to find the correct solution to the ancient riddle of planetary motion. About this event, Kepler wrote:

> If I had believed that we could ignore these eight minutes [of arc], I would have patched up my hypothesis accordingly. But, since it was not permissible to ignore, those eight minutes pointed the road to a complete reformation in astronomy.

Kepler's key discovery was that planetary orbits are not circles but instead are a special type of oval called an **ellipse.** You can draw a circle by putting a pencil on the end of a string, tacking the string to a board, and pulling the pencil around (Figure 3.13a). Drawing an ellipse is similar, except that you must stretch the string around *two* tacks (Figure 3.13b). The locations of the two tacks are called the **foci** (singular, **focus**) of the ellipse. The long axis of the ellipse is called its *major axis*, each half of which is called a **semimajor axis;** as we'll see shortly, the length of the semimajor axis is particularly important in astronomy. The short axis is called the *minor axis*. By altering the distance between the two foci while keeping the length of string the same, you can draw ellipses of varying **eccentricity,** a quantity that describes how much an ellipse is stretched out compared to a perfect circle (Figure 3.13c). A circle is an ellipse with zero eccentricity, and greater eccentricity means a more elongated ellipse.

▲ **FIGURE 3.12**

Tycho Brahe in his naked-eye observatory, which worked much like a giant protractor. He could sit and observe a planet through the rectangular hole in the wall as an assistant used a sliding marker to measure the angle on the protractor.

Johannes Kepler (1571–1630)

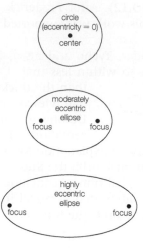

a Drawing a circle with a string of fixed length.

b Drawing an ellipse with a string of fixed length.

c Eccentricity describes how much an ellipse deviates from a perfect circle.

▲ **FIGURE 3.13**

An ellipse is a special type of oval. These diagrams show how an ellipse differs from a circle and how different ellipses vary in their eccentricity.

▲ **FIGURE 3.14**

Kepler's first law: The orbit of each planet about the Sun is an ellipse with the Sun at one focus. (The eccentricity shown here is exaggerated compared to the actual eccentricities of the planets.)

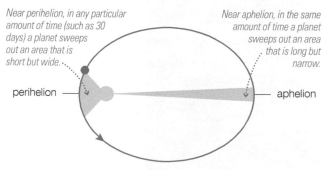

▲ **FIGURE 3.15**

Kepler's second law: As a planet moves around its orbit, an imaginary line connecting it to the Sun sweeps out equal areas (the shaded regions) in equal times.

Kepler's decision to trust the data over his preconceived beliefs marked an important transition point in the history of science. Once he abandoned perfect circles in favor of ellipses, Kepler soon came up with a model that could predict planetary positions with far greater accuracy than Ptolemy's Earth-centered model. Kepler's model withstood the test of time and became accepted not only as a model of nature but also as a deep, underlying truth about planetary motion.

> By using elliptical orbits, Kepler created a Sun-centered model that predicted planetary positions with outstanding accuracy.

◆ What are Kepler's three laws of planetary motion?

Kepler summarized his discoveries with three simple laws that we now call **Kepler's laws of planetary motion.** He published the first two laws in 1609 and the third in 1619.

Kepler's first law tells us that the orbit of each planet about the Sun is an ellipse with the Sun at one focus (Figure 3.14). This law tells us that a planet's distance from the Sun varies during its orbit. It is closest at the point called **perihelion** (from the Greek for "near the Sun") and farthest at the point called **aphelion** ("away from the Sun"). The *average* of a planet's perihelion and aphelion distances is the length of its *semimajor axis*. We will refer to this simply as the planet's average distance from the Sun.

> Kepler's first law: The orbit of each planet about the Sun is an ellipse with the Sun at one focus.

Kepler's second law states that as a planet moves around its elliptical orbit, it moves faster when it is nearer the Sun and slower when it is farther from the Sun, sweeping out equal areas in equal times. As shown in Figure 3.15, the "sweeping" refers to an imaginary line connecting the planet to the Sun, and keeping the areas equal means that the planet moves a greater distance (and hence is moving faster) when it is near perihelion than it does in the same amount of time near aphelion.

> Kepler's second law: A planet moves faster in the part of its orbit nearer the Sun and slower when farther from the Sun, sweeping out equal areas in equal times.

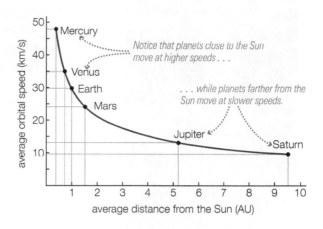

a This graph shows that Kepler's third law ($p^2 = a^3$) holds true; the graph shows only the planets known in Kepler's time.

b This graph, based on Kepler's third law and modern values of planetary distances, shows that more distant planets orbit the Sun more slowly.

▲ **FIGURE 3.16**

Graphs based on Kepler's third law.

Kepler's third law tells us that more distant planets orbit the Sun at slower average speeds. Mathematically, it states that planets obey the relationship $p^2 = a^3$, where p is the planet's orbital period in years and a is its average distance from the Sun in astronomical units. Figure 3.16a shows the $p^2 = a^3$ law graphically; notice that the square of each planet's orbital period (p^2) is indeed equal to the cube of its average distance from the Sun (a^3). Because Kepler's third law relates orbital distance to orbital time (period), we can use the law to calculate a planet's average orbital speed. Figure 3.16b shows the result, confirming that more distant planets orbit the Sun more slowly.

Kepler's third law: More distant planets orbit the Sun at slower average speeds, obeying the relationship $p^2 = a^3$.

> **think about it** Suppose a comet has an orbit that brings it quite close to the Sun at its perihelion and beyond Mars at its aphelion, but with an average distance (semimajor axis) of 1 AU. How long would the comet take to complete each orbit of the Sun? Would it spend most of its time close to the Sun, far from the Sun, or somewhere in between? Explain.

The fact that more distant planets move more slowly led Kepler to suggest that planetary motion might be the result of a force from the Sun. He did not know the nature of the force, which was later identified as gravity by Isaac Newton.

◆ How did Galileo solidify the Copernican revolution?

The success of Kepler's laws in matching Tycho's data provided strong evidence in favor of Copernicus's placement of the Sun at the center of the solar system. Nevertheless, many scientists still voiced objections to the Copernican view. There were three basic objections, all rooted in the 2000-year-old beliefs of Aristotle and other ancient Greeks.

- First, Aristotle had held that Earth could not be moving because, if it were, objects such as birds, falling stones, and clouds would be left behind as Earth moved along its way.

cosmic calculations 3.2

Kepler's Third Law

Kepler's third law in its original form, $p^2 = a^3$, applies to any orbiting object that meets the following two conditions:

1. it orbits the Sun *or* a star of the same mass, and
2. we measure *period in years* and *distance in AU*.

(Newton extended the law to *all* orbiting objects; see Cosmic Calculations 4.1.)

Example 1: Find the orbital period of the dwarf planet (and largest asteroid) Ceres, which orbits the Sun at an average distance (semimajor axis) of 2.77 AU.

Solution: Both conditions are met, so we solve Kepler's third law for the orbital period p and substitute the given orbital distance, $a = 2.77$ AU:

$$p^2 = a^3 \Rightarrow p = \sqrt{a^3} = \sqrt{2.77^3} = 4.6$$

Ceres has an orbital period of 4.6 years.

Example 2: Find the orbital distance of a planet that orbits a star of the same mass as our Sun with a period of 3 months.

Solution: The first condition is met, and we can satisfy the second by converting the orbital period from months to years: $p = 3$ months $= 0.25$ year. We now solve Kepler's third law for the average distance a:

$$p^2 = a^3 \Rightarrow a = \sqrt[3]{p^2} = \sqrt[3]{0.25^2} = 0.40$$

The planet orbits its star at an average distance of 0.40 AU, which is slightly greater than Mercury's orbital distance from the Sun.

Galileo (1564–1642)

- Second, the idea of noncircular orbits contradicted Aristotle's claim that the heavens—the realm of the Sun, Moon, planets, and stars—must be perfect and unchanging.

- Third, no one had detected the stellar parallax that should occur if Earth orbits the Sun [Section 2.4].

Galileo Galilei (1564–1642), usually known by his first name, answered all three objections.

Galileo's Evidence   Galileo defused the first objection with experiments that almost single-handedly overturned the Aristotelian view of physics. In particular, he used experiments with rolling balls to demonstrate that a moving object remains in motion *unless* a force acts to stop it (an idea now codified in Newton's first law of motion [Section 4.2]). This insight explained why objects that share Earth's motion through space—such as birds, falling stones, and clouds—should *stay* with Earth rather than falling behind as Aristotle had argued. This same idea explains why passengers stay with a moving airplane even when they leave their seats.

The second objection had already been challenged by Tycho's supernova and comet observations, which demonstrated that the heavens could change. Galileo shattered the idea of heavenly perfection after he built a telescope in late 1609. (Galileo did not invent the telescope, but his innovations made it much more powerful.) Through his telescope, Galileo saw sunspots on the Sun, which were considered "imperfections" at the time. He also used his telescope to observe that the Moon has mountains and valleys like the "imperfect" Earth by noticing the shadows cast near the dividing line between the light and dark portions of the lunar face (Figure 3.17). If the heavens were in fact not perfect, then the idea of elliptical orbits (as opposed to "perfect" circles) was not so objectionable.

The third objection—the absence of observable stellar parallax—had been of particular concern to Tycho. Based on his estimates of the distances of stars, Tycho believed that his naked-eye observations were sufficiently precise to detect stellar parallax if Earth did in fact orbit the Sun. Refuting Tycho's argument required showing that the stars were more distant than Tycho had thought and therefore too distant for him to have

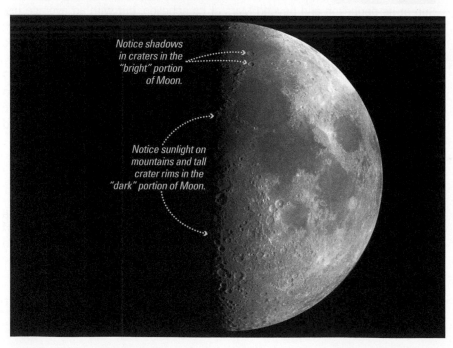

Notice shadows in craters in the "bright" portion of Moon.

Notice sunlight on mountains and tall crater rims in the "dark" portion of Moon.

▶ **FIGURE 3.17**

The shadows cast by mountains and crater rims near the dividing line between the light and dark portions of the lunar face show that the Moon's surface is not perfectly smooth.

obscrved stellar parallax. Although Galileo didn't actually prove this fact, he provided strong evidence in its favor. For example, he saw with his telescope that the Milky Way resolved into countless individual stars. This discovery helped him argue that the stars were far more numerous and more distant than Tycho had believed.

In hindsight, the final nails in the coffin of the Earth-centered model came with two of Galileo's earliest discoveries through the tele-

Galileo's experiments and telescopic observations overcame remaining scientific objections to the Copernican idea, sealing the case for the Sun-centered solar system.

scope. First, he observed four moons clearly orbiting Jupiter, not Earth (Figure 3.18). Soon thereafter, he observed that Venus goes through phases in a way that meant that it must orbit the Sun and not Earth (Figure 3.19).

Galileo and the Church Although we now recognize that Galileo won the day, the story was more complex in his own time, when Catholic Church doctrine still held Earth to be the center of the universe. On June 22, 1633, Galileo was brought before a Church inquisition in Rome and ordered to recant his claim that Earth orbits the Sun. Nearly 70 years old and fearing for his life, Galileo did as ordered. His life was spared. However, legend has it that as he rose from his knees he whispered under his breath, *Eppur si muove*—Italian for "And yet it moves." (Given the likely consequences if Church officials had heard him say this, most historians doubt the legend.)

The Church did not formally vindicate Galileo until 1992, but Church officials gave up the argument long before that: In 1757, all works backing the idea of a Sun-centered solar system were removed from the Church's Index of banned books. Moreover, Catholic scientists have long worked at the forefront of much astronomical research, and today's official Church teachings are compatible not only with Earth's planetary status but also with the theories of the Big Bang and the subsequent evolution of the cosmos and of life.

▲ **FIGURE 3.18**

A page from Galileo's notebook written in 1610. His sketches show four "stars" near Jupiter (the circle) but in different positions at different times (and sometimes hidden from view). Galileo soon realized that the "stars" were actually moons orbiting Jupiter.

▼ **FIGURE 3.19**

Galileo's telescopic observations of Venus showed that it orbits the Sun rather than Earth.

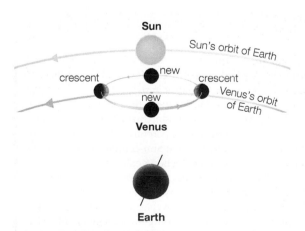

a In the Ptolemaic system, Venus orbits Earth, moving around a smaller circle on its larger orbital circle; the center of the smaller circle lies on the Earth–Sun line. If this view were correct, Venus's phases would range only from new to crescent.

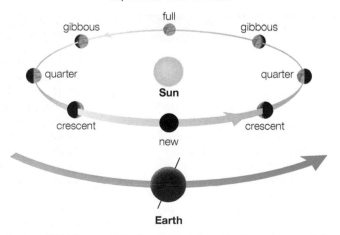

b In reality, Venus orbits the Sun, so from Earth we can see it in many different phases. This is just what Galileo observed, which convinced him that Venus orbits the Sun.

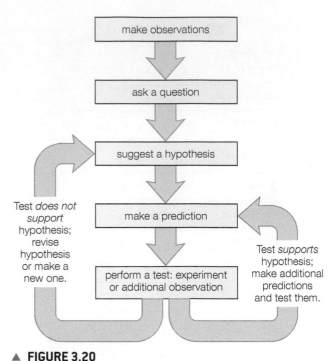

▲ FIGURE 3.20
This diagram illustrates what we often call the *scientific method.*

Flow diagram boxes:
- make observations
- ask a question
- suggest a hypothesis
- make a prediction
- perform a test: experiment or additional observation

Test *does not support* hypothesis; revise hypothesis or make a new one.

Test *supports* hypothesis; make additional predictions and test them.

3.4 The Nature of Science

The story of how our ancestors gradually figured out the basic architecture of the cosmos exhibits many features of what we now consider "good science." For example, we have seen how models were formulated and tested against observations and modified or replaced when they failed those tests. The story also illustrates some classic mistakes, such as the apparent failure of anyone before Kepler to question the belief that orbits must be circles. The ultimate success of the Copernican revolution led scientists, philosophers, and theologians to reassess the various modes of thinking that played a role in the 2000-year process of discovering Earth's place in the universe. Let's examine how the principles of modern science emerged from the lessons of the Copernican revolution.

◆ How can we distinguish science from nonscience?

It's surprisingly difficult to define the term *science* precisely. The word comes from the Latin *scientia*, meaning "knowledge," but not all knowledge is science. For example, you may know what music you like best, but your musical taste is not a result of scientific study.

Approaches to Science One reason science is difficult to define is that not all science works in the same way. For example, you've probably heard that science is supposed to proceed according to something called the "scientific method." As an idealized illustration of this method, consider what you would do if your flashlight suddenly stopped working. You might *hypothesize* that the flashlight's batteries have died. This type of tentative explanation, or **hypothesis,** is sometimes called an *educated guess*—in this case, it is "educated" because you already know that flashlights need batteries. Your hypothesis allows you to make a simple prediction: If you replace the batteries with new ones, the flashlight should work. You can test this prediction by replacing the batteries. If the flashlight now works, you've confirmed your hypothesis. If it doesn't, you must revise or discard your hypothesis, perhaps in favor of some other one that you can also test (such as that the bulb is burned out). Figure 3.20 illustrates the basic flow of this process.

The scientific method can be a useful idealization, but real science rarely progresses in such an orderly way. Scientific progress often begins

---

extraordinary claims | Earth Orbits the Sun

In the 21st century, claiming that Earth orbits the Sun will not raise any eyebrows, but it was quite an extraordinary claim in the 3rd century B.C., when Greek astronomer Aristarchus of Samos put it forward [Section 2.4]. To almost everyone else of his time, the idea that the Sun moves while Earth remains stationary seemed like plain common sense. However, Aristarchus was also a mathematician and he used mathematical reasoning to conclude that observations of the sky made more sense if the Sun, and not Earth, were at the center of the solar system.

In this and similar boxes elsewhere in the book, we will look at scientific claims that seemed extraordinary in their time. As astronomer Carl Sagan was fond of saying, "extraordinary claims require extraordinary evidence," and we will discuss how scientific evidence ended up supporting or debunking those claims, or in some cases leaving them still unanswered. Each case will illustrate the self-correcting nature of

science: Mistaken ideas are eventually disproved, while a few ideas that once appeared extraordinary end up gaining widespread acceptance.

In the case of Aristarchus, the evidence proving his claim did not become strong enough to convince most other scholars until almost two millennia after his death. Nevertheless, Aristarchus's Sun-centered idea remained alive throughout this time, and apparently influenced Copernicus when he proposed his own, more detailed Sun-centered model. As discussed in this chapter, others including Tycho, Kepler, and Galileo then collected the evidence that ultimately led to widespread acceptance of Aristarchus's extraordinary claim. The case was later sealed after Newton provided a physical understanding of *why* Kepler's laws hold and after astronomers collected direct evidence, including measurements of stellar parallax, that proved beyond a shadow of doubt that Earth orbits the Sun.

Verdict: Clearly correct.

---

with someone going out and looking at nature in a general way, rather than by conducting a careful set of experiments. For example, Galileo wasn't looking for anything in particular when he pointed his telescope at the sky and made his first startling discoveries.

The scientific method is a useful idealization of scientific thinking, but science rarely progresses in such an orderly way.

Furthermore, scientists are human beings, and their intuition and personal beliefs inevitably influence their work. Copernicus, for example, adopted the idea that Earth orbits the Sun not because he had carefully tested it but because he believed it made more sense than the prevailing view of an Earth-centered universe. While his intuition guided him to the right general idea, he erred in the specifics because he still held Plato's ancient belief that heavenly motion must be in perfect circles.

Given that the idealized scientific method is an overly simplistic characterization of science, how can we tell what is science and what is not? To answer this question, we must look a little deeper at the distinguishing characteristics of scientific thinking.

Hallmarks of Science

One way to define scientific thinking is to list the criteria that scientists use when they judge competing models of nature. Historians and philosophers of science have examined (and continue to examine) this issue in great depth, and different experts express different viewpoints on the details. Nevertheless, everything we now consider to be science shares the following three basic characteristics, which we will refer to as the "hallmarks" of science (Figure 3.21):

- Modern science seeks explanations for observed phenomena that rely solely on natural causes.
- Science progresses through the creation and testing of models of nature that explain the observations as simply as possible.
- A scientific model must make testable predictions about natural phenomena that would force us to revise or abandon the model if the predictions did not agree with observations.

Each of these hallmarks is evident in the story of the Copernican revolution. The first shows up in the way Tycho's careful measurements of planetary motion motivated Kepler to come up with a better explanation for those motions. The second is evident in the way several competing models were compared and tested, most notably those of Ptolemy, Copernicus, and Kepler. We see the third in the fact that each model could make precise predictions about the future motions of the Sun, Moon, planets, and stars in our sky. Kepler's model gained acceptance because it worked, while the competing models lost favor because their predictions failed to match the observations. Figure 3.22 summarizes the Copernican revolution and how it illustrates the hallmarks of science.

Science seeks to explain observed phenomena using testable models of nature that explain the observations as simply as possible.

Occam's Razor

The criterion of simplicity in the second hallmark deserves additional explanation. Remember that Copernicus's original model did *not* match the data noticeably better than Ptolemy's model. If scientists had judged this model solely on the accuracy of its predictions, they might have rejected it immediately. However, many scientists found elements of the Copernican model appealing, such as its simple explanation for apparent retrograde motion. They therefore kept the model alive until Kepler found a way to make it work.

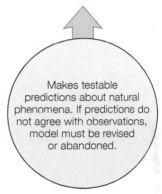

Hallmarks of Science

Seeks explanations for observed phenomena that rely solely on natural causes.

Progresses through creation and testing of models of nature that explain the observations as simply as possible.

Science

Makes testable predictions about natural phenomena. If predictions do not agree with observations, model must be revised or abandoned.

▲ **FIGURE 3.21**
Hallmarks of science.

If agreement with data were the sole criterion for judgment, we could imagine a modern-day Ptolemy adding millions or billions of additional circles to the geocentric model in an effort to improve its agreement with observations. A sufficiently complex geocentric model could in principle reproduce the observations with almost perfect accuracy—but it still would not convince us that Earth is the center of the universe. We would still choose the Copernican view over the geocentric view because its predictions would be just as accurate but follow a much simpler model of nature. The idea that scientists should prefer the simpler of two models that agree equally well with observations is called *Occam's razor*, after the medieval scholar William of Occam (1285–1349).

Verifiable Observations The third hallmark of science forces us to face the question of what counts as an "observation" against which a prediction can be tested. Consider the claim that aliens are visiting Earth in UFOs. Proponents of this claim say that thousands of eyewitness reports of UFO encounters provide evidence that it is true. But do these personal testimonials count as *scientific* evidence? On the surface, the answer isn't obvious, because all scientific studies involve eyewitness accounts on some level. For example, only a handful of scientists have personally made detailed tests of Einstein's theory of relativity, and it is their personal reports of the results that have convinced other scientists of the theory's validity. However, there's an important difference between personal testimony about a scientific test and a UFO: The first can be verified by anyone, at least in principle, while the second cannot.

Understanding this difference is crucial to understanding what counts as science and what does not. Even though you may never have conducted a test of Einstein's theory of relativity yourself, there's nothing stopping you from doing so. It might require several years of study before you had the necessary background to conduct the test, but you could then confirm the results reported by other scientists. In other words, while you may currently be trusting the eyewitness testimony of scientists, you always have the option of verifying their testimony for yourself.

In contrast, there is no way for you to verify someone's eyewitness account of a UFO. Moreover, scientific studies of eyewitness testimony show it to be notoriously unreliable, because different eyewitnesses often disagree on what they saw even immediately after an event has occurred. As time passes, memories of the event may change further. In some cases in which memory has been checked against reality, people have reported vivid memories of events that never happened at all. This explains something that virtually all of us have experienced: disagreements with a friend about who did what and when. Since both people cannot be right in such cases, at least one person must have a memory that differs from reality.

The demonstrated unreliability of eyewitness testimony explains why it is generally considered insufficient for a conviction in criminal court; at least some other evidence is required. For the same reason, we cannot accept eyewitness testimony by itself as sufficient evidence in science, no matter who reports it or how many people offer similar testimony.

Objectivity in Science It's important to realize that science is not the only valid way of seeking knowledge. For example, suppose you are shopping for a car, learning to play drums, or pondering the meaning of life. In each case, you might make observations, exercise logic, and test hypotheses. Yet these pursuits are not science, because they are not directed at developing testable explanations for observed natural phenomena. As long as nonscientific searches for knowledge make no claims about how the natural world works, they do not conflict with science. Unfortunately, the boundaries between science and nonscience are not always so clear cut.

common misconceptions

Eggs on the Equinox

One of the hallmarks of science holds that you needn't take scientific claims on faith. In principle, at least, you can always test them for yourself. Consider the claim, repeated in news reports every year, that the spring equinox is the only day on which you can balance an egg on its end. Many people believe this claim, but you'll be immediately skeptical if you think about the nature of the spring equinox. The equinox is merely a point in time at which sunlight strikes both hemispheres equally (see Figure 2.15). It's difficult to see how sunlight could affect an attempt to balance eggs (especially if the eggs are indoors), and there's nothing special about either Earth's or the Sun's gravity on that day.

More important, you can test this claim directly. It's not easy to balance an egg on its end, but with practice you can do it on any day of the year, not just on the spring equinox. Not all scientific claims are so easy to test for yourself, but the basic lesson should be clear: Before you accept any scientific claim, you should demand at least a reasonable explanation of the evidence that backs it up.

We generally think of science as being objective, meaning that all people should be able to find the same scientific results. However, there is a difference between the overall objectivity of science and the objectivity of individual scientists. Science is practiced by human beings, and individual scientists may bring their personal biases and beliefs to their scientific work. For example, most scientists choose their research projects based on personal interests rather than on some objective formula. In extreme cases, scientists have been known to cheat—either deliberately or subconsciously—to obtain a result they desire. For example, in the late 19th century, astronomer Percival Lowell claimed to see a network of artificial canals in blurry telescopic images of Mars, leading him to conclude that there was a great Martian civilization. But no such canals exist, so Lowell must have allowed his beliefs about extraterrestrial life to influence the way he interpreted what he saw—in essence, a form of cheating, though almost certainly not intentional.

Bias can occasionally show up even in the thinking of the scientific community as a whole. Some valid ideas may not be considered by any scientist because they fall too far outside the general patterns of thought, or **paradigm,** of the time. Einstein's theory of relativity is an example. Many scientists in the decades before Einstein had gleaned hints of the theory but did not investigate them, at least in part because they seemed too outlandish.

The beauty of science is that it encourages continued testing by many people. Even if personal biases affect some results, tests by others should eventually uncover the mistakes. Similarly, if a new idea is correct but falls outside the accepted paradigm, sufficient testing and verification of the idea should eventually force a paradigm shift. In that sense, *science ultimately provides a means of bringing people to agreement*, at least on topics that can be subjected to scientific study.

Individual scientists inevitably carry personal biases into their work, but the collective action of many scientists should ultimately make science objective.

---

special topic   Astrology

The terms *astrology* and *astronomy* sound very similar, but today they describe very different practices. In ancient times, however, astrology and astronomy often went hand in hand, and astrology played an important role in the historical development of astronomy. Indeed, astronomers and astrologers were usually one and the same.

The basic tenet of astrology is that human events are influenced by the apparent positions of the Sun, Moon, and planets among the stars in our sky. The origins of this idea are easy to understand. The position of the Sun in the sky clearly influences our lives—it determines the seasons and hence the times of planting and harvesting, of warmth and cold, and of daylight and darkness. Similarly, the Moon determines the tides, and the cycle of lunar phases coincides with many biological cycles. Because the planets also appear to move among the stars, it seemed reasonable to imagine that planets also influence our lives, even if these influences were much more difficult to discover.

Ancient astrologers hoped that they might learn *how* the positions of the Sun, Moon, and planets influence our lives. They charted the skies, seeking correlations with events on Earth. For example, if an earthquake occurred when Saturn was entering the constellation of Leo, might Saturn's position have caused the earthquake? If the king became ill when Mars was in Gemini and the first-quarter moon was in Scorpio, might it mean another misfortune for the king when this particular alignment of the Moon and Mars next recurred? Ancient astrologers thought that the patterns of influence eventually would become clear and they would then be able to forecast human events with the same reliability with which observations of the Sun could forecast the coming of spring.

This hope was never realized. Although many astrologers still attempt to predict future events, scientific tests have shown that their predictions come true no more often than would be expected by pure chance. Moreover, in light of our current understanding of the universe, the original ideas behind astrology no longer make sense. For example, today we use ideas of gravity and energy to explain the influences of the Sun and the Moon, and these same ideas tell us that the planets are too far from Earth to have a similar influence.

Of course, many people continue to practice astrology, perhaps because of its ancient and rich traditions. Scientifically, we cannot say anything about such traditions, because traditions are not testable predictions. But if you want to understand the latest discoveries about the cosmos, you'll need a science that can be tested and refined—and astrology fails to meet these requirements.

◆ What is a scientific theory?

The most successful scientific models explain a wide variety of observations in terms of just a few general principles. When a powerful yet simple model makes predictions that survive repeated and varied testing, scientists elevate its status and call it a **theory.** Some famous examples are Isaac Newton's theory of gravity, Charles Darwin's theory of evolution, and Albert Einstein's theory of relativity.

Note that the scientific meaning of the word *theory* is quite different from its everyday meaning, in which we equate a theory more closely with speculation or a hypothesis. For example, someone might say, "I have a new theory about why people enjoy the beach." Without the support of a broad range of evidence that others have tested and confirmed, this "theory" is really only a guess. In contrast, Newton's theory of gravity qualifies as a scientific theory because it uses simple physical principles to explain many observations and experiments. *Theory* is just one of many terms that are used with different meaning in science than in everyday life. Table 3.2 summarizes a few of the most common of these terms.

Despite its success in explaining observed phenomena, a scientific theory can never be proved true beyond all doubt, because future

TABLE 3.2 Scientific Terminology

This table lists some words you will encounter in the media that have a different meaning in science than in everyday life. (Adapted from a table published by Richard Somerville and Susan Joy Hassol in Physics Today, Oct. 2011.)

Term	Everyday Meaning	Scientific Meaning	Example
model	something you build, like a model airplane	a representation of nature, sometimes using mathematics or computer simulations, that is intended to explain or predict observed phenomena	A model of planetary motion can be used to calculate exactly where planets should appear in our sky.
hypothesis	a guess or assumption of almost any type	a model that has been proposed to explain some observations, but which has not yet been rigorously confirmed	Scientists hypothesize that the Moon was formed by a giant impact, but there is not enough evidence to be fully confident in this model.
theory	speculation	a particularly powerful model that has been so extensively tested and verified that we have extremely high confidence in its validity	Einstein's theory of relativity successfully explains a broad range of natural phenomena and has passed a great many tests of its validity.
bias	distortion, political motive	tendency toward a particular result	Current techniques for detecting extrasolar planets are biased toward detecting large planets.
critical	really important; involving criticism, often negative	right on the edge	A boiling point is a "critical value" because above that temperature, a liquid will boil away.
deviation	strangeness or unacceptable behavior	change or difference	The recent deviation in global temperatures from their long-term average implies that something is heating the planet.
enhance/enrich	improve	increase or add more, but not necessarily to make something "better"	"Enhanced colors" means colors that have been brightened. "Enriched with iron" means containing more iron.
error	mistake	range of uncertainty	The "margin of error" tells us how closely measured values are likely to reflect true values.
feedback	a response	a self-regulating (negative feedback) or self-reinforcing (positive feedback) cycle	Gravity can provide positive feedback to a forming planet: Adding mass leads to stronger gravity, which leads to more added mass, and so on.
state (as a noun)	a place or location	a description of current condition	The Sun is in a state of balance, and so it shines steadily.
uncertainty	ignorance	a range of possible values around some central value	The measured age of our solar system is 4.55 billion years with an uncertainty of 0.02 billion years.
values	ethics, monetary value	numbers or quantities	The speed of light has a measured value of 300,000 km/s.

observations may disagree with its predictions. However, anything that qualifies as a scientific theory must be supported by a large, compelling body of evidence.

A scientific theory is a simple yet powerful model whose predictions have been borne out by repeated and varied testing.

In this sense, a scientific theory is not at all like a hypothesis or any other type of guess. We are free to change a hypothesis at any time, because it has not yet been carefully tested. In contrast, we can discard or replace a scientific theory only if we have an alternative way of explaining the evidence that supports it.

Again, the theories of Newton and Einstein offer good examples. A vast body of evidence supports Newton's theory of gravity, but by the late 19th century scientists had begun to discover cases where its predictions did not perfectly match observations. These discrepancies were explained only when Einstein developed his general theory of relativity, which was able to match the observations. Still, the many successes of Newton's theory could not be ignored, and Einstein's theory would not have gained acceptance if it had not been able to explain these successes equally well. It did, and that is why we now view Einstein's theory as a broader theory of gravity than Newton's theory. Some scientists today are seeking a theory of gravity that will go beyond Einstein's. If any new theory ever gains acceptance, it will have to match all the successes of Einstein's theory as well as apply to new realms where Einstein's theory does not.

think about it When people claim that something is "only a theory," what do you think they mean? Does this meaning of "theory" agree with the definition of a theory in science? Do scientists always use the word *theory* in its "scientific" sense? Explain.

---

the big picture — Putting Chapter 3 into Perspective

In this chapter, we focused on the scientific principles through which we have learned so much about the universe. Key "big picture" concepts from this chapter include the following:

- The basic ingredients of scientific thinking—careful observation and trial-and-error testing—are a part of everyone's experience. Modern science simply provides a way of organizing this thinking to facilitate the learning and sharing of new knowledge.

- Although our understanding of the universe is growing rapidly today, each new piece of knowledge builds on ideas that came before.

- The Copernican revolution, which overthrew the ancient Greek belief in an Earth-centered universe, unfolded over a period of more than a century. Many of the characteristics of modern science first appeared during this time.

- Science exhibits several key features that distinguish it from nonscience and that in principle allow anyone to come to the same conclusions when studying a scientific question.

my cosmic perspective All of us are connected to ancient astronomy through our ancestors, and to modern astronomy through the fact that it was driven by the Copernican revolution, which also drove the development of virtually all modern science and technology.

3.1 The Ancient Roots of Science

◆ **In what ways do all humans use scientific thinking?**
Scientific thinking relies on the same type of trial-and-error thinking that we use in our everyday lives, but done in a carefully organized way.

◆ **How is modern science rooted in ancient astronomy?**

Ancient astronomers were accomplished observers who learned to tell the time of day and the time of year, to track cycles of the Moon, and to observe planets and stars. The care and effort that went into these observations helped set the stage for modern science.

3.2 Ancient Greek Science

◆ **Why does modern science trace its roots to the Greeks?**
The Greeks developed **models** of nature and emphasized the importance of agreement between the predictions of those models and observations of nature.

◆ **How did the Greeks explain planetary motion?**

retrograde loop

The Greek **geocentric model** reached its culmination with the **Ptolemaic model,** which explained apparent retrograde motion by having each planet move on a small circle whose center moves around Earth on a larger circle.

3.3 The Copernican Revolution

◆ **How did Copernicus, Tycho, and Kepler challenge the Earth-centered model?**
Copernicus created a Sun-centered model of the solar system designed to replace the Ptolemaic model, but it was no more accurate than Ptolemy's because Copernicus still used perfect circles. Tycho's accurate, naked-eye observations provided the data needed to improve on Copernicus's model. Kepler developed a model of planetary motion that fit Tycho's data.

◆ **What are Kepler's three laws of planetary motion?**

(1) The orbit of each planet is an ellipse with the Sun at one focus.
(2) A planet moves faster in the part of its orbit nearer the Sun and slower when farther from the Sun, sweeping out equal areas in equal times.
(3) More distant planets orbit the Sun at slower average speeds, obeying the precise mathematical relationship $p^2 = a^3$.

◆ **How did Galileo solidify the Copernican revolution?**

Venus

Earth

Galileo's experiments and telescopic observations overcame remaining objections to the Copernican idea of Earth as a planet orbiting the Sun. Although not everyone accepted his results immediately, in hindsight we see that Galileo sealed the case for the Sun-centered solar system.

3.4 The Nature of Science

◆ **How can we distinguish science from nonscience?**
Science generally exhibits three hallmarks: (1) Modern science seeks explanations for observed phenomena that rely solely on natural causes. (2) Science progresses through the creation and testing of models of nature that explain the observations as simply as possible. (3) A scientific model must make testable predictions about natural phenomena that would force us to revise or abandon the model if the predictions did not agree with observations.

◆ **What is a scientific theory?**
A scientific **theory** is a simple yet powerful model that explains a wide variety of observations using just a few general principles, and that has survived repeated and varied testing.

a

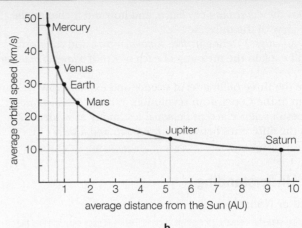

b

Use the information in the graphs to answer the following questions.

1. Approximately how fast is Jupiter orbiting the Sun?
   a. cannot be determined from the information provided
   b. 20 km/s
   c. 10 km/s
   d. a little less than 15 km/s

2. An asteroid with an average orbital distance of 2 AU will orbit the Sun at an average speed that is _____.
   a. a little slower than the orbital speed of Mars
   b. a little faster than the orbital speed of Mars
   c. the same as the orbital speed of Mars

3. Uranus, not shown on the graph, orbits about 19 AU from the Sun. Based on the graph, its approximate orbital speed is between about _____.
   a. 20 and 25 km/s
   b. 15 and 20 km/s
   c. 10 and 15 km/s
   d. 5 and 10 km/s

4. Kepler's third law is often stated as $p^2 = a^3$. The value a^3 for a planet is shown on _____.
   a. the horizontal axis of Figure a
   b. the vertical axis of Figure a
   c. the horizontal axis of Figure b
   d. the vertical axis of Figure b

5. On Figure a, you can see Kepler's third law ($p^2 = a^3$) from the fact that _____.
   a. the data fall on a straight line
   b. the axes are labeled with values for p^2 and a^3
   c. the planet names are labeled on the graph

6. Suppose Figure a showed a planet on the red line directly above a value of 1000 AU³ along the horizontal axis. On the vertical axis, this planet would be at _____.
   a. 1000 years²
   b. 1000² years²
   c. $\sqrt{1000}$ years²
   d. 100 years

7. How far does the planet in question 6 orbit from the Sun?
   a. 10 AU
   b. 100 AU
   c. 1000 AU
   d. $\sqrt{1000}$ AU

MasteringAstronomy®   For instructor-assigned homework and other learning materials, go to MasteringAstronomy®.

Review Questions

1. In what way is scientific thinking natural to all of us, and how does modern science build upon this everyday type of thinking?
2. Why did ancient peoples study astronomy? Describe the astronomical origins of our day, week, month, and year.

3. What is a lunar calendar? How can it be kept roughly synchronized with a solar calendar?
4. What do we mean by a *model* in science? Briefly summarize the Greek *geocentric model*.

5. What do we mean by the *Ptolemaic model*? How did this model account for the apparent retrograde motion of planets in our sky?

6. What was the *Copernican revolution,* and how did it change the human view of the universe?

7. What is an *ellipse*? Define its *foci, semimajor axis,* and *eccentricity*.

8. State and explain the meaning of each of *Kepler's laws of planetary motion*.

9. Describe the three hallmarks of science and explain how we can see them in the Copernican revolution. What is *Occam's razor*? Why doesn't science accept personal testimony as evidence?

10. What is the difference between a *hypothesis* and a *theory* in science?

Test Your Understanding

 Science or Nonscience?

Each of the following statements makes some type of claim. Decide in each case whether the claim could be evaluated scientifically or whether it falls into the realm of nonscience. Explain clearly; not all of these have definitive answers, so your explanation is more important than your chosen answer.

11. The Yankees are the best baseball team of all time.

12. Several kilometers below its surface, Jupiter's moon Europa has an ocean of liquid water.

13. My house is haunted by ghosts who make the creaking noises I hear each night.

14. There are no lakes or seas on the surface of Mars today.

15. Dogs are smarter than cats.

16. Children born when Jupiter is in the constellation Taurus are more likely to be musicians than other children.

17. Aliens can manipulate time so that they can abduct and perform experiments on people who never realize they were taken.

18. Newton's law of gravity works as well for explaining the orbits of planets around other stars as it does for explaining the orbits of planets in our own solar system.

19. God created the laws of motion that were discovered by Newton.

20. A huge fleet of alien spacecraft will land on Earth and introduce an era of peace and prosperity on January 1, 2035.

Quick Quiz

Choose the best answer to each of the following. Explain your reasoning with one or more complete sentences.

21. In the Greek geocentric model, the retrograde motion of a planet occurs when (a) Earth is about to pass the planet in its orbit around the Sun. (b) the planet actually goes backward in its orbit around Earth. (c) the planet is aligned with the Moon in our sky.

22. Which of the following was *not* a major advantage of Copernicus's Sun-centered model over the Ptolemaic model? (a) It made significantly better predictions of planetary positions in our sky. (b) It offered a more natural explanation for the apparent retrograde motion of planets in our sky. (c) It allowed calculation of the orbital periods and distances of the planets.

23. When we say that a planet has a highly *eccentric* orbit, we mean that (a) it is spiraling in toward the Sun. (b) its orbit is an ellipse with the Sun at one focus. (c) in some parts of its orbit it is much closer to the Sun than in other parts.

24. Earth is closer to the Sun in January than in July. Therefore, in accord with Kepler's second law, (a) Earth travels faster in its orbit around the Sun in July than in January. (b) Earth travels faster in its orbit around the Sun in January than in July. (c) it is summer in January and winter in July.

25. According to Kepler's third law, (a) Mercury travels fastest in the part of its orbit in which it is closest to the Sun. (b) Jupiter orbits the Sun at a faster speed than Saturn. (c) all the planets have nearly circular orbits.

26. Tycho Brahe's contribution to astronomy included (a) inventing the telescope. (b) proving that Earth orbits the Sun. (c) collecting data that enabled Kepler to discover the laws of planetary motion.

27. Galileo's contribution to astronomy included (a) discovering the laws of planetary motion. (b) discovering the law of gravity. (c) making observations and conducting experiments that dispelled scientific objections to the Sun-centered model.

28. Which of the following is *not* true about scientific progress? (a) Science progresses through the creation and testing of models of nature. (b) Science advances only through the scientific method. (c) Science avoids explanations that invoke the supernatural.

29. Which of the following is *not* true about a scientific theory? (a) A theory must explain a wide range of observations or experiments. (b) Even the strongest theories can never be proved true beyond all doubt. (c) A theory is essentially an educated guess.

30. When Einstein's theory of gravity (general relativity) gained acceptance, it demonstrated that Newton's theory had been (a) wrong. (b) incomplete. (c) really only a guess.

Process of Science

31. *What Makes It Science?* Choose a single idea in the modern view of the cosmos discussed in Chapter 1, such as "The universe is expanding," or "We are made from elements manufactured by stars," or "The Sun orbits the center of the Milky Way Galaxy once every 230 million years."
    a. Describe how this idea reflects each of the three hallmarks of science, discussing how it is based on observations, how our understanding of it depends on a model, and how that model is testable.
    b. Describe a hypothetical observation that, if it were actually made, might cause us to call the idea into question. Then briefly discuss whether you think that, overall, the idea is likely or unlikely to hold up to future observations.

32. *Earth's Shape.* It took thousands of years for humans to deduce that Earth is spherical. For each of the following alternative models of Earth's shape, identify one or more observations that you could make for yourself that would invalidate the model.
    a. A flat Earth
    b. A cylindrical Earth [which was actually proposed by the Greek philosopher Anaximander (c. 610–546 B.C.)]
    c. A football-shaped Earth

Group Work Exercise

33. *Galileo on Trial.* **Roles:** *Scribe* (takes notes on the group's activities), *Galileo* (argues in favor of the idea that Earth orbits the Sun), *Prosecutor* (argues against the idea that Earth orbits the Sun), and *Moderator* (leads group discussion and makes sure the debate remains civil). **Activity:** Conduct a mock trial in which you consider the following three pieces of evidence: (1) observations of mountains and valleys on the Moon; (2) observations of moons orbiting Jupiter; (3) observations of

the phases of Venus. *Galileo* should explain why the evidence indicates that Earth orbits the Sun. The *Prosecutor* should present a rebuttal. The *Scribe* and *Moderator* should serve as jury to decide whether the evidence is convincing beyond a reasonable doubt, somewhat convincing, or not convincing. The group should record the final verdict along with an explanation of their reasoning.

Investigate Further

Short-Answer/Essay Questions

34. *Copernican Players.* Using a bulleted list format, make a one-page "executive summary" of the major roles that Copernicus, Tycho, Kepler, and Galileo played in overturning the ancient belief in an Earth-centered universe.

35. *Influence on History.* Based on what you have learned about the Copernican revolution, write a one- to two-page essay about how you believe it altered the course of human history.

36. *Cultural Astronomy.* Choose a particular culture of interest to you, and research the astronomical knowledge and accomplishments of that culture. Write a two- to three-page summary of your findings.

Quantitative Problems

Be sure to show all calculations clearly and state your final answers in complete sentences.

37. *Method of Eratosthenes.* You are an astronomer on planet Nearth, which orbits a distant star. It has recently been accepted that Nearth is spherical in shape, though no one knows its size. One day, while studying in the library of Alectown, you learn that on the equinox your sun is directly overhead in the city of Nyene, located 1000 km due north of you. On the equinox, you go outside in Alectown and observe that the altitude of your sun is 80°. What is the circumference of Nearth? (*Hint:* Apply the technique used by Eratosthenes to measure Earth's circumference.)

38. *Eris Orbit.* The dwarf planet Eris orbits the Sun every 557 years. What is its average distance (semimajor axis) from the Sun? How does its average distance compare to that of Pluto?

39. *Halley Orbit.* Halley's comet orbits the Sun every 76.0 years and has an orbital eccentricity of 0.97.
    a. Find its average distance (semimajor axis).
    b. Halley's perihelion distance is approximately 90 million km. Approximately what is its aphelion distance?

Discussion Questions

40. *The Impact of Science.* The modern world is filled with ideas, knowledge, and technology that developed through science and application of the scientific method. Discuss some of these things and how they affect our lives. Which of these impacts do you think are positive? Which are negative? Overall, do you think science has benefited the human race? Defend your opinion.

41. *The Importance of Ancient Astronomy.* Why was astronomy important to people in ancient times? Discuss both the practical importance of astronomy and the importance it may have had for religious or other traditions. Which do you think was more important in the development of ancient astronomy: its practical or its philosophical role? Defend your opinion.

42. *Astronomy and Astrology.* Why do you think astrology remains so popular around the world even though it has failed all scientific tests of its validity? Do you think this popularity has any social consequences? Defend your opinions.

Web Projects

43. *The Ptolemaic Model.* This chapter gives only a very brief description of Ptolemy's model of the universe. Investigate this model in greater depth. Using diagrams and text as needed, create a two- to three-page description of the model.

44. *The Galileo Affair.* In recent years, the Roman Catholic Church has devoted a lot of resources to learning more about the trial of Galileo and to understanding past actions of the Church in the Galilean case. Learn more about these studies, and write a two- to three-page report about the current Vatican view of the case.

45. *Astrology.* Find out about at least one scientific test of the validity of astrology. Write a short summary of the methods and results of the test.

46. *Your Test of Astrology.* Collect the 12 astrological predictions for the previous day or month from any astrology site. Remove the names of the astrological signs from the predictions, and then ask other students to identify which prediction best fits what happened to them over the prior day or month. (Be sure to randomize the order in which you show your list.) Also ask students their astrological sign, so that you can check whether the prediction they picked matches their sign. What fraction of students choose their own sign? What does your test suggest about the validity of astrological predictions? (Note: You can do a simplified version of the test by showing each student just three predictions: one that corresponds to his or her "correct" sign and the other two randomly drawn from the rest.)

causing your velocity to decrease. Turning means a change in direction—which therefore means a change in velocity—so turning is a form of acceleration even if your speed remains constant.

You can often feel the effects of acceleration. For example, as you speed up in a car, you feel yourself being pushed back into your seat. As you slow down, you feel yourself being pulled forward. As you drive around a curve, you feel yourself being pushed away from the direction of your turn. In contrast, you don't feel such effects when moving at *constant velocity*. That is why you don't feel any sensation of motion when you're traveling in an airplane on a smooth flight.

The Acceleration of Gravity One of the most important types of acceleration is the acceleration caused by gravity. In a legendary experiment in which he supposedly dropped weights from the Leaning Tower of Pisa, Galileo demonstrated that gravity accelerates all objects by the same amount, regardless of their mass. This fact may be surprising because it seems to contradict everyday experience: A feather floats gently to the ground, while a rock plummets. However, air resistance causes this difference in acceleration. If you dropped a feather and a rock on the Moon, where there is no air, both would fall at exactly the same rate.

see it for yourself Find a piece of paper and a small rock. Hold both at the same height and let them go at the same instant. The rock, of course, hits the ground first. Next, crumple the paper into a small ball and repeat the experiment. What happens? Explain how this experiment suggests that gravity accelerates all objects by the same amount.

The acceleration of a falling object is called the **acceleration of gravity,** abbreviated g. On Earth, the acceleration of gravity causes falling objects to fall faster by 9.8 meters per second (m/s), or about 10 m/s, with each passing second. For example, suppose you drop a rock from a tall building. At the moment you let it go, its speed is 0 m/s. After 1 second, the rock will be falling downward at about 10 m/s. After 2 seconds, it will be falling at about 20 m/s. In the absence of air resistance, its speed will continue to increase by about 10 m/s each second until it hits the ground (Figure 4.2). We therefore say that the acceleration of gravity is about 10 *meters per second per second,* or 10 *meters per second squared,* which we write as 10 m/s^2 (more precisely, $g = 9.8$ m/s^2).

Momentum and Force The concepts of speed, velocity, and acceleration describe how an individual object moves, but most of the interesting phenomena we see in the universe result from *interactions* between objects. We need two additional concepts to describe these interactions:

- An object's **momentum** is the product of its mass and its velocity; that is, momentum = mass × velocity.
- The only way to change an object's momentum is to apply a **force** to it.

We can understand these concepts by considering the effects of collisions. Imagine that you're stopped in your car at a red light when a bug flying at a velocity of 30 km/hr due south slams into your windshield. What will happen to your car? Not much, except perhaps a bit of a mess on your windshield. Next, imagine that a 2-ton truck runs the red light and hits you head-on with the same velocity as the bug. Clearly, the truck will cause far more damage. We can understand why by considering the momentum and force in each collision.

$t = 0$
$v = 0$

$t = 1$ s
$v \approx 10$ m/s

Acceleration of gravity: Downward velocity increases by about 10 m/s with each passing second. (Gravity does not affect horizontal velocity.)

$t = 2$ s
$v \approx 20$ m/s

t = time
v = velocity
    (downward)

▲ **FIGURE 4.2**
On Earth, gravity causes an unsupported object to accelerate downward at about 10 m/s^2, which means its downward velocity increases by about 10 m/s with each passing second. (Gravity does not affect horizontal velocity.)

Before the collisions, the truck's much greater mass means it has far more momentum than the bug, even though both the truck and the bug are moving with the same velocity. During the collisions, the bug and the truck each transfer some of their momentum to your car. The bug has very little momentum to give to your car, so it does not exert much of a force. In contrast, the truck imparts enough of its momentum to cause a dramatic and sudden change in your car's momentum. You feel this sudden change in momentum as a force, and it can do great damage to you and your car.

The mere presence of a force does not always cause a change in momentum. For example, a moving car is always affected by forces of air resistance and friction with the road—forces that will slow your car if you take your foot off the gas pedal. However, you can maintain a constant velocity, and hence constant momentum, if you step on the gas pedal hard enough to overcome the slowing effects of these forces.

In fact, forces of some kind are always present, such as the force of gravity or the electromagnetic forces acting between atoms. The **net force** (or *overall force*) acting on an object represents the combined effect of all the individual forces put together. There is no net force on your car when you are driving at constant velocity, because the force generated by the engine to turn the wheels precisely offsets the forces of air resistance and road friction. A change in momentum occurs only when the net force is not zero. (The car is experiencing a net force in all three examples in Figure 4.1.)

Changing an object's momentum means changing its velocity, as long as its mass remains constant. A net force that is not zero therefore causes an object to accelerate. Conversely, whenever an object accelerates, a net force must be causing the acceleration. That is why you feel forces (pushing you forward, backward, or to the side) when you accelerate in your car. We can use the same ideas to understand many astronomical processes. For example, planets are always accelerating as they orbit the Sun, because their direction of travel constantly changes as they go around their orbits. We can therefore conclude that some force must be causing this acceleration. As we'll discuss shortly, Isaac Newton identified this force as gravity.

An object must accelerate whenever a net force acts on it.

◆ How is mass different from weight?

In daily life, we usually think of *mass* as something you can measure with a bathroom scale, but technically the scale measures your *weight,* not your mass. The distinction between mass and weight rarely matters when we are talking about objects on Earth, but it is very important in astronomy:

- Your **mass** is the amount of matter in your body.
- Your **weight** (or **apparent weight***) is the *force* that a scale measures when you stand on it; that is, weight depends both on your mass and on the forces (including gravity) acting on your mass.

To understand the difference between mass and weight, imagine standing on a scale in an elevator (Figure 4.3). Your mass will be the same no matter how the elevator moves, but your weight can vary. When the elevator is stationary or moving at constant velocity, the scale

---

*Some physics texts distinguish between "true weight" due only to gravity and "apparent weight" that also depends on other forces (as in an elevator).

When the elevator moves at constant velocity (or is stationary)...

... your weight is normal.

When the elevator **accelerates** upward...

... you weigh more.

When the elevator **accelerates** downward...

... you weigh less.

If the cable breaks so that you are in **free-fall**...

... you are weightless.

▲ **FIGURE 4.3**

Mass is not the same as weight. In an elevator, your mass never changes, but your weight is different when the elevator accelerates.

common **misconceptions**

No Gravity in Space?

If you ask people why astronauts are weightless in space, one of the most common answers is "There is no gravity in space." But you can usually convince people that this answer is wrong by following up with another simple question: Why does the Moon orbit Earth? Most people know that the Moon orbits Earth because of gravity, proving that there is gravity in space. In fact, at the altitude of the International Space Station's orbit, the acceleration of gravity is only about 10% less than it is on Earth's surface.

The real reason astronauts are weightless is that they are in a constant state of free-fall. Imagine being an astronaut. You'd have the sensation of free-fall—just as when you jump from a diving board—the entire time you were in orbit. This constant falling sensation makes many astronauts sick to their stomachs when they first experience weightlessness. Fortunately, they quickly get used to the sensation, which allows them to work hard and enjoy the view.

reads your "normal" weight. When the elevator accelerates upward, the floor exerts a greater force than it does when you are at rest. You feel heavier, and the scale verifies your greater weight. When the elevator accelerates downward, the floor and the scale exert a weaker force on you, so the scale registers less weight. Note that the scale shows a weight different from your "normal" weight only when the elevator is *accelerating*, not when it is going up or down at constant speed.

see it for yourself Take a small bathroom scale on an elevator and stand on it. How does your weight change when the elevator accelerates upward or downward? Does it change when the elevator is moving at constant speed? Explain your observations.

Your mass is the same no matter where you are, but your weight can vary. Your mass therefore depends only on the amount of matter in your body and is the same anywhere, but your weight can vary because the forces acting on you can vary. For example, your mass would be the same on the Moon as on Earth, but you would weigh less on the Moon because of its weaker gravity.

Free-Fall and Weightlessness Now consider what happens if the elevator cable breaks (see the last frame in Figure 4.3). The elevator and you are suddenly in **free-fall**—falling without any resistance to slow you down. The floor drops away at the same rate that you fall, allowing you to "float" freely above it, and the scale reads zero because you are no longer held to it. In other words, your free-fall has made you **weightless.**

In fact, you are in free-fall whenever there's nothing to *prevent* you from falling. For example, you are in free-fall when you jump off a chair or spring from a diving board or trampoline. Surprising as it may seem, you have therefore experienced weightlessness many times in your life.

You can experience it right now simply by jumping off your chair—though your weightlessness lasts for only a very short time until you hit the ground.

Weightlessness in Space You've probably seen videos of astronauts floating weightlessly in the International Space Station. But why are they weightless? Many people guess that there's no gravity in space, but that's not true. After all, it is gravity that makes the Space Station orbit Earth. Astronauts are weightless for the same reason that you are weightless when you jump off a chair: They are in free-fall.

> People or objects are weightless whenever they are falling freely, and astronauts in orbit are weightless because they are in a constant state of free-fall.

Astronauts are weightless the entire time they orbit Earth because they are in a *constant state of free-fall*. To understand this idea, imagine a tower that reaches all the way to the Space Station's orbit, about 350 kilometers above Earth (Figure 4.4). If you stepped off the tower, you would fall downward, remaining weightless until you hit the ground (or until air resistance had a noticeable effect on you). Now, imagine that instead of stepping off the tower, you ran and jumped out of the tower. You'd still fall to the ground, but because of your forward motion you'd land a short distance away from the base of the tower.

The faster you ran out of the tower, the farther you'd go before landing. If you could somehow run fast enough—about 28,000 km/hr (17,000 mi/hr) at the orbital altitude of the Space Station—a very interesting thing would happen: By the time gravity had pulled you downward as far as the length of the tower, you'd already have moved far enough around Earth that you'd no longer be going down at all. Instead, you'd be just as high above Earth as you'd been all along, but a good portion of the way around the world. In other words, you'd be orbiting Earth.

The Space Station and all other orbiting objects stay in orbit because they are constantly "falling around" Earth. Their constant state of free-fall makes spacecraft and everything in them weightless.

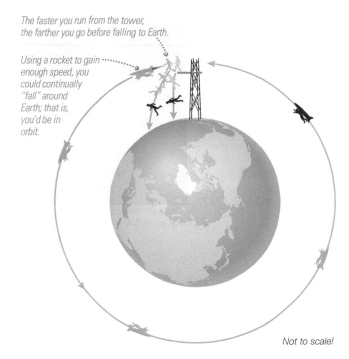

The faster you run from the tower, the farther you go before falling to Earth.

Using a rocket to gain enough speed, you could continually "fall" around Earth; that is, you'd be in orbit.

Not to scale!

▲ **FIGURE 4.4**
This figure explains why astronauts are weightless and float freely in space. If you could leap from a tall tower with enough speed, you could travel forward so fast that you'd orbit Earth. You'd then be in a constant state of free-fall, which means you'd be weightless. *Note:* On the scale shown here, the tower extends far higher than the Space Station's orbit; the rocket's orientation shows it rotating once with each orbit. The rocket has also been given a slight amount of rotation so that the driver remains facing Earth. (Adapted from *Space Station Science* by Marianne Dyson.)

4.2 Newton's Laws of Motion

The complexity of motion in daily life might lead you to guess that the laws governing motion would also be complex. For example, if you watch a falling piece of paper waft lazily to the ground, you'll see it rock back and forth in a seemingly unpredictable pattern. However, the complexity of this motion arises because the paper is affected by a variety of forces, including gravity and the changing forces caused by air currents. If you could analyze the forces individually, you'd find that each force affects the paper's motion in a simple, predictable way. Sir Isaac Newton (1642–1727) discovered the remarkably simple laws that govern motion.

◆ How did Newton change our view of the universe?

Newton was born in Lincolnshire, England, on Christmas Day in 1642. He had a difficult childhood and showed few signs of unusual talent. He attended Trinity College at Cambridge, where he earned his keep by

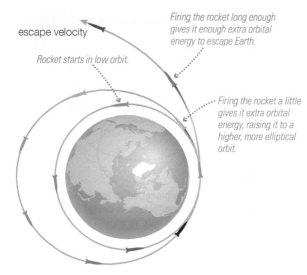

escape velocity

Rocket starts in low orbit.

Firing the rocket long enough gives it enough extra orbital energy to escape Earth.

Firing the rocket a little gives it extra orbital energy, raising it to a higher, more elliptical orbit.

▲ **FIGURE 4.18**
An object with escape velocity has enough orbital energy to escape Earth completely.

common misconceptions

The Origin of Tides

Many people believe that tides arise because the Moon pulls Earth's oceans toward it. But if that were the whole story, there would be a bulge only on the side of Earth facing the Moon, and hence only one high tide each day. The correct explanation for tides must account for why Earth has two tidal bulges.

Only one explanation works: Earth must be stretching from its center in both directions (toward and away from the Moon). This stretching force, or tidal force, arises from the difference between the force of gravity attracting different parts of Earth to the Moon. In fact, stretching due to tides affects many objects, not just Earth. Many moons are stretched into slightly oblong shapes by tidal forces caused by their parent planets, and mutual tidal forces stretch close binary stars into teardrop shapes. In regions where gravity is extremely strong, such as near a black hole, tides can have even more dramatic effects.

Atmospheric Drag Friction can cause objects to lose orbital energy. A satellite in low-Earth orbit (a few hundred kilometers above Earth's surface) experiences a bit of drag from Earth's thin upper atmosphere. This drag gradually causes the satellite to lose orbital energy until it finally plummets to Earth. The satellite's lost orbital energy is converted to thermal energy in the atmosphere, which is why a falling satellite usually burns up.

Friction may also help explain why the outer planets have so many small moons. These moons may once have orbited the Sun independently, and their orbits could not have changed spontaneously. However, the outer planets probably once were surrounded by clouds of gas [Section 6.3], and friction would have slowed objects passing through this gas. Some of these small objects may have lost just enough energy to friction to allow them to be "captured" as moons. Mars may have captured its two small moons in a similar way.

Escape Velocity An object that gains orbital energy moves into an orbit with a higher average altitude. For example, if we want to boost the orbital altitude of a spacecraft, we can give it more orbital energy by firing a rocket. The chemical potential energy released by the rocket fuel is converted to orbital energy for the spacecraft.

If we give a spacecraft enough orbital energy, it may end up in an unbound orbit that allows it to *escape* Earth completely (Figure 4.18).

A spacecraft that achieves escape velocity can escape Earth completely.

For example, when we send a space probe to Mars, we must use a large rocket that gives the probe enough energy to leave Earth orbit. Although it would probably make more sense to say that the probe achieves "escape energy," we instead say that it achieves **escape velocity.** The escape velocity from Earth's surface is about 40,000 km/hr, or 11 km/s; this is the minimum velocity required to escape Earth's gravity for a spacecraft that starts near the surface.

Note that the escape velocity does not depend on the mass of the escaping object—*any* object must travel at a velocity of 11 km/s to escape from Earth, whether it is an individual atom or molecule escaping from the atmosphere, a spacecraft being launched into deep space, or a rock blasted into the sky by a large impact. Escape velocity *does* depend on whether you start from the surface or from someplace high above the surface. Because gravity weakens with distance, it takes less energy—and hence a lower velocity—to escape from a point high above Earth than from Earth's surface.

◆ How does gravity cause tides?

Newton's universal law of gravitation has applications that go far beyond explaining Kepler's laws and orbits. For our purposes, however, there is just one more topic we need to cover: how gravity causes tides.

If you've spent time near an ocean, you've probably observed the rising and falling of the tides. In most places, tides rise and fall twice each day. Tides arise because gravity attracts Earth and the Moon toward each other (with the Moon staying in orbit as it "falls around" Earth), but it affects different parts of Earth slightly differently: Because the strength of gravity declines with distance, the gravitational attraction of each part of Earth to the Moon becomes weaker as we go from the side of Earth facing the Moon to the side facing away from the Moon. This difference in attraction creates a "stretching force," or **tidal force,** that stretches the entire Earth to create two tidal bulges, one facing the Moon and one opposite the Moon (Figure 4.19). If you are still unclear about why there are *two* tidal bulges, think about a rubber band: If you pull on a rubber band, it will stretch in both directions relative to its center, even if you pull on only one side (while holding the other side still). In the same way, Earth stretches on both sides even though the Moon is tugging harder on only one side.

Tides affect both land and ocean, but we generally notice only the ocean tides because water flows much more readily than land. Earth's

Tidal forces cause the entire Earth to stretch along the Earth–Moon line, creating two tidal bulges.

rotation carries any location through each of the two bulges each day, creating two high tides. Low tides occur when the location is at the points halfway between the two tidal bulges. The height and timing of ocean tides varies considerably from place to place on Earth. For example, while the tide rises gradually in most locations,

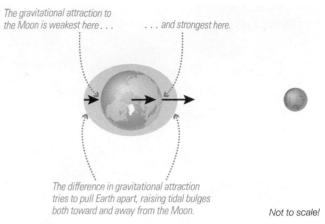

The gravitational attraction to the Moon is weakest here . . . . . . and strongest here.

The difference in gravitational attraction tries to pull Earth apart, raising tidal bulges both toward and away from the Moon.

Not to scale!

▲ **FIGURE 4.19**

Tides are created by the difference in the force of attraction between different parts of Earth and the Moon. The two daily high tides occur as a location on Earth rotates through the two tidal bulges. (The diagram highly exaggerates the tidal bulges, which raise the oceans only about 2 meters and the land only about a centimeter.)

---

special topic | **Why Does the Moon Always Show the Same Face to Earth?**

Tidal effects explain the Moon's *synchronous rotation*, in which the Moon keeps the same face toward Earth because its orbital period is the same as its rotation period. To understand why, let's start by considering the Moon's tidal effect on Earth.

By itself, the Moon's gravity would keep Earth's two tidal bulges on the Earth–Moon line. However, because the tidal bulges stretch Earth itself, Earth's rotation generates friction with the bulges that tries to pull them around with it. The resulting "compromise" keeps the bulges just ahead of the Earth–Moon line at all times (see the figure), which causes two important effects. First, the Moon's gravity always pulls back on the bulges, slowing Earth's rotation. Second, the gravity of the bulges pulls the Moon slightly ahead in its orbit, adding orbital energy that causes the Moon to move farther from Earth. These effects are barely noticeable on human time scales, but they add up over billions of years. Early in Earth's history, a day may have been only 5 or 6 hours long and the Moon may have been one-tenth or less of its current distance from Earth. These changes also provide a great example of conservation of angular momentum: The Moon's growing orbit gains the angular momentum that Earth loses as its rotation slows.

Now consider Earth's tidal force on the Moon, which must be greater than the Moon's tidal force on Earth because of Earth's greater mass. This tidal force gives the Moon two tidal bulges along the Earth–Moon line, much like the two tidal bulges that the Moon creates on Earth. (The Moon's tidal bulges are not visible but can be measured in terms of excess mass along the Earth–Moon line.) If the Moon rotated relative to its tidal bulges in the same way as

If Earth didn't rotate, tidal bulges would be oriented along the Earth–Moon line.

Friction with the rotating Earth pulls the tidal bulges slightly ahead of the Earth–Moon line.

The Moon's gravity tries to pull the bulges back into line, slowing Earth's rotation.

The gravity of the bulges pulls the Moon ahead, increasing its orbital distance. Moon

Not to scale!

Earth's rotation pulls its tidal bulges slightly ahead of the Earth–Moon line, leading to gravitational effects that gradually slow Earth's rotation and increase the Moon's orbital distance.

Earth, the resulting tidal friction would cause the Moon's rotation to slow down. This is exactly what we think happened long ago.

The Moon probably once rotated much faster than it does today. As a result, it *did* rotate through its tidal bulges, and its rotation gradually slowed. Once the Moon's rotation slowed to the point at which the Moon and its bulges rotated at the same rate—that is, synchronously with the orbital period—there was no further source for tidal friction. The Moon's synchronous rotation was therefore a natural outcome of Earth's tidal effects on the Moon.

Similar tidal friction has led to synchronous rotation in many other cases. For example, Jupiter's four large moons (Io, Europa, Ganymede, and Callisto) keep nearly the same face toward Jupiter at all times, as do many other moons. Pluto and its moon Charon *both* rotate synchronously: Like two dancers, they always keep the same face toward each other. Many binary star systems also rotate in this way. Tidal forces may be most familiar because of their effects on our oceans, but they are important throughout the universe.

▲ **FIGURE 4.20**
Photographs of high and low tide at the abbey of Mont-Saint-Michel, France. Here the tide rushes in much faster than a person can swim. Before a causeway was built (visible at the far left), the Mont was accessible by land only at low tide. At high tide, it became an island.

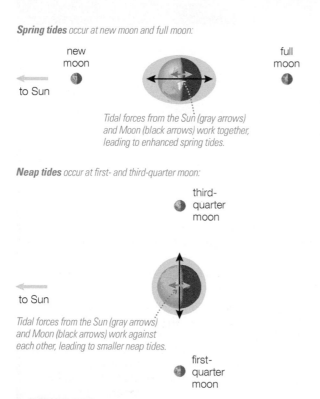

Spring tides occur at new moon and full moon:

Tidal forces from the Sun (gray arrows) and Moon (black arrows) work together, leading to enhanced spring tides.

Neap tides occur at first- and third-quarter moon:

Tidal forces from the Sun (gray arrows) and Moon (black arrows) work against each other, leading to smaller neap tides.

▲ **FIGURE 4.21**
The Sun exerts a tidal force on Earth less than half as strong as that from the Moon. When the tidal forces from the Sun and Moon work together at new moon and full moon, we get enhanced *spring tides*. When they work against each other, at first- and third-quarter moons, we get smaller *neap tides*.

the incoming tide near the famous abbey on Mont-Saint-Michel, France, moves much faster than a person can swim (Figure 4.20). In centuries past, the Mont was an island twice a day at high tide but was connected to the mainland at low tide. Many pilgrims drowned when they were caught unprepared by the tide rushing in. Another unusual tidal pattern occurs in coastal states along the northern shore of the Gulf of Mexico, where topography and other factors combine to make only one noticeable high tide and low tide each day.

The Sun also affects the tides. Although the Sun is much more massive than the Moon, its tidal effect on Earth is smaller because its much greater distance means that the *difference* in the Sun's pull on the near and far sides of Earth is relatively small. The overall tidal force caused by the Sun is a little less than half that caused by the Moon (Figure 4.21). When the tidal forces of the Sun and the Moon work together, as is the case at both new moon and full moon, we get the especially pronounced *spring tides* (so named because the water tends to "spring up" from Earth). When the tidal forces of the Sun and the Moon counteract each other, as is the case at first- and third-quarter moon, we get the relatively small tides known as *neap tides*.

think about it Explain why any tidal effects on Earth caused by the other planets would be unnoticeably small.

Tidal forces affect many objects in the solar system and universe. For example, Earth exerts tidal forces on the Moon that explain why the Moon always shows the same face to Earth (see Special Topic on page 99), and in Chapter 8 we'll see how tidal forces have led to the astonishing volcanic activity of Jupiter's moon Io and the possibility of a subsurface ocean on its moon Europa.

We've covered a lot of ground in this chapter, from the scientific terminology of motion to the overarching principles that govern motion throughout the universe. Be sure you understand the following "big picture" ideas:

- Understanding the universe requires understanding motion. Motion may seem complex, but it can be described simply using Newton's three laws of motion.

- Today, we know that Newton's laws of motion stem from deeper physical principles, including the laws of conservation of angular momentum and of energy.

These principles enable us to understand a wide range of astronomical phenomena.

- Newton also discovered the universal law of gravitation, which explains how gravity holds planets in their orbits and much more—including how satellites can reach and stay in orbit, the nature of tides, and why the Moon rotates synchronously around Earth.

- Newton's discoveries showed that the same physical laws we observe on Earth apply throughout the universe. The universality of physics opens up the entire cosmos as a possible realm of human study.

my cosmic perspective The laws of physics that we use today in everything from building bridges to sending spacecraft to distant objects were first inspired and tested by astronomical observations.

summary of key concepts

4.1 Describing Motion: Examples from Daily Life

◆ **How do we describe motion?**

Speed is the rate at which an object is moving. **Velocity** is speed in a certain direction. **Acceleration** is a change in velocity, meaning a change in either speed or direction. **Momentum** is mass × velocity. A **force** can change an object's momentum, causing it to accelerate.

◆ **How is mass different from weight?**

An object's **mass** is the same no matter where it is located, but its **weight** varies with the strength of gravity or other forces acting on the object. An object becomes **weightless** when it is in **free-fall**, even though its mass is unchanged.

4.2 Newton's Laws of Motion

◆ **How did Newton change our view of the universe?**

Newton showed that the same physical laws that operate on Earth also operate in the heavens, making it possible to learn about the universe by studying physical laws on Earth.

◆ **What are Newton's three laws of motion?**

(1) An object moves at constant velocity if there is no net force acting upon it. (2) Force = mass × acceleration ($F = ma$). (3) For any force, there is always an equal and opposite reaction force.

4.3 Conservation Laws in Astronomy

◆ **What keeps a planet rotating and orbiting the Sun?**

Conservation of angular momentum means that a planet's rotation and orbit cannot change unless it transfers angular momentum to another object. The planets in our solar system do not exchange substantial angular momentum with each other or anything else, so their orbits and rotation rates remain fairly steady.

◆ **Where do objects get their energy?**

kinetic energy

radiative energy   potential energy

Energy is always conserved—it can be neither created nor destroyed. Objects received whatever energy they now have from exchanges of energy with other objects. Energy comes in three basic categories—**kinetic, radiative, and potential.**

4.4 The Force of Gravity

◆ **What determines the strength of gravity?**

The **universal law of gravitation** states that every object attracts every other object with a gravitational force that is directly proportional to the product of the objects' masses and declines with the square of the distance between their centers:

$$F_g = G \frac{M_1 M_2}{d^2}$$

◆ **How does Newton's law of gravity extend Kepler's laws?**

 (1) Newton showed that Kepler's first two laws apply to all orbiting objects, not just planets. (2) He showed that elliptical **bound orbits** are not the only possible orbital shape—orbits can also be **unbound** (taking the shape of a parabola or a hyperbola). (3) **Newton's version of Kepler's third law** allows us to calculate the masses of orbiting objects from their orbital periods and distances.

◆ **How do gravity and energy allow us to understand orbits?**

Gravity determines orbits, and an object cannot change its orbit unless it gains or loses **orbital energy**—the sum of its kinetic and gravitational potential energy—through energy exchange with other objects. If an object gains enough orbital energy, it may achieve **escape velocity** and leave the gravitational influence of the object it was orbiting.

◆ **How does gravity cause tides?**

 The Moon's gravity creates a **tidal force** that stretches Earth along the Earth–Moon line, causing Earth to bulge both toward and away from the Moon. Earth's rotation carries us through the two bulges each day, giving us two daily high tides and two daily low tides.

---

visual skills check

Check your understanding of some of the many types of visual information used in astronomy. For additional practice, try the Chapter 4 Visual Quiz at MasteringAstronomy®.

The figure represents how the Moon causes tides on Earth; the diagram looks down from above the North Pole, so the numbers 1 through 4 label points along Earth's equator.

1. What do the three black arrows represent?
   a. the tidal force Earth exerts on the Moon
   b. the Moon's gravitational force at different points on Earth
   c. the direction in which Earth's water is flowing
   d. Earth's orbital motion

2. Where is it high tide?
   a. point 1 only   b. point 2 only
   c. points 1 and 3   d. points 2 and 4

3. Where is it low tide?
   a. point 1 only   b. point 2 only
   c. points 1 and 3   d. points 2 and 4

4. What time is it at point 1?
   a. noon
   b. midnight
   c. 6 a.m.
   d. cannot be determined from the information in the figure

5. The light blue region represents tidal bulges. In what way are these bulges drawn inaccurately?
   a. There should be only one bulge rather than two.
   b. They should be aligned with the Sun rather than the Moon.
   c. They should be much smaller compared to Earth.
   d. They should be more pointy in shape.

---

exercises and problems

MasteringAstronomy® For instructor-assigned homework and other learning materials, go to MasteringAstronomy®.

Review Questions

1. Define *speed, velocity,* and *acceleration*. What are the units of acceleration? What is the *acceleration of gravity*?
2. Define *momentum* and *force*. What do we mean when we say that momentum can be changed only by a *net force*?
3. What is *free-fall,* and why does it make you *weightless*? Briefly describe why astronauts are weightless in the International Space Station.
4. State *Newton's three laws of motion*. For each law, give an example of its application.
5. Describe the laws of *conservation of angular momentum* and *conservation of energy*. Give an example of how each is important in astronomy.
6. Define *kinetic energy, radiative energy,* and *potential energy*, with at least two examples for each.
7. Define and distinguish *temperature* and *thermal energy*.

8. What is *mass-energy*? Explain the formula $E = mc^2$.

9. Summarize the *universal law of gravitation* both in words and with an equation.

10. What is the difference between a *bound* and an *unbound orbit*?

11. Under what conditions can we use *Newton's version of Kepler's third law* to calculate an object's mass, and what quantities must we measure in order to complete the calculation?

12. Explain why orbits cannot change spontaneously, and how a *gravitational encounter* can cause a change. How can an object achieve *escape velocity*?

13. Explain how the Moon creates tides on Earth. Why do we have two high and low tides each day?

14. How do the tides vary with the phase of the Moon? Why?

Test Your Understanding

◔ Does It Make Sense?

Decide whether the statement makes sense (or is clearly true) or does not make sense (or is clearly false). Explain clearly; not all of these have definitive answers, so your explanation is more important than your chosen answer.

15. I've never been to space, so I've never experienced weightlessness.

16. Suppose you could enter a vacuum chamber (a chamber with no air in it) on Earth. Inside this chamber, a feather would fall at the same rate as a rock.

17. If an astronaut goes on a space walk outside the Space Station, she will quickly float away from the station unless she has a tether holding her to the station.

18. I used Newton's version of Kepler's third law to calculate Saturn's mass from orbital characteristics of its moon Titan.

19. If the Sun were magically replaced with a giant rock that had precisely the same mass, Earth's orbit would not change.

20. The fact that the Moon rotates once in precisely the time it takes to orbit Earth once is such an astonishing coincidence that scientists probably never will be able to explain it.

21. Venus has no oceans, so it could not have tides even if it had a moon (which it doesn't).

22. If an asteroid passed by Earth at just the right distance, Earth's gravity would capture it and make it our second moon.

23. When I drive my car at 30 miles per hour, it has more kinetic energy than it does at 10 miles per hour.

24. Someday soon, scientists are likely to build an engine that produces more energy than it consumes.

Quick Quiz

Choose the best answer to each of the following. Explain your reasoning with one or more complete sentences.

25. A car is accelerating when it is (a) traveling on a straight, flat road at 50 miles per hour. (b) traveling on a straight uphill road at 30 miles per hour. (c) going around a circular track at a steady 100 miles per hour.

26. Compared to their values on Earth, on another planet your (a) mass and weight would both be the same. (b) mass would be the same but your weight would be different. (c) weight would be the same but your mass would be different.

27. Which person is weightless? (a) a child in the air as she plays on a trampoline (b) a scuba diver exploring a deep-sea wreck (c) an astronaut on the Moon

28. Consider the statement "There's no gravity in space." This statement is (a) completely false. (b) false if you are close to a planet or moon, but true in between the planets. (c) completely true.

29. To make a rocket turn left, you need to (a) fire an engine that shoots out gas to the left. (b) fire an engine that shoots out gas to the right. (c) spin the rocket clockwise.

30. Compared to its angular momentum when it is farthest from the Sun, Earth's angular momentum when it is nearest to the Sun is (a) greater. (b) less. (c) the same.

31. The gravitational potential energy of a contracting interstellar cloud (a) stays the same at all times. (b) gradually transforms into other forms of energy. (c) gradually grows larger.

32. If Earth were twice as far from the Sun, the force of gravity attracting Earth to the Sun would be (a) twice as strong. (b) half as strong. (c) one-quarter as strong.

33. According to the law of universal gravitation, what would happen to Earth if the Sun were somehow replaced by a black hole of the same mass? (a) Earth would be quickly sucked into the black hole. (b) Earth would slowly spiral into the black hole. (c) Earth's orbit would not change.

34. If the Moon were closer to Earth, high tides would (a) be higher than they are now. (b) be lower than they are now. (c) occur three or more times a day rather than twice a day.

◔ Process of Science

35. *Testing Gravity.* Scientists are constantly trying to learn whether our current understanding of gravity is complete or must be modified. Describe how the observed motion of spacecraft headed out of the solar system (such as the *Voyager* spacecraft) can be used to test the accuracy of our current theory of gravity.

36. *How Does the Table Know?* Thinking deeply about seemingly simple observations sometimes reveals underlying truths that we might otherwise miss. For example, think about holding a golf ball in one hand and a bowling ball in the other. To keep them motionless, you must actively adjust the tension in your arm muscles so that each arm exerts a different upward force that exactly balances the weight of each ball. Now, think about what happens when you set the balls on a table. Somehow, the table exerts exactly the right amount of upward force to keep the balls motionless, even though their weights are very different. How does a table "know" to make the same type of adjustment that you make consciously when you hold the balls motionless in your hands? (*Hint:* Think about the origin of the force pushing upward on the objects.)

Group Work Exercise

37. *Your Ultimate Energy Source.* **Roles:** *Scribe* (takes notes on the group's activities), *Proposer* (proposes explanations to the group), *Skeptic* (points out weaknesses in proposed explanations), *Moderator* (leads group discussion and makes sure the group works as a team). **Activity:** According to the law of conservation of energy, the energy your body is using right now had to come from somewhere else. Make a list going backwards in time describing how the energy you are using right now has proceeded through time. For each item on the list, identify the energy as kinetic energy, gravitational potential energy, chemical potential energy, electrical potential energy, mass-energy, or radiative energy.

Investigate Further

Short-Answer/Essay Questions

38. *Weightlessness.* Astronauts are weightless when in orbit in the Space Station. Are they also weightless during launch to the station? How about during their return to Earth? Explain.

39. *Einstein's Famous Formula.*
   a. What is the meaning of the formula $E = mc^2$? Define each variable.
   b. How does this formula explain the generation of energy by the Sun?
   c. How does this formula explain the destructive power of nuclear bombs?

40. *The Gravitational Law.*
   a. How does quadrupling the distance between two objects affect the gravitational force between them?
   b. Suppose the Sun were somehow replaced by a star with twice as much mass. What would happen to the gravitational force between Earth and the Sun?
   c. Suppose Earth were moved to one-third of its current distance from the Sun. What would happen to the gravitational force between Earth and the Sun?

41. *Allowable Orbits?*
   a. Suppose the Sun were replaced by a star with twice as much mass. Could Earth's orbit stay the same? Why or why not?
   b. Suppose Earth doubled in mass (but the Sun stayed the same as it is now). Could Earth's orbit stay the same? Why or why not?

42. *Head-to-Foot Tides.* You and Earth attract each other gravitationally, so you should also be subject to a tidal force resulting from the difference between the gravitational attraction felt by your feet and that felt by your head (at least when you are standing). Explain why you can't feel this tidal force.

Quantitative Problems

Be sure to show all calculations clearly and state your final answers in complete sentences.

43. *Energy Comparisons.* Use the data in Table 4.1 to answer each of the following questions.
   a. Compare the energy of a 1-megaton H-bomb to the energy released by a major earthquake.
   b. If the United States obtained all its energy from oil, how much oil would be needed each year?
   c. Compare the Sun's annual energy output to the energy released by a supernova.

44. *Fusion Power.* No one has yet succeeded in creating a commercially viable way to produce energy through nuclear fusion. However, suppose we could build fusion power plants using the hydrogen in water as a fuel. Based on the data in Table 4.1, how much water would we need each minute to meet U.S. energy needs? Could such a reactor power the entire United States with the water flowing from your kitchen sink? Explain. (*Hint:* Use the annual U.S. energy consumption to find the energy consumption per minute, and then divide by the energy yield from fusing 1 liter of water to figure out how many liters would be needed each minute.)

45. *Understanding Newton's Version of Kepler's Third Law.* Find the orbital period for the planet in each case. (*Hint:* The calculations for this problem are so simple that you will not need a calculator.)
   a. A planet with twice Earth's mass orbiting at a distance of 1 AU from a star with the same mass as the Sun.
   b. A planet with the same mass as Earth orbiting at a distance of 1 AU from a star with four times the Sun's mass.

46. *Using Newton's Version of Kepler's Third Law.*
   a. Find Earth's approximate mass from the fact that the Moon orbits Earth in an average time of 27.3 days at an average distance of 384,000 kilometers. (*Hint:* The Moon's mass is only about $\frac{1}{80}$ of Earth's.)
   b. Find Jupiter's mass from the fact that its moon Io orbits every 42.5 hours at an average distance of 422,000 kilometers.
   c. You discover a planet orbiting a distant star that has about the same mass as the Sun, with an orbital period of 63 days. What is the planet's orbital distance?
   d. Pluto's moon Charon orbits Pluto every 6.4 days with a semimajor axis of 19,600 kilometers. Calculate the *combined* mass of Pluto and Charon.
   e. Calculate the orbital period of a spacecraft in an orbit 300 kilometers above Earth's surface.
   f. Estimate the mass of the Milky Way Galaxy from the fact that the Sun orbits the galactic center every 230 million years at a distance of 27,000 light-years. (As we'll discuss in Chapter 15, this calculation actually tells us only the mass of the galaxy *within* the Sun's orbit.)

Discussion Questions

47. *Knowledge of Mass-Energy.* Einstein's discovery that energy and mass are equivalent has led to technological developments that are both beneficial and dangerous. Discuss some of these developments. Overall, do you think the human race would be better or worse off if we had never discovered that mass is a form of energy? Defend your opinion.

48. *Perpetual Motion Machines.* Every so often, someone claims to have built a machine that can generate energy perpetually from nothing. Why isn't this possible according to the known laws of nature? Why do you think claims of perpetual motion machines sometimes receive substantial media attention?

Web Projects

49. *Space Station.* Visit a NASA site with pictures from the International Space Station. Choose two photos that illustrate some facet of Newton's laws. Explain how Newton's laws apply to each photo.

50. *Nuclear Power.* There are two basic ways to generate energy from atomic nuclei: through nuclear fission (splitting nuclei) and through nuclear fusion (combining nuclei). All current nuclear reactors are based on fission, but using fusion would have many advantages if we could develop the technology. Research some of the advantages of fusion and some of the obstacles to developing fusion power. Do you think fusion power will be a reality in your lifetime? Explain.

51. *Space Elevator.* Some people have proposed using a "space elevator" to reach orbit high above Earth. Learn about the concept and write a short report on how it works, what advantages it would have over rockets, and whether it is feasible.

5 Light
The Cosmic Messenger

The visible light spectrum of the Sun.

LEARNING GOALS

5.1 Basic Properties of Light and Matter
- What is light?
- What is matter?
- How do light and matter interact?

5.2 Learning from Light
- What are the three basic types of spectra?
- How does light tell us what things are made of?
- How does light tell us the temperatures of planets and stars?
- How does light tell us the speed of a distant object?

5.3 Collecting Light with Telescopes
- How do telescopes help us learn about the universe?
- Why do we put telescopes in space?

105

Ancient observers could discern only the most basic features of the light that they saw, such as color and brightness, but we now know that light carries far more information. Today, we can analyze the light of distant objects to learn what they are made of, how hot they are, how fast they are moving, and much more. Light is truly the cosmic messenger, bringing the stories of distant objects to Earth.

In this chapter, we'll explore the basic properties of light and matter that allow us to understand the messages encoded in light. We'll also discuss telescopes and technologies that allow us to collect and study light.

5.1 Basic Properties of Light and Matter

The chapter opening photo shows a detailed view of the Sun's **spectrum,** in which the colors of sunlight are spread out in horizontal rows from the upper left to the lower right. The rainbow of color probably reminds you of what we see when we pass white light through a prism (Figure 5.1). However, notice that the Sun's spectrum contains hundreds of dark lines, representing places where a small piece of the rainbow is missing. We see similar dark or bright lines when we look at almost any spectrum in detail, whether it is the spectrum of the flame from a backyard gas grill or the spectrum of a distant galaxy whose light we collect with a gigantic telescope.

The features in an object's spectrum are created by interactions between light and matter in the object. As a result, careful study of a spectrum can tell us a great deal about the object from which it comes— but only if we first understand the basic properties of light and matter.

◆ What is light?

Light is familiar to all of us, but its nature remained a mystery for most of human history. Experiments performed by Isaac Newton in the 1660s provided the first real insights into the nature of light. It was already known that passing white light through a prism produced a rainbow of color, but many people thought the colors came from the prism rather than from the light itself. Newton demonstrated that the colors came from the light by placing a second prism in front of the light of just one color, such as red, from the first prism. If the rainbow of color came from the prism itself, the second prism would have produced a rainbow just like the first. But it did not: When only red light entered the second prism, only red light emerged, proving that the color was a property of the light and not of the prism.

Newton's experiment showed that *white* light is a mix of all the colors in the rainbow. Later scientists found that just as there are sounds that our ears cannot hear (such as the sound of a dog whistle), there is light "beyond the rainbow" that our eyes cannot see. In fact, the **visible light** that splits into the rainbow of color is only a tiny part of the complete spectrum of light, usually called the **electromagnetic spectrum** for reasons that will soon be clear (Figure 5.2). Light itself is often called **electromagnetic radiation.**

Light is also known as electromagnetic radiation.

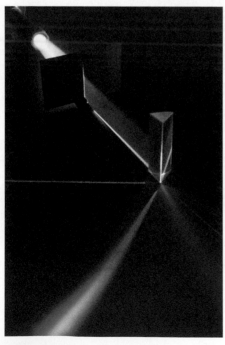

▲ **FIGURE 5.1**

When we pass white light through a prism, it disperses into a rainbow of color that we call a *spectrum.*

The Electromagnetic Spectrum

gamma rays | X rays | ultraviolet | infrared | radio

visible

microwaves

← shorter   longer →

wavelength (meters)

10^{-12} 10^{-10} 10^{-8} 10^{-6} 10^{-4} 10^{-2} 1 10^2

size of wavelength

hydrogen atom   protein   bacterium   animal cell   pinhead   baseball   football field

← higher   lower →

10^{20} 10^{18} 10^{16} 10^{14} 10^{12} 10^{10} 10^8 10^6

frequency (hertz)

energy (electron-volts)

10^6 10^4 10^2 1 10^{-2} 10^{-4} 10^{-6} 10^{-8}

sources on Earth

radioactive elements   X-ray machines   light bulb   people   radar   microwave oven   radio transmitter

cosmic sources

gamma ray burst   black hole accretion disk   Sun's chromosphere   Sun   planets, star-forming clouds   cosmic microwave background   radio galaxy

▲ **FIGURE 5.2**

The electromagnetic spectrum. Notice that wavelength increases as we go from gamma rays to radio waves, while frequency and energy increase in the opposite direction. (Energy is given in units of electron-volts [eV]: 1 eV = 1.60×10^{-19} joule.)

Wave Properties of Light   You've probably heard that light is a wave, but what does that mean? In general, a wave is something that can transmit energy without carrying material along with it. For example, shaking the end of a rope makes every piece of the rope bob up and down, creating a wave of peaks and troughs that move along the rope even though the rope itself doesn't go anywhere (Figure 5.3a). The **wavelength** is the distance between adjacent peaks and the **frequency** is the number of times that any piece of the rope moves up and down each second. For example, if a piece of the rope moves up and down three times each second, the wave has a frequency of three cycles per second, or three *hertz* for short.

Light is different from waves on a rope because we cannot see anything moving up and down as it travels. However, we can tell that light is a wave from its effect on matter. If you could set up a row of electrically charged particles such as electrons, it would wriggle like a snake as a wave of light passed by (Figure 5.3b). The distance between adjacent peaks would tell us the wavelength and the number of times each electron bobbed up and down would tell us the frequency (Figure 5.3c). Because light can interact with both electrically charged particles and magnetic

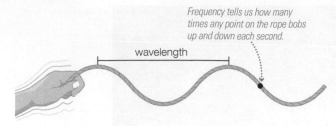

Frequency tells us how many times any point on the rope bobs up and down each second.

wavelength

a Shaking one end of a rope up and down generates waves moving along it.

b If you could line up electrons, they would wriggle up and down as light passes by, demonstrating that light is a wave.

Wavelength is the distance between adjacent peaks of the electric (and magnetic) field . . .

. . . while frequency is the number of times each second that the electric (and magnetic) field vibrates up and down (or side to side) at any point.

wavelength

All light travels with speed c = 300,000 km/s.

c Light can affect both electrically charged particles and magnets, so we say that light is an *electromagnetic wave.*

▲ **FIGURE 5.3**

These diagrams explain the wave properties of light.

1 cm

Longer wavelength means lower frequency.

wavelength = 1 cm,
frequency = 30 GHz

0.5 cm

wavelength = $\frac{1}{2}$ cm,
frequency = 2 × 30 GHz = 60 GHz

0.25 cm

wavelength = $\frac{1}{4}$ cm,
frequency = 4 × 30 GHz = 120 GHz

Shorter wavelength means higher frequency.

▲ **FIGURE 5.4**

Because all light travels through space at the same speed, light of longer wavelength must have lower frequency, and vice versa. (GHz stands for gigahertz, or 10^9 hertz.)

fields, we say that light is an **electromagnetic wave** (which explains the origin of the terms *electromagnetic radiation* and *electromagnetic spectrum*).

All light travels through empty space at the same speed—the **speed of light**—which is about 300,000 kilometers per second. The speed of

The longer the wavelength of light, the lower its frequency and energy.

any wave is its wavelength times its frequency, and this fact leads to an important relationship between wavelength and frequency for light: *The longer the wavelength, the lower the frequency, and vice versa* (Figure 5.4).

Particle Properties of Light   In everyday life, waves seem very different from particles. A wave exists only as a pattern of motion with a wavelength and a frequency, while a particle is a "thing" such as a marble, a baseball, or an individual atom. However, experiments show that light can behave both as a wave and as a particle.

The idea that light can be both a wave and a particle may seem quite strange, but it is fundamental to our modern understanding of physics. We think of light as consisting of many individual "pieces," or **photons.** Like baseballs, photons of light can be counted individually and can hit a wall one

Light comes in "pieces" called photons, each with a precise wavelength, frequency, and energy.

at a time. Like waves, each photon travels at the speed of light and is characterized by a wavelength and frequency. Moreover, each photon carries a particular amount of energy that depends on its frequency: The higher the frequency of the photon, the more energy it carries. That is why energy increases in the same direction as frequency in Figure 5.2.

think about it   Does the energy of a photon also depend on its wavelength? Explain.

The Many Forms of Light   Figure 5.2 also shows the names we give to different portions of the electromagnetic spectrum. Visible light has wavelengths ranging from about 400 nm at the blue or violet end of the rainbow to about 700 nm at the red end. (A nanometer [nm] is a billionth of a meter.) Light with wavelengths somewhat longer than red light is called **infrared,** because it lies beyond the red end of the rainbow. **Radio waves** are the longest-wavelength light. The region near the border between infrared and radio waves, where wavelengths range from micrometers to centimeters, is often called **microwaves.** In astronomy, microwaves are sometimes divided further: Wavelengths from about one to a few millimeters are called *millimeter waves*, while wavelengths of tenths of a millimeter are called *submillimeter waves*.

On the other side of the spectrum, light with wavelengths somewhat shorter than blue light is called **ultraviolet,** because it lies beyond the blue (or violet) end of the rainbow. Light with even shorter wavelengths is called **X rays,** and the shortest-wavelength light is called **gamma rays.** Notice that visible light is an extremely small part of the entire electromagnetic spectrum: The reddest red that our eyes can see has only about twice the wavelength of the bluest blue, but the radio waves from your favorite radio station are a billion times as long as the X rays used in a doctor's office.

Radio waves, microwaves, infrared, visible light, ultraviolet, X rays, and gamma rays are all forms of light.

The various energies of light explain many familiar effects in everyday life. Radio waves carry so little energy that they have no noticeable effect on our bodies, but they can make electrons move up and down in an antenna, making them useful for radio communication. Molecules moving in a warm object emit infrared light, which is why we sometimes associate infrared light with heat. Receptors in our eyes respond to visible-light photons, making vision possible. Ultraviolet photons carry enough energy to damage skin cells, causing sunburn or cancer. X-ray photons have enough energy to penetrate skin and muscle but can be blocked by bones or teeth, which is why they can be used to make images of bone or tooth structures.

◆ What is matter?

We are usually more interested in the matter that light is coming from—such as planets, stars, and galaxies—than we are in the light itself. We must therefore explore the nature of matter if we are to decode the messages carried by light.

The ancient Greeks imagined that all material was made of four elements: fire, water, earth, and air. Some Greeks, beginning with the philosopher Democritus (c. 470–380 B.C.), further imagined that these four elements came in the form of tiny particles they called *atoms*, a Greek term meaning "indivisible." Modern ideas are similar in spirit but differ in many details. For example, we now know of more than 100 chemical **elements,** each composed of a different type of atom. Some of the most familiar elements are hydrogen, helium, carbon, oxygen, silicon, iron, gold, silver, lead, and uranium. (See Appendix D for a complete list.) Moreover, the atoms that make up the elements are composed of even smaller particles.

Atomic Structure   Atoms are made of particles that we call **protons, neutrons,** and **electrons** (Figure 5.5). Protons and neutrons are found in the tiny **nucleus** at the center of the atom. The rest of the atom's volume contains the electrons that surround the nucleus. Although

> The chemical elements are made of atoms, which in turn are made of protons, neutrons, and electrons.

the nucleus is very small compared to the atom as a whole, it contains most of the atom's mass, because protons and neutrons are each about 2000 times as massive as an electron. Note that atoms are incredibly small: Millions could fit end to end across the period at the end of this sentence. The number of atoms in a single drop of water (typically, 10^{22} to 10^{23} atoms) may exceed the number of stars in the observable universe.

The properties of an atom depend mainly on the **electrical charge** in its nucleus. Electrical charge is a fundamental physical property that describes how strongly an object will interact with electromagnetic fields; total electrical charge is always conserved, just as energy is always conserved. We define the electrical charge of a proton as the basic unit of positive charge, which we write as +1. An electron has an electrical charge that is precisely opposite that of a proton, so we say it has negative charge (−1). Neutrons are electrically neutral, meaning that they have no charge.

Oppositely charged particles attract, and similarly charged particles repel. The attraction between the positively charged protons in the nucleus and the negatively charged electrons that surround it is what holds an atom together. Ordinary atoms have identical numbers of electrons and protons, making them electrically neutral overall. (You may wonder why electrical repulsion doesn't cause the positively charged protons in

common misconceptions

Is Radiation Dangerous?

Many people associate the word *radiation* with danger. However, the word *radiate* simply means "to spread out from a center" (note the similarity between *radiation* and *radius* [of a circle]), and *radiation* is just a term to describe energy carried through space. Energy carried by particles of matter, such as protons or neutrons, is called *particle radiation*. Energy carried by light is called *electromagnetic radiation*. In general, radiation is dangerous only if it has high energies that allow it to penetrate and cause damage to body tissues. Lower-energy forms of radiation, such as radio waves, are usually harmless, and visible-light radiation from the Sun is necessary to life on Earth. So while some forms of radiation are dangerous, others are harmless or beneficial.

common misconceptions

Can You Hear Radio Waves or See an X Ray?

Most people associate the term *radio* with sound, but radio waves are a form of *light* with long wavelengths—too long for our eyes to see. Radio stations encode sounds (such as voices and music) as electrical signals, which they broadcast as radio waves. What we call "a radio" in daily life is an electronic device that receives these radio waves and decodes them to re-create the sounds played at the radio station. Televisions, cell phones, and other wireless devices also work by encoding and decoding information in the form of light called radio waves.

X rays are also a form of light, with wavelengths far too short for our eyes to see. In a medical office, a special machine works somewhat like the flash on an ordinary camera but emits X rays instead of visible light. This machine flashes the X rays at you, and a detector placed behind you records the X rays transmitted through your body. You never see the X rays themselves—you see only the image recorded by the detector.

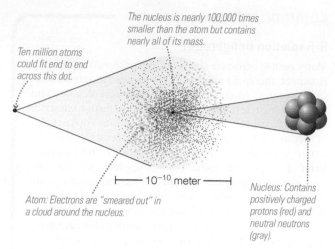

Ten million atoms could fit end to end across this dot.

The nucleus is nearly 100,000 times smaller than the atom but contains nearly all of its mass.

├── 10^{-10} meter ──┤

Atom: Electrons are "smeared out" in a cloud around the nucleus.

Nucleus: Contains positively charged protons (red) and neutral neutrons (gray).

▲ **FIGURE 5.5**

The structure of a typical atom. Note that atoms are extremely tiny: The atom shown in the middle is magnified to about 1 billion times its actual size, and the nucleus on the right is magnified to about 100 trillion times its actual size.

atomic number = number of protons
atomic mass number = number of protons + neutrons
(A neutral atom has the same number of electrons as protons.)

Hydrogen (^{1}H)   **Helium (^{4}He)**   **Carbon (^{12}C)**

atomic number = 1   atomic number = 2   atomic number = 6
atomic mass   atomic mass   atomic mass
number = 1   number = 4   number = 12
(1 electron)   (2 electrons)   (6 electrons)

Different *isotopes* of a given element contain the same number of protons, but different numbers of neutrons.

Isotopes of Carbon

carbon-12   carbon-13   carbon-14

^{12}C ^{13}C ^{14}C
(6 protons   (6 protons   (6 protons
+ 6 neutrons)   + 7 neutrons)   + 8 neutrons)

▲ **FIGURE 5.6**

Terminology of atoms.

a nucleus to fly apart from one another. The answer is that an even stronger force, called the **strong force,** overcomes electrical repulsion and holds the nucleus together [Section 11.2].)

Although we can think of electrons as tiny particles, they are not quite like tiny grains of sand and they don't orbit the nucleus the way planets orbit the Sun. Instead, the electrons in an atom form a kind of "smeared out" cloud that surrounds the nucleus and gives the atom its apparent size. The electrons aren't really cloudy, but it is impossible to pinpoint their positions in the atom. The electrons therefore give the atom a size far larger than its nucleus even though they represent only a tiny portion of the atom's mass. If we imagine an atom on a scale that makes its nucleus the size of your fist, its electron cloud would be many kilometers wide.

Atomic Terminology   You've probably learned the basic terminology of atoms in past science classes, but let's review it just to be sure. Figure 5.6 summarizes the key terminology we will use in this book.

Each different chemical element contains a different number of protons in its nucleus. This number is its **atomic number.** For example, a hydrogen nucleus contains just one proton, so its atomic number is 1. A helium nucleus contains two protons, so its atomic number is 2. The *combined* number of protons and neutrons in an atom is called its **atomic mass number.** The atomic mass number of ordinary hydrogen is 1 because its nucleus is just a single proton. Helium usually has two neutrons in addition to its two protons, giving it an atomic mass number of 4. Carbon usually has six protons and six neutrons, giving it an atomic mass number of 12.

Atoms of different chemical elements have different numbers of protons.

Every atom of a given element contains exactly the same number of protons, but the number of neutrons can vary. For example, all carbon atoms have six protons, but they may have six, seven, or eight neutrons. Versions of an element with different numbers of neutrons are called **isotopes** of that element. Isotopes are named with their element name and atomic mass number. For example, the most common isotope of carbon has six protons and six neutrons, giving it atomic mass number $6 + 6 = 12$, so we call it *carbon-12.* Other isotopes of carbon are carbon-13 (six protons and seven neutrons) and carbon-14 (six protons and eight neutrons). We sometimes write the atomic mass number as a superscript to the left of the element symbol: ^{12}C, ^{13}C, ^{14}C. We read ^{12}C as "carbon-12."

Isotopes of a particular chemical element all have the same number of protons but different numbers of neutrons.

think about it   The symbol ^{4}He represents helium with an atomic mass number of 4. ^{4}He is the most common form of helium, containing two protons and two neutrons. What does the symbol ^{3}He represent?

The number of different material substances is far greater than the number of chemical elements because atoms can combine to form **molecules.** Some molecules consist of two or more atoms of the same element. For example, we breathe O_2, oxygen molecules made of two oxygen atoms. Other molecules, such as water, are made up of atoms of two or more different elements. The symbol H_2O tells us that a water molecule contains two hydrogen atoms and one oxygen atom. The chemical properties of a molecule are different from those of its individual atoms. For example, water behaves very differently than pure hydrogen or pure oxygen.

How do light and matter interact?

Now that we have discussed the nature of light and of matter individually, we are ready to explore how light and matter interact. Energy carried by light can interact with matter in four general ways:

- **Emission:** A light bulb *emits* visible light; the energy of the light comes from electrical potential energy supplied to the bulb.
- **Absorption:** When you place your hand near an incandescent light bulb, your hand *absorbs* some of the light, and this absorbed energy warms your hand.
- **Transmission:** Some forms of matter, such as glass and air, *transmit* light, which means allowing it to pass through.
- **Reflection/scattering:** Light can bounce off matter, leading to what we call *reflection* (when the bouncing is all in the same general direction) or *scattering* (when the bouncing is more random).

Materials that transmit light are said to be *transparent*, and materials that absorb light are called *opaque*. Many materials are neither perfectly transparent nor perfectly opaque. For example, dark sunglasses and clear eyeglasses are both partially transparent, but the dark glasses absorb more light and transmit less. Materials often interact differently with different colors of light. For example, red glass transmits red light but absorbs other colors, while a green lawn reflects (scatters) green light but absorbs all other colors.

Matter can emit, absorb, transmit, or reflect light.

Let's put these ideas together to understand what happens when you walk into a room and turn on the light switch (Figure 5.7). The light bulb begins to emit white light, which is a mix of all the colors in the spectrum. Some of this light exits the room, transmitted through the windows. The rest of the light strikes the surfaces of objects inside the room, and the material properties of each object determine the colors it absorbs or reflects. The light coming from each object therefore carries an enormous amount of information about the object's location, shape and structure, and composition. You acquire this information

▼ **FIGURE 5.7**

This diagram shows examples of the four basic interactions between light and matter: emission, absorption, transmission, and reflection (or scattering).

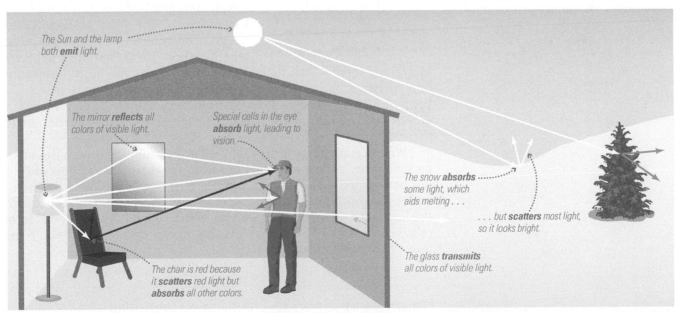

The Sun and the lamp both **emit** light.

The mirror **reflects** all colors of visible light.

Special cells in the eye **absorb** light, leading to vision.

The snow **absorbs** some light, which aids melting . . .

. . . but **scatters** most light, so it looks bright.

The glass **transmits** all colors of visible light.

The chair is red because it **scatters** red light but **absorbs** all other colors.

when light enters your eyes, where special cells in your retina absorb it and send signals to your brain. Your brain interprets the messages that light carries, recognizing materials and objects in the process we call *vision*.

5.2 Learning from Light

Light carries much more information than our naked eyes can recognize. Modern instruments can reveal otherwise hidden details in spectra, and special telescopes can record forms of light that are invisible to our eyes. In this section, we'll explore how detailed studies of light help us unlock the secrets of the universe.

◆ What are the three basic types of spectra?

Laboratory studies show that spectra come in three basic types,* summarized in Figure 5.8:

1. The spectrum of a traditional, or incandescent, light bulb is a rainbow of color. Because the rainbow spans a broad range of wavelengths without interruption, we call it a **continuous spectrum.**

2. A thin or low-density cloud of gas emits light only at specific wavelengths that depend on its composition and temperature. The spectrum therefore consists of bright **emission lines** against a black background and is called an **emission line spectrum.**

3. If the cloud of gas lies between us and a light bulb (and the cloud is cooler than the light bulb or other light source), we still see most of the continuous spectrum of the light bulb. However, the cloud absorbs light of specific wavelengths, so the spectrum shows dark **absorption lines** over the background rainbow. We call this an **absorption line spectrum.**

Notice that each of the spectra in Figure 5.8 is shown both as a band of light and as a graph. The band of light is essentially what you would see if you projected the light that passes through the prism onto a wall. The graph shows the amount, or **intensity,** of the light at each wavelength; the intensity is high at wavelengths where there is a lot of light and low where there is little light. For example, the graph of the absorption line spectrum shows dips in intensity at the wavelengths where the band of light shows dark lines. Astronomers usually display spectra as graphs because they make it easier to see how intensity varies across the spectrum.

The three basic types of spectra are continuous, emission line, and absorption line.

We can apply these ideas to the solar spectrum that opens this chapter. The many dark absorption lines over a background rainbow of color tell us that we are essentially looking at a hot light source through a cooler gas, much like the situation in Figure 5.8c. For the solar spectrum, the hot light source is the hot interior of the Sun, while the "cloud" is the relatively cool and low-density gas that makes up the Sun's visible surface, or *photosphere* [Section 11.1].

---

*The rules that specify the conditions producing each type are often called *Kirchhoff's laws*.

a *The light bulb produces light of all visible wavelengths (colors).*

hot light source

prism

intensity

wavelength

Continuous Spectrum

The spectrum shows a smooth, continuous rainbow of light.

A graph of the spectrum is also continuous; notice that intensity varies slightly at different wavelengths.

b *The atoms in a warm gas cloud emit light only at specific wavelengths (colors) determined by the cloud's composition and temperature.*

cloud of gas

prism

intensity

wavelength

Emission Line Spectrum

We see bright emission lines at specific wavelengths (colors), but no other light.

The graph shows an upward spike at the wavelength of each emission line.

c *If light from a hot source passes through a cooler gas cloud, atoms in the cloud absorb light at wavelengths determined by the cloud's composition and temperature.*

hot light source

cloud of gas

prism

intensity

wavelength

Absorption Line Spectrum

We see dark absorption lines where the cloud has absorbed light of specific wavelengths (colors).

The graph shows a dip in intensity at the wavelength of each absorption line.

▲ **FIGURE 5.8**
These diagrams show examples of the conditions under which we see the three basic types of spectra.

◆ How does light tell us what things are made of?

We have just seen *how* different viewing conditions lead to different types of spectra, so it is time to discuss *why*. Let's start with absorption and emission line spectra. As we'll see, the lines in these spectra can tell us what distant objects are made of.

Energy Levels in Atoms   To understand why we sometimes see emission and absorption lines, we must first discuss a strange fact about electrons in atoms: The electrons can have only particular amounts of energy, and not other energies in between. As an analogy, suppose you're washing windows on a building. If you use an adjustable platform to reach high windows, you can stop the platform at any height above the ground. But if you use a ladder, you can stand only at *particular* heights—the heights of the rungs of the ladder—and not at other heights in between. The possible energies of electrons in atoms are like the possible heights on a ladder. Only a few particular energies are possible, and energies between these special few are not possible. The possible energies are known as the **energy levels** of an atom.

Electrons in atoms can have only particular amounts of energy, and not other energies in between.

ionization
level
                                                                        ⤴ ⟵····· This electron
                                                                              gains enough
                                                                              energy to
                                                                              escape the
                                                                              atom.

                                                                        13.6 eV

level 4 ——————————————————————————————————————— 12.8 eV
level 3 ——————————————————————————————————————— 12.1 eV

level 2 ——————————————————————————————————————— 10.2 eV

                                         │   ┌─────────────┐
                                         │   │ Dropping from│
                              ⤴   │   │ level 2 to   │
                           ┌──────────┐ │Exactly │ level 1 requires│
                           │ Electron │ │10.2 eV │ electron to │
                    ⤴····· │ cannot   │ │allows │ give up 10.2 eV.│
                  ┌───────┐│ accept   │ │electron│   │
                  │Electron││ 11 eV.   │ │to rise │   │
                  │cannot ││   │ │to level 2.│   │
                  │accept ││   │ │   ↓ ⟵   │
level 1   │5 eV.   ││   │ │   │   │
(ground ——————————┴────────┴┴──────────┴──┴─────────┴─────————— 0 eV
state)

▲ FIGURE 5.9

Energy levels for the electron in a hydrogen atom. The electron can change energy levels only if it gains or loses the amount of energy separating the levels. If the electron gains enough energy to reach the ionization level, it can escape from the atom, leaving behind a positively charged ion.

Figure 5.9 shows the energy levels in hydrogen, the simplest of all atoms. The energy levels are labeled on the left in numerical order and on the right with energies in units of *electron-volts*, or *eV* for short. (1 eV = 1.60×10^{-19} joule.) The lowest possible energy level—called level 1 or the *ground state*—is defined as an energy of 0 eV. Each of the higher energy levels (sometimes called *excited states*) is labeled with the extra energy of an electron in that level compared to the ground state.

An electron can rise from a low energy level to a higher one or fall from a high level to a lower one. Such changes are called **energy level transitions.** Because energy must be conserved, energy level transitions can occur only when an electron gains or loses the specific amount of energy separating two levels. For example, an electron in level 1 can rise to level 2 only if it gains 10.2 eV of energy. If you try to give the electron 5 eV of energy, it won't accept it because that is not enough energy to reach level 2. Similarly, if you try to give it 11 eV, it won't accept it because it is too much for level 2 but not enough to reach level 3. Once in level 2, the electron can return to level 1 by giving up 10.2 eV of energy.

Notice that the amount of energy separating the various levels gets smaller at higher levels. For example, it takes more energy to raise the electron from level 1 to level 2 than from level 2 to level 3, which in turn takes more energy than the transition from level 3 to level 4. If the electron gains enough energy to reach the *ionization level*, it escapes the atom completely. Because the escaping electron carries away negative electrical charge, the atom is left with positive electrical charge. Electrically charged atoms are called **ions,** so we say that the escape of the electron *ionizes* the atom.

think about it Are there any circumstances under which an electron in a hydrogen atom can gain 2.6 eV of energy? Explain.

Other atoms also have distinct energy levels, but the levels correspond to different amounts of energy than those of hydrogen. Every type of ion and every type of molecule also has a distinct set of energy levels.

Emission and Absorption Lines The fact that each type of atom, ion, or molecule possesses a unique set of energy levels is what causes emission and absorption lines to appear at specific wavelengths in spectra. It is also what allows us to learn the compositions of distant objects in the universe. To see how, let's consider what happens in a cloud of gas consisting solely of hydrogen atoms.

The atoms in any cloud of gas are constantly colliding with one another, exchanging energy in each collision. Most of the collisions simply send the atoms careening off in new directions. However, a few of the collisions transfer the right amount of energy to bump an electron from a low energy level to a higher energy level. Electrons can't stay in higher energy levels for long. They always fall back down to level 1, usually in a

The photons that produce emission lines are created when electrons fall to lower energy levels.

tiny fraction of a second. The energy the electron loses when it falls to a lower energy level must go somewhere, and often it goes to *emitting* a photon of light. The emitted photon must have the same amount of energy that the electron loses, which means that it has a specific wavelength and frequency. Figure 5.10a shows the energy levels in hydrogen that we saw in Figure 5.9, but it is also labeled with the wavelengths of the photons emitted by various downward transitions of an electron from a higher energy level to a lower one. For example, the transition from level 2 to level 1 emits an ultraviolet photon of wavelength 121.6 nm, and the transition from level 3 to level 2 emits a red visible-light photon of wavelength 656.3 nm.

As long as the gas remains moderately warm, collisions will continually bump some electrons into higher levels from which they fall back down and emit photons with some of the wavelengths shown in Figure 5.10a. The gas therefore emits light with these specific wavelengths. That is why a warm gas cloud produces an emission line spectrum (Figure 5.10b). The bright emission lines appear at the wavelengths that correspond to downward transitions of electrons, and the rest of the spectrum is dark (black). The specific set of lines that we see depends on the cloud's temperature as well as its composition: At higher temperatures, electrons are more likely to be bumped to higher energy levels.

think about it If nothing continues to heat the hydrogen gas, all the electrons eventually will end up in the lowest energy level (the ground state, or level 1). Use this fact to explain why we should *not* expect to see an emission line spectrum from a very cold cloud of hydrogen gas.

Absorption lines occur when photons cause electrons to rise to higher energy levels.

Now, suppose a light bulb illuminates the hydrogen gas from behind (as in Figure 5.8c). The light bulb emits light of all wavelengths, producing a spectrum that looks like a rainbow of color. However, the hydrogen atoms can absorb those photons that have the right amount of energy needed to raise an electron from a low energy level to a higher one.* Figure 5.10c shows the result. It is an absorption line spectrum, because the light bulb produces a continuous rainbow of color while the hydrogen atoms absorb light at specific wavelengths.

You should now understand why the dark absorption lines in Figure 5.10c occur at the same wavelengths as the emission lines in Figure 5.10b: Both types of lines represent the same energy level transitions, except in opposite directions. For example, electrons moving downward from level 3 to level 2 in hydrogen can emit photons of wavelength 656.3 nm (producing an emission line at this wavelength), while electrons absorbing photons with this wavelength can rise up from level 2 to level 3 (producing an absorption line at this wavelength).

Chemical Fingerprints
The fact that hydrogen emits and absorbs at specific wavelengths makes it possible to detect its presence in distant objects. For example, imagine that you look through a telescope at an interstellar gas cloud, and its spectrum looks like that shown in Figure 5.10b. Because only hydrogen produces this particular set of lines, you can conclude that the cloud is made of hydrogen. In essence, the spectrum contains a "fingerprint" left by hydrogen atoms.

Every kind of atom, ion, and molecule produces a unique spectral "fingerprint."

Real interstellar clouds are not made solely of hydrogen. However, the other chemical constituents in the cloud leave fingerprints on the spectrum in much the same way. Every type of atom, ion, and molecule has its own unique spectral fingerprint, because it has its own unique set of energy levels. Over the past century, scientists have done laboratory experiments to

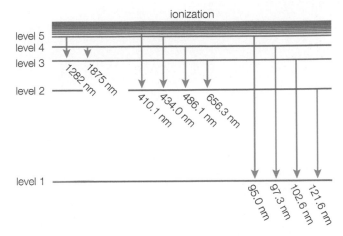

a Energy level transitions in hydrogen correspond to photons with specific wavelengths. Only a few of the many possible transitions are labeled.

410.1 434.0   486.1   656.3
nm   nm   nm   nm

b This spectrum shows emission lines produced by downward transitions between higher levels and level 2 in hydrogen.

410.1 434.0   486.1   656.3
nm   nm   nm   nm

c This spectrum shows absorption lines produced by upward transitions between level 2 and higher levels in hydrogen.

▲ **FIGURE 5.10**
An atom emits or absorbs light only at specific wavelengths that correspond to changes in the atom's energy as an electron undergoes transitions between its allowed energy levels.

---

*Of course, the electrons quickly fall back down, which means they can emit photons of the same wavelength they absorbed. However, these photons are emitted in random directions, so we still see absorption lines because photons that were originally coming toward us have been redirected away from our line of sight.

identify the spectral lines of every chemical element and many ions and molecules. When we see any of those lines in the spectrum of a distant object, we can determine what chemicals produced them. For example, if we see spectral lines of hydrogen, helium, and carbon in the spectrum of a distant star, we know that all three elements are present in the star. With more detailed analysis, we can determine the relative proportions of the various elements. That is how we have learned the chemical compositions of objects throughout the universe.

◆ How does light tell us the temperatures of planets and stars?

We next turn our attention to continuous spectra. Although continuous spectra can be produced in more than one way, light bulbs, planets, and stars produce a particular kind of continuous spectrum that can help us determine their temperatures.

Thermal Radiation: Every Body Does It In a cloud of gas that produces a simple emission or absorption line spectrum, the individual atoms or molecules are essentially independent of one another. Most photons pass easily through such a gas, except those that cause energy level transitions in the atoms or molecules of the gas. However, the atoms and molecules within most of the objects we encounter in everyday life—such as rocks, light bulb filaments, and people—cannot be considered independent and therefore have much more complex sets of energy levels. These objects tend to absorb light across a broad range of wavelengths, which means light cannot easily pass through them and light emitted inside them cannot easily escape. The same is true of almost any large or dense object, including planets and stars.

In order to understand the spectra of such objects, let's consider an idealized case in which an object absorbs all photons that strike it and does not allow photons inside it to escape easily. Photons tend to bounce around randomly inside such an object, constantly exchanging energy with its atoms or molecules. By the time the photons finally escape the object, their radiative energies have become randomized so that they are spread over a wide range of wavelengths. The wide wavelength range of the photons explains why the spectrum of light from such an object is smooth, or *continuous*, like a pure rainbow without any absorption or emission lines.

Most important, the spectrum from such an object depends on only one thing: the object's *temperature*. To understand why, remember that temperature represents the average kinetic energy of the atoms or molecules in an object [Section 4.3]. Because the randomly bouncing photons interact so many times with those atoms or molecules, they end up with energies that match the kinetic energies of the object's atoms or molecules—which means the photon energies depend only on the object's temperature, regardless of what the object is made of. The temperature dependence of this light explains why we call it **thermal radiation** (sometimes known as *blackbody* radiation) and why its spectrum is called a **thermal radiation spectrum.**

No real object emits a perfect thermal radiation spectrum, but almost all familiar objects—including the Sun, the planets, rocks, and even you—emit light that approximates thermal radiation. Figure 5.11 shows a graph of the idealized thermal radiation spectra of three stars and a human, each with its temperature given on the Kelvin scale (see Figure 4.10). Be sure to notice that these spectra show the intensity of light *per unit surface area*, not the total

Planets, stars, rocks, and people emit thermal radiation that depends only on temperature.

Law 1: The curve for a hotter object is everywhere above the curve for a cooler object, showing that hotter objects emit more radiation per unit surface area at every wavelength.

Law 2: The peak wavelength is further to the left for hotter objects, showing that hotter objects emit more of their light at shorter wavelength (high energy).

▲ **FIGURE 5.11**

Graphs of idealized thermal radiation spectra demonstrate the two laws of thermal radiation: (1) Each square meter of a hotter object's surface emits more light at all wavelengths; (2) hotter objects emit photons with a higher average energy. Notice that the graph uses power-of-10 scales on both axes, so that we can see all the curves even though the differences between them are quite large.

amount of light emitted by the object. For example, a very large 3000 K star can emit more total light than a small 15,000 K star, even though the hotter star emits much more light per unit area of its surface.

The Two Laws of Thermal Radiation If you compare the spectra in Figure 5.11, you'll see that they obey two laws of thermal radiation:

- **Law 1** (Stefan-Boltzmann law): *Each square meter of a hotter object's surface emits more light at all wavelengths.* For example, each square meter on the surface of the 15,000 K star emits a lot more light at every wavelength than each square meter of the 3000 K star, and the hotter star emits light at some ultraviolet wavelengths that the cooler star does not emit at all.

- **Law 2** (Wien's [pronounced *veen's*] law): *Hotter objects emit photons with a higher average energy,* which means a shorter average wavelength. That is why the peaks of the spectra are at shorter wavelengths for hotter objects. For example, the peak for the 15,000 K star is in ultraviolet light, the peak for the 5800 K Sun is in visible light, and the peak for the 3000 K star is in the infrared.

You can see these laws in action with a fireplace poker (Figure 5.12). While the poker is still relatively cool, it emits only infrared light, which we cannot see. As it gets hot (above about 1500 K), it begins to glow with visible light, and it glows more brightly as it gets hotter, demonstrating the first law. Its color demonstrates the second law. At first it glows "red hot," because red light has the longest wavelengths of visible light. As it gets even hotter, the average wavelength of the emitted photons moves toward the blue (short wavelength) end of the visible spectrum. The mix of colors emitted at this higher temperature makes the poker look white to your eyes, which is why "white hot" is hotter than "red hot."

see it for yourself Find an incandescent light that has a dimmer switch. What happens to the bulb temperature (which you can check by placing your hand near it) as you turn the switch up? How does the light change color? Explain how these observations demonstrate the two laws of thermal radiation.

Because thermal radiation spectra depend only on temperature, we can use them to measure the temperatures of distant objects. In many cases we can estimate temperatures simply from the object's colors. Notice that while hotter objects emit more light at *all* wavelengths, the biggest difference appears at the shortest wavelengths. With a human body temperature of about 310 K,

Hotter objects emit more total light per unit surface area and emit photons with a higher average energy.

people emit infrared light but not visible light—which explains why we don't glow in the dark! A relatively cool star, with a 3000 K surface temperature, emits mostly red light. That is why some bright stars in our sky, such as Betelgeuse (in Orion) and Antares (in Scorpius), appear reddish in color. The Sun's 5800 K surface emits most strongly in green light (around 500 nm), but the Sun looks yellow or white to our eyes because it also emits other colors throughout the visible spectrum. Hotter stars emit mostly in the ultraviolet but appear blue-white in color because our eyes cannot see their ultraviolet light. If an object were heated to a temperature of millions of degrees, it would radiate mostly X rays. Some astronomical objects are indeed hot enough to emit X rays, such as the Sun's *corona* and hot *accretion disks* around black holes.

At relatively low temperatures, the poker emits only infrared light that we cannot see. ⋯⋯⋯

As it gets hotter, it begins to glow. ⋯⋯⋯

It gets brighter as it heats up (demonstrating Law 1) . . .

. . . and changes from red to white in color (demonstrating Law 2).

▲ **FIGURE 5.12**
A fireplace poker shows the two laws of thermal radiation in action.

cosmic **calculations 5.1**

Laws of Thermal Radiation

The two laws of thermal radiation have simple mathematical formulas.

Law 1 (Stefan-Boltzmann law):
emitted power (per square meter of surface) $= \sigma T^4$

where T is temperature (in Kelvin), σ (Greek letter *sigma*) is a constant with measured value $\sigma = 5.7 \times 10^{-8} \frac{\text{watt}}{(\text{m}^2 \times \text{K}^4)}$, and a *watt* is a unit of power equal to 1 joule per second.

Law 2 (Wien's law): $\lambda_{max} \approx \dfrac{2,900,000}{T \, (\text{in Kelvin})} \text{ nm}$

where λ_{max} (read as "lambda max") is the wavelength (in nanometers) of maximum intensity, which is located at the peak in a thermal radiation spectrum.

Example: Find the emitted power per square meter and the wavelength of peak intensity for a 10,000 K object that emits thermal radiation.

Solution: We use the first law to calculate the emitted power per square meter for an object with $T = 10,000$ K:

$$\sigma T^4 = 5.7 \times 10^{-8} \frac{\text{watt}}{\text{m}^2 \times \text{K}^4} \times (10,000 \text{ K})^4$$
$$= 5.7 \times 10^8 \text{ watt}/\text{m}^2$$

The second law gives the wavelength of maximum intensity:

$$\lambda_{max} \approx \frac{2,900,000}{10,000 \, (\text{in Kelvin})} \text{ nm} \approx 290 \text{ nm}$$

A 10,000 K object emits a total power of 570 million watts per square meter of surface. Its wavelength of maximum intensity is 290 nm, which is in the ultraviolet.

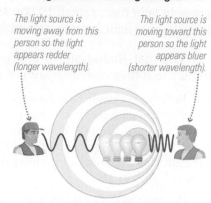

The pitch this person hears . . .   *. . . is the same as the pitch this person hears.*

Behind the train, sound waves stretch to longer wavelength (lower frequency and pitch).   *In front of the train, sound waves bunch up to shorter wavelength (higher frequency and pitch).*

The light source is moving away from this person so the light appears redder (longer wavelength).   *The light source is moving toward this person so the light appears bluer (shorter wavelength).*

a The whistle sounds the same no matter where you stand near a stationary train.

b For a moving train, the sound you hear depends on whether the train is moving toward you or away from you.

c We get the same basic effect from a moving light source (although the shifts are usually too small to notice with our eyes).

▲ **FIGURE 5.13**
The Doppler effect. Each circle represents the crests of sound (or light) waves going in all directions from the source. For example, the circles from the train might represent waves emitted 0.001 second apart.

cosmic **calculations 5.2**

The Doppler Shift

We can calculate an object's radial velocity from its Doppler shift. For velocities that are small compared to the speed of light (less than a few percent of c), the formula is

$$\frac{v_{rad}}{c} = \frac{\lambda_{shift} - \lambda_{rest}}{\lambda_{rest}}$$

where v_{rad} is the object's radial velocity, λ_{rest} is the rest wavelength of a particular spectral line, and λ_{shift} is the shifted wavelength of the same line. (As always, c is the speed of light.) A positive answer means the object is redshifted and moving away from us; a negative answer means it is blueshifted and moving toward us.

Example: One of the visible lines of hydrogen has a rest wavelength of 656.285 nm, but it appears in the spectrum of the star Vega at 656.255 nm. How is Vega moving relative to us?

Solution: We use the rest wavelength $\lambda_{rest} = 656.285$ nm and the shifted wavelength $\lambda_{shift} = 656.255$ nm:

$$\frac{v_{rad}}{c} = \frac{\lambda_{shift} - \lambda_{rest}}{\lambda_{rest}}$$

$$= \frac{656.255 \text{ nm} - 656.285 \text{ nm}}{656.285 \text{ nm}}$$

$$\approx -4.6 \times 10^{-5}$$

The negative answer tells us that Vega is moving *toward* us. Its speed is about 4.6×10^{-5} of the speed of light c. Because $c = 300{,}000$ km/s, this is equivalent to about $4.6 \times 10^{-5} \times (3 \times 10^5 \text{ km/s}) \approx 13.8$ km/s.

◆ How does light tell us the speed of a distant object?

There is still more that we can learn from light: We can use light to learn about the motion of distant objects (relative to us) from changes in their spectra caused by the **Doppler effect.**

The Doppler Effect You've probably noticed the Doppler effect on the *sound* of a train whistle near train tracks. If the train is stationary, the pitch of its whistle sounds the same no matter where you stand (Figure 5.13a). But if the train is moving, the pitch sounds higher when the train is coming toward you and lower when it's moving away from you. Just as the train passes by, you can hear the dramatic change from high to low pitch—a sort of "weeeeeeee–ooooooooooh" sound. To understand why, we have to think about what happens to the sound waves coming from the train (Figure 5.13b). When the train is moving toward you, each pulse of a sound wave is emitted a little closer to you. The result is that waves are bunched up between you and the train, giving them a shorter wavelength and higher frequency (pitch). After the train passes you by, each pulse comes from farther away, stretching out the wavelengths and giving the sound a lower frequency.

The Doppler effect causes similar shifts in the wavelengths of light (Figure 5.13c). If an object is moving toward us, the light waves bunch up between us and the object, so that its entire spectrum is shifted to shorter wavelengths. Because shorter wavelengths of visible light are bluer, the Doppler shift of an object coming toward us is called a **blueshift.** If an object is moving away from us, its light is shifted to longer wavelengths. We call this a **redshift** because longer wavelengths of visible light are redder. For convenience, astronomers use the terms *blueshift* and *redshift* even when they aren't talking about visible light.

Spectral lines shift to shorter wavelengths when an object is moving toward us, and to longer wavelengths when an object is moving away from us.

Spectral lines provide the reference points we use to identify and measure Doppler shifts (Figure 5.14). For example, suppose we recognize the pattern of hydrogen lines in the spectrum of a distant object. We know the **rest wavelengths** of the hydrogen lines—that is, their wavelengths in stationary clouds of hydrogen gas—from laboratory experiments in which a tube of hydrogen gas is heated so that the wavelengths of the spectral lines can be measured. If the hydrogen lines from the object appear at longer wavelengths, then we know they are redshifted and the object is moving away from us. The larger the shift, the faster the object is moving. If the lines appear at shorter wavelengths, then we know they are blueshifted and the object is moving toward us.

think about it Suppose the hydrogen emission line with a rest wavelength of 121.6 nm (the transition from level 2 to level 1) appears at a wavelength of 120.5 nm in the spectrum of a particular star. Given that these wavelengths are in the ultraviolet, is the shifted wavelength closer to or farther from blue visible light? Why, then, do we say that this spectral line is *blueshifted*?

Note that a Doppler shift tells us only the part of an object's full motion that is directed toward or away from us (the *radial* component of motion). Doppler shifts do not give us any information about how fast an object is moving across our line of sight (the *tangential* component of motion). For example, consider three stars moving at the same speed: one moving directly away from us, one moving across our line of sight, and one moving diagonally away from us (Figure 5.15). The Doppler shift will tell us the full speed only of the first star. It will not indicate any speed for the second star, and for the third star it will tell us only the part of the star's speed that is directed away from us. To measure how fast an object is moving across our line of sight, we must observe it long enough to notice how its position gradually shifts across our sky.

Spectral Summary We've covered the major ways in which we can learn from an object's spectrum, discussing how we learn about an object's composition, temperature, and motion. Figure 5.16 (pages 120–121) summarizes the ways in which we learn from spectra.

5.3 Collecting Light with Telescopes

Light carries a great deal of information, but we can obtain only a little of that information with our naked eyes. We need telescopes to learn more, and most great advances in astronomy are directly tied to advances in telescope technology.

◆ How do telescopes help us learn about the universe?

Telescopes are essentially giant eyes that can collect far more light than our own eyes. By combining this light-collecting capacity with cameras and other instruments—such as *spectrographs* that disperse the light into spectra—we can record and analyze light in detail.

Two Key Telescope Properties The first key property of a telescope is its **light-collecting area,** which determines how much total light the telescope can collect at one time. Telescopes are generally round, so we usually characterize a telescope's "size" as the *diameter* of its light-collecting area. For example, a "10-meter telescope" has a light-collecting area 10 meters in diameter.

Laboratory spectrum
Lines at rest wavelengths.

Object 1 *Lines redshifted: Object moving away from us.*

Object 2 *Greater redshift: Object moving away faster than Object 1.*

Object 3 *Lines blueshifted: Object moving toward us.*

Object 4 *Greater blueshift: Object moving toward us faster than Object 3.*

▲ **FIGURE 5.14**
Spectral lines provide the crucial reference points for measuring Doppler shifts.

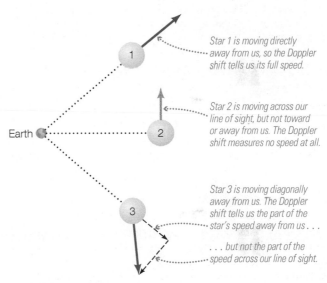

Star 1 is moving directly away from us, so the Doppler shift tells us its full speed.

Star 2 is moving across our line of sight, but not toward or away from us. The Doppler shift measures no speed at all.

Star 3 is moving diagonally away from us. The Doppler shift tells us the part of the star's speed away from us . . .

. . . but not the part of the speed across our line of sight.

▲ **FIGURE 5.15**
The Doppler shift tells us only the portion of an object's speed that is directed toward or away from us. It does not give us any information about how fast an object is moving across our line of sight.

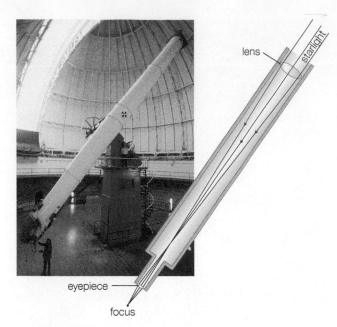

lens

starlight

eyepiece

focus

▲ **FIGURE 5.17**

A refracting telescope collects light with a large transparent lens (see diagram). The photo shows the just-over-1-meter (40-inch) refractor at the University of Chicago's Yerkes Observatory, the world's largest refracting telescope.

Because area is proportional to the *square* of diameter, a small increase in diameter can mean a big increase in light-collecting area. A 10-meter telescope has five times the diameter of a 2-meter telescope, which means $5^2 = 25$ times the light-collecting area.

think about it How does the light-collecting area of a 10-meter telescope compare to that of a human eye, which collects light through an opening (the pupil) about 5 millimeters in diameter?

A second key property of a telescope is the amount of detail it allows us to see, which we characterize by its **angular resolution**—the smallest angle over which we can tell that two dots (or two stars) are distinct. The human eye has an angular resolution of about 1 arcminute (1/60 degree), meaning that two stars can appear distinct only if they have at least this much angular separation in the sky. If the stars are separated by less than 1 arcminute, our eyes will not be able to distinguish them individually and they will look like a single star.

Telescopes collect far more light and allow us to see far more detail than does the naked eye.

Large telescopes can have amazing angular resolution. The 2.4-meter Hubble Space Telescope has an angular resolution of about 0.05 arcsecond (for visible light), which would allow you to read this book from a distance of almost 1 kilometer. Larger telescopes can have even better (smaller) angular resolution, though Earth's atmosphere usually prevents ground-based telescopes from achieving their theoretical limits.

Basic Telescope Design Telescopes come in two basic designs: *refracting* and *reflecting*. A **refracting telescope** operates similar to an eye, using transparent glass lenses to collect and focus light (Figure 5.17). The earliest telescopes, including Galileo's, were refracting telescopes. The world's largest refracting telescope, completed in 1897, has a lens that is 1 meter in diameter and a telescope tube that is 19.5 meters long.

---

extraordinary claims | We Can Never Learn the Composition of Stars

The limits of science have long been a topic of great debate among both scientists and philosophers. One of the most famous claims about such limits came in 1835, when the prominent French philosopher Auguste Comte declared that science could never allow us to learn the composition of stars. His rationale was based primarily on the idea that while we could observe things like the sizes of distant objects, we could not learn what they were made of without collecting physical samples to study here on Earth.

As you know from this chapter, Comte's extraordinary claim was proven wrong a few decades later with the advent of spectroscopy. Less than a century after he made his claim, Cecilia Payne-Gaposchkin used spectroscopy and an understanding of quantum mechanics to unlock the secret to the composition of stars [Section 12.1]. Moreover, even if spectroscopy had not been discovered, Comte's claim might still have been proven wrong, because it also presumed that we would never travel out into space to collect samples of distant objects. While stars besides the Sun remain far beyond our reach, sample

collection within our solar system is now well within our abilities. It's also worth noting that the possibility of space travel was already being considered seriously by Comte's time. For example, in 1593, Johannes Kepler wrote a letter to Galileo in which he made an extraordinary claim of his own: "Provide ships or sails adapted to the heavenly breezes, and there will be some who will not fear even that void . . . ." Of course, that didn't stop many people from claiming that space travel would prove impossible, some of them holding to that view almost right up until we achieved it.

There may well be limits to what we can learn through science, but the history of science teaches us to be wary of claims about what we may or may not do or learn in the future. Some questions that seem unanswerable today, such as why the universe exists or what (if anything) came before the Big Bang, may remain unanswerable, but we should be open to the possibility that science may yet open doors to knowledge that we cannot yet envision.

Verdict: Rejected.

A **reflecting telescope** uses a precisely curved *primary mirror* to gather light (Figure 5.18). This mirror reflects the gathered light to a *secondary mirror* that lies in front of it. The secondary mirror then reflects the light to a focus at a place where the eye or instruments can observe it—sometimes through a hole in the primary mirror and sometimes through the side of the telescope (often with the aid of additional small mirrors). The fact that the secondary mirror prevents some light from reaching the primary mirror might seem like a drawback, but in practice it is not a problem because only a small fraction of the incoming light is blocked.

Nearly all telescopes used in current astronomical research are reflectors. For a long time, the main factor limiting the size of reflecting telescopes was the sheer weight of the glass needed for their primary mirrors.

The world's largest reflecting telescopes have primary mirrors 10 meters or more in diameter.

Recent technological innovations have made it possible to build lighter-weight mirrors, such as the 8-meter mirror in the Gemini telescope (see Figure 5.18), or to make many small mirrors work together as one large one, as in the twin 10-meter Keck telescopes (Figure 5.19). Several other large telescopes are currently in planning or construction, including the Large Synoptic Survey Telescope (8.4 meters, but with a very wide field of view), the Giant Magellan Telescope (effective size of 21 meters), the Thirty Meter Telescope (30 meters), and the European Extremely Large Telescope (39 meters).

Telescopes Across the Spectrum If we studied only visible light, we'd be missing much of the picture. Planets are relatively cool and emit primarily infrared light. The hot upper layers of stars emit ultraviolet and X-ray light. Some violent events produce gamma rays. In fact, most objects emit light over a broad range of wavelengths, so astronomers seek to study light across the entire spectrum.

Telescopes specialized to observe different wavelengths of light allow us to learn far more than we could learn from visible light alone.

The basic idea behind nearly all telescopes is the same: Light is collected by a primary mirror (sometimes more than one) and ultimately focused on cameras or other instruments. However, different wavelengths pose different challenges for telescope design.

▲ **FIGURE 5.18**
A reflecting telescope collects light with a precisely curved primary mirror (see diagram). The photo shows the Gemini North telescope (Mauna Kea, Hawaii), which has an 8-meter-diameter primary mirror. The secondary mirror, located in the smaller central lattice, reflects light back down through the hole visible in the center of the primary mirror.

▲ **FIGURE 5.19**
The primary mirror of one of the Keck telescopes (Mauna Kea, Hawaii), with a man in the center for scale. It is made up of 36 hexagonal mirrors arranged in a honeycomb pattern. The inset shows the two Keck telescopes from above.

common misconceptions

Magnification and Telescopes

Many people guess that magnification is the most important function of a telescope. However, even though telescopes can magnify images—much like telephoto camera lenses or binoculars—the amount of magnification a telescope can provide is *not* one of its crucial properties. No matter how much a telescope image is magnified, you cannot see details if the telescope does not collect enough light to show them, or if they are smaller than the angular resolution of the telescope. Magnifying an image too much just makes it look blurry, which is why a telescope's light-collecting area and angular resolution are much more important than its magnification.

▲ **FIGURE 5.20**
China's Five-hundred-meter Aperture Spherical Telescope (FAST) is a radio dish with a diameter of 50 meters. It is nestled in a natural valley in southwest Guizhou province.

Some portions of the infrared and ultraviolet lie near enough to visible wavelengths that the light behaves similarly to visible light. This light can therefore be focused by visible-light telescopes, which is why the Hubble Space Telescope can be used to study infrared and ultraviolet light as well as visible light.

At longer infrared wavelengths, the heat of a telescope itself can create problems, because the telescope may emit thermal radiation at the same wavelengths it is trying to observe. To alleviate this problem, infrared telescopes in space generally have shielding to block the Sun, which allows them to cool to temperatures of 30–50 K. Some, like the Spitzer Space Telescope during its first 5 years (until the coolant ran out), are cooled further with liquid helium, which can take them down to temperatures only a few degrees above absolute zero.

Radio waves present a different challenge. For a telescope of a particular size, the angular resolution is poorer (larger) for longer wavelengths of light. For example, the Hubble Space Telescope has lower angular resolution for infrared light than for visible light. The long wavelengths of radio waves therefore mean that very large telescopes are necessary to achieve reasonable angular resolution. The world's largest single telescope is China's Five-hundred-meter Aperture Spherical Telescope, or FAST, a 500-meter-diameter radio dish nestled in a natural valley (Figure 5.20). Completed in 2016, FAST surpassed the previous record holder, Puerto Rico's 305-meter Arecibo radio telescope. Despite their large sizes, these telescopes have an angular resolution of only about 1 arcminute at commonly observed radio wavelengths—about 1000 times worse than the visible-light resolution of the Hubble Space Telescope.

special topic — Would You Like Your Own Telescope?

Just a couple decades ago, a decent telescope would have set you back a few thousand dollars and taken weeks of practice to learn to use. Today, you can get a good-quality telescope for a few hundred dollars, and built-in computer drives can make it very easy to use.

Before you consider buying a telescope, you should understand what a personal telescope can and cannot do. A telescope will allow you to look for yourself at light that has traveled vast distances through space to reach your eyes. This can be a rewarding experience, but the images in your telescope will *not* look like the beautiful photographs in this book, which were obtained with much larger telescopes and sophisticated cameras. In addition, while your telescope can in principle let you see many distant objects, including star clusters, nebulae, and galaxies, it won't allow you to find anything unless you first set it up properly. Even computer-driven telescopes (sometimes called "go to" telescopes) typically take 15 minutes to a half-hour to set up for each use, and longer when you are first learning.

If your goal is just to see the Moon and a few other objects with relatively little effort, you may want to skip the telescope in favor of a good pair of binoculars, which is usually less expensive. Binoculars are generally described by two numbers, such as 7 × 35 or 12 × 50. The first number is the magnification; for example, "7×" means that objects will look 7 times closer through the binoculars than to your eye. The second number is the diameter of each lens in millimeters. As with telescopes, larger lenses mean more light and better views. However, larger lenses also tend to be heavier and more difficult to hold steady, which means you may need a tripod.

If you decide to get a telescope, the first rule to remember is that magnification is *not* the key factor, and telescopes advertised only by their magnification (such as "650 power") are rarely high quality. Instead, focus on three factors when choosing your telescope:

1. *The light-collecting area (also called aperture).* Most personal telescopes are reflectors, so a "6-inch" telescope means it has a primary mirror that is 6 inches in diameter.
2. *Optical quality.* A poorly made telescope won't do you much good. If you cannot do side-by-side comparisons, stick with a major telescope manufacturer (such as Meade, Celestron, or Orion).
3. *Portability.* A large, bulky telescope can be great if you plan to keep it on a deck, but it will be difficult to carry on camping trips. Depending on how you plan to use your telescope, you'll need to make trade-offs between size and portability.

Most important, remember that a telescope is an investment that you will keep for many years. As with any investment, learn all you can before you settle on a particular model. Read buyers' guides and reviews of telescopes from sources such as *Astronomy*, *Sky and Telescope*, or the Astronomical Society of the Pacific. Talk to knowledgeable salespeople at stores that specialize in telescopes. And find a nearby astronomy club that holds observing sessions so that you can try out some telescopes and learn from experienced telescope owners.

Fortunately, astronomers have developed a technology known as **interferometry,** which can allow multiple telescopes to work together to achieve an angular resolution equivalent to that of a much larger single telescope. The Karl G. Jansky Very Large Array (JVLA) in New Mexico links 27 individual radio dishes laid out in the shape of a Y (Figure 5.21); when spaced as widely as possible, the JVLA can achieve an angular resolution that otherwise would require a single radio telescope with a diameter of almost 40 kilometers. Astronomers can achieve even higher angular resolution by linking radio telescopes around the world.

Interferometry is more difficult for shorter-wavelength (higher-frequency) light, but astronomers have achieved many successes. One spectacular example is the Atacama Large Millimeter/submillimeter Array

Interferometry allows small telescopes to work together to obtain the angular resolution of a much larger telescope

(ALMA), in Chile, which combines light from 66 individual telescopes working at millimeter and submillimeter wavelengths (Figure 5.22).

Perhaps even more impressively, the Event Horizon Telescope project seeks to link ALMA and other radio and submillimeter telescopes around the world, with the goal of achieving the angular resolution needed to obtain an image of the Milky Way Galaxy's central black hole [Section 15.4]. Interferometry is also being used at infrared and visible wavelengths with telescopes built in pairs (such as the Keck and Magellan telescope pairs) or with more than one telescope on a common mount (such as the Large Binocular Telescope).

At the short-wavelength end of the spectrum, astronomers face a different challenge in building telescopes. Trying to focus high-energy ultraviolet or X-ray photons is somewhat like trying to focus a stream of bullets. If the bullets are fired directly at a metal sheet, they will puncture or damage the sheet. However, if the metal sheet is angled so that the bullets barely graze its surface, then it will slightly deflect the bullets. The mirrors of X-ray telescopes, such as NASA's Chandra X-Ray Observatory and the NuSTAR mission, are designed to deflect X rays in much the same way (Figure 5.23). Gamma rays have even more energy and

▲ **FIGURE 5.21**
The Karl G. Jansky Very Large Array (JVLA) in New Mexico consists of 27 telescopes that can be moved along train tracks. The telescopes work together through interferometry and can achieve an angular resolution equivalent to that of a single radio telescope almost 40 kilometers across.

◄ **FIGURE 5.22**
The Atacama Large Millimeter/submillimeter Array (ALMA) is located in a high desert (altitude 5000 meters) in Chile.

a Artist's illustration of the Chandra X-Ray Observatory, which orbits Earth.

X rays

The first set of nested mirrors deflects X rays to the second set . . .

10 meters

X rays

focus

. . . and the second set deflects X rays a second time to the focus point.

b This diagram shows the arrangement of Chandra's nested, cylindrical X-ray mirrors. Each mirror is 0.8 meter long and between 0.6 and 1.2 meters in diameter.

▲ **FIGURE 5.23**

The Chandra X-Ray Observatory focuses X rays that enter the front of the telescope by deflecting them twice so that they end up focused at the back of the telescope.

▲ **FIGURE 5.24**

This photo shows an aerial view of a detector in Hanford, Washington, for the Advanced Laser Interferometer Gravitational-Wave Observatory (LIGO). A second detector is located in Livingston, Louisiana.

cannot generally be focused by mirrors, so gamma-ray telescopes (such as the Fermi Gamma-Ray Space Telescope) typically use massive detectors to capture photons and determine the direction they came from.

Looking Beyond Light Light is not the only form of information that travels through the universe, and astronomers have begun to build and use telescopes designed to observe at least three other types of "cosmic messengers." First, there's an extremely lightweight type of subatomic particle known as the *neutrino* [Section 11.2] that is produced by nuclear reactions, including nuclear fusion in the Sun and the reactions that accompany the explosions of distant stars. Astronomers have used "neutrino telescopes"—typically located in deep mines or under water or ice—to gain valuable insights about the Sun and stellar explosions. Second, Earth is continually bombarded by very high-energy subatomic particles from space known as *cosmic rays* [Section 15.2]. We still know relatively little about the origin of cosmic rays, but astronomers are now using both satellites and ground-based detectors to catch and study them. Third, Einstein's general theory of relativity (see Special Topic, page 373) predicts the existence of something called *gravitational waves*, which are different in nature from light but travel at the speed of light. For decades, we've had indirect evidence that gravitational waves really exist, but until recently, direct detection of them was beyond our technological capabilities. Today, the first gravitational wave telescopes are up and running (Figure 5.24), and they have already successfully detected gravitational waves from the mergers of pairs of black holes [Section 14.4].

◆ Why do we put telescopes in space?

Many telescopes are now placed in space, including the Hubble Space Telescope, the Chandra X-Ray Observatory, and the James Webb Space Telescope slated for launch in 2018. To understand why we do this despite the high cost of launching a telescope into space, we must understand the ways in which Earth's atmosphere hinders observations from the ground.

Atmospheric Effects on Visible Light Some of the problems created by Earth's atmosphere are obvious. The brightness of the daytime sky limits visible-light observations to nighttime, and clouds can block night observations. In addition, our atmosphere scatters the bright lights of cities, creating **light pollution** that can obscure the view even for the best telescopes (Figure 5.25). For example, the 2.5-meter telescope at Mount Wilson, the world's largest when it was built in 1917, would be much more useful today if it weren't located so close to the lights of what was once the small town of Los Angeles.

A somewhat less obvious problem is the blurring of light by the atmosphere. The ever-changing motion, or **turbulence,** of air in the atmosphere

Telescopes in space are above the distorting effects of Earth's atmosphere.

bends light in constantly shifting patterns. This turbulence causes the familiar twinkling of stars. Twinkling may be beautiful to the naked eye, but it causes problems for astronomers because it blurs astronomical images.

see it for yourself Put a coin at the bottom of a cup of water. If you stir the water, the coin will appear to move around, even if it remains stationary on the bottom. What makes the coin appear to move? How is this similar to the way that our atmosphere makes stars appear to twinkle?

▲ FIGURE 5.25
Earth at night: It's pretty, but to astronomers it's light pollution. This image, a composite made from hundreds of satellite photos, shows the bright lights of cities as they appear from Earth orbit at night.

▲ FIGURE 5.26
Observatories on the summit of Mauna Kea in Hawaii. Mauna Kea meets all the key criteria for an observing site: It is far from big-city lights, high in altitude, and located in an area where the air tends to be calm and dry.

Astronomers can partially mitigate effects of weather, light pollution, and atmospheric blurring by choosing observing sites that are *dark* (limiting light pollution), *dry* (limiting rain and clouds), *calm* (limiting turbulence), and *high* (placing them above at least part of the atmosphere). Three particularly important sites are the 4300-meter (14,000-foot) summit of Mauna Kea on the Big Island of Hawaii (Figure 5.26), a 2400-meter-high site on the island of La Palma in Spain's Canary Islands, and, for the southern hemisphere, the 2600-mctcr-high Paranal Observatory site in Chile.

Of course, the ultimate solution to atmospheric distortion is to put telescopes in space, above the atmosphere. That is one reason why the Hubble Space Telescope (Figure 5.27) was built and why it has been so successful despite the relatively small size (2.4 meters) of its primary mirror.

Atmospheric Absorption and Emission of Light As we'll discuss shortly, new technologies sometimes make it possible for ground-based observatories to equal or better the visible-light observations of the Hubble Space Telescope. However, Earth's atmosphere poses one major problem that no Earth-bound technology can overcome: *Our atmosphere prevents most forms of light from reaching the ground at all* (Figure 5.28). Moreover, the atmosphere itself glows at many infrared wavelengths, generating a background glare for most infrared observations from the ground. Only radio waves, visible light (and the very longest wavelengths of ultraviolet light), and small parts of the infrared spectrum can be observed from the ground.

The most important reason for putting telescopes in space is to allow us to observe light that does not penetrate Earth's atmosphere. That is why all X-ray telescopes are in space—an X-ray telescope would be completely useless on the ground—

Much of the electromagnetic spectrum can be observed only from space and not from the ground.

and the same is true for telescopes observing in most portions of the infrared, ultraviolet, and gamma rays. Indeed, the Hubble Space Telescope often observes ultraviolet or infrared wavelengths that do not reach the ground (or that would be

▲ FIGURE 5.27
The Hubble Space Telescope orbits Earth. Its position above the atmosphere allows it an undistorted view of space. Hubble can observe infrared and ultraviolet light as well as visible light.

▲ FIGURE 5.28

This diagram shows the approximate depths to which different wavelengths of light penetrate Earth's atmosphere. Note that most of the electromagnetic spectrum can be observed only from very high altitudes or from space. Major space observatories for different wavelengths are also shown.

interfered with by atmospheric infrared emissions), which is why it would remain a valuable observatory even if ground-based telescopes matched its visible-light capabilities. The James Webb Space Telescope is being optimized for infrared observations, which will allow it to study the highly redshifted light of the most distant galaxies in the universe. Because we see distant objects as they were long ago, this will enable us to observe galaxies as they first began to form in the early universe. The telescope will be kept far from Earth's heat by being put in an orbit around the Sun at a greater distance than Earth, while an attached Sun shield will prevent sunlight from heating the telescope (Figure 5.29).

think about it Find the current status of the James Webb Space Telescope. Is it on track for launch or already launched? List at least three science objectives of the telescope.

common **misconceptions**

Closer to the Stars?

Many people mistakenly believe that space telescopes are advantageous because their locations above Earth put them closer to the stars. You can see why this is wrong by thinking about scale. On the scale of the Voyage model solar system (see Section 1.1), the Hubble Space Telescope is so close to the surface of the millimeter-diameter Earth that you would need a microscope to resolve its altitude, while the nearest stars are thousands of kilometers away. The distances to the stars are effectively the same whether a telescope is on the ground or in space. The real advantages of space telescopes arise from their being above Earth's atmosphere and the observational problems it presents.

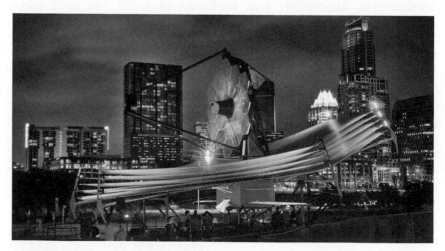

▲ FIGURE 5.29

This photo shows a full-size model of the James Webb Space Telescope, with the sunshield at the bottom, on display in Austin, Texas, during the South by Southwest festival.

Adaptive Optics   Despite the many advantages of putting telescopes in space, it is still much less expensive to build large telescopes on the ground. However, while these telescopes can obviously collect a lot of light, until recently they were unable to achieve the angular resolution that would in principle be allowed by their sizes, because air turbulence inevitably blurred their images.

Today, an amazing technology known as **adaptive optics** can eliminate much of the blurring caused by our atmosphere. The tech-

Adaptive optics allows ground-based telescopes to overcome atmospheric distortions.

nology works like this: Turbulence causes rays of light from a star to dance around as they reach a telescope. Adaptive optics essentially makes a telescope's mirrors do an opposite dance, canceling out the atmospheric distortions (Figure 5.30). The shape of a mirror (often the secondary or even a third or fourth mirror) is changed slightly many times each second to compensate for the rapidly changing atmospheric distortions. A computer calculates the necessary changes by monitoring distortions in the image of a bright star near the object under study. If there is no bright star near the object of interest, the observatory may shine a laser into the sky to create an *artificial star* (a point of light in Earth's atmosphere) that it can monitor for distortions.

Together, the combination of space telescopes, adaptive optics for ground-based telescopes, and interferometry is helping astronomers achieve unprecedented views of the heavens. Technology is rapidly advancing, and it seems reasonable to imagine that, within a few decades, new telescopes may offer views of distant objects that may be as detailed in comparison to Hubble Space Telescope images as Hubble's images are in comparison to those of the naked eye.

a Atmospheric blurring makes this ground-based image of a double star look like a single star.

b When the same telescope is used with adaptive optics, the two stars are clearly distinguished. The angular separation between the two stars is 0.28 arcsecond.

▲ **FIGURE 5.30**

The technology of adaptive optics can enable a ground-based telescope to overcome most of the blurring caused by Earth's atmosphere. Both images were taken in near-infrared light with the Canada-France-Hawaii Telescope. The colors represent infrared brightness, with the brightest light shown in white (center of each star image) and the faintest light in blue to black.

---

the big picture   Putting Chapter 5 into Perspective

This chapter's main purpose was to show how we learn about the universe by observing the light of distant objects. "Big picture" ideas that will help you keep your understanding in perspective include the following:

- Most of what we know about the universe comes from information that we receive from light, because matter leaves "fingerprints" that we can read by carefully analyzing the light of distant objects.

- The visible light that our eyes can see is only a small portion of the complete electromagnetic spectrum. Different portions of the spectrum contain different pieces

of the story of a distant object, so it is important to study all forms of light.

- Images are pretty, but we can often learn more by dispersing the light of a distant object into a spectrum, which can reveal the object's composition, surface temperature, motion toward or away from us, and more.

- Technology drives astronomical discovery. Every time we build a bigger telescope, develop a more sensitive detector, or open up a new wavelength region to study, we learn more about the universe.

my cosmic perspective   The methods of learning from light that we've discussed for astronomy are also used to learn about many things on Earth. For example, we use light to learn about the atmosphere and global warming, to identify toxic chemicals in water, and for medical scans that help diagnose injuries and disease.

5.1 Basic Properties of Light and Matter

◆ What is light?

Light is an **electromagnetic wave,** but also comes in individual "pieces" called **photons.** Each photon has a precise wavelength, frequency, and energy: the shorter the wavelength, the higher the frequency and energy. In order of decreasing wavelength, the forms of light are **radio waves, microwaves, infrared, visible light, ultraviolet, X rays,** and **gamma rays.**

◆ What is matter?

Ordinary matter is made of **atoms,** which are made of **protons, neutrons,** and **electrons.** Atoms of different **chemical elements** have different numbers of protons. **Isotopes** of a particular chemical element all have the same number of protons but different numbers of neutrons. **Molecules** are made from two or more atoms.

◆ How do light and matter interact?

Matter can emit, absorb, transmit, or reflect (or scatter) light.

5.2 Learning from Light

◆ What are the three basic types of spectra?

There are three basic types of spectra: a **continuous spectrum,** which looks like a rainbow; an **absorption line spectrum,** in which specific colors are missing from the rainbow; and an **emission line spectrum,** in which we see lines of specific colors against a black background.

◆ How does light tell us what things are made of?

Emission or absorption lines occur only at specific wavelengths that correspond to particular energy level transitions in atoms or molecules. Every kind of atom, ion, and molecule produces a unique set of spectral lines, so we can determine an object's composition by identifying these lines.

◆ How does light tell us the temperatures of planets and stars?

Objects such as planets and stars produce **thermal radiation** spectra, the most common type of continuous spectra. We can determine temperature from these spectra because hotter objects emit more total radiation per unit area and emit photons with a higher average energy.

◆ How does light tell us the speed of a distant object?

The **Doppler effect** tells us how fast an object is moving toward or away from us. Spectral lines are shifted to shorter wavelengths (a **blueshift**) for objects moving toward us and to longer wavelengths (a **redshift**) for objects moving away from us.

5.3 Collecting Light with Telescopes

◆ How do telescopes help us learn about the universe?

Telescopes allow us to see fainter objects and to see more detail than we can see with our eyes, and to study light from all portions of the spectrum. **Light-collecting area** describes how much light a telescope can collect. **Angular resolution** determines the amount of detail in telescopic images; it is better (smaller) for larger telescopes and, for a given telescope size, better for shorter-wavelength light. Multiple telescopes can sometimes be used together through **interferometry** to achieve the angular resolution of a much larger telescope.

◆ Why do we put telescopes in space?

Telescopes in space are above Earth's atmosphere and not subject to problems caused by **light pollution,** atmospheric distortion and emission of light, or the fact that most forms of light do not penetrate through the atmosphere to the ground. However, for visible light, it is now possible to overcome some of the blurring effects of Earth's atmosphere through **adaptive optics.**

Refer to the numbered features on the above graph, which is a schematic spectrum of the planet Mars.

1. Which of the six numbered features represents emission lines?

2. Which of the six numbered features represents absorption lines?

3. Which portion(s) of the spectrum represent(s) reflected sunlight?
   a. 1 only
   b. 2, 3, and 4
   c. 3 and 6
   d. the entire spectrum

4. What does the wavelength of the peak labeled 6 tell us about Mars?
   a. its color
   b. its surface temperature
   c. its chemical composition
   d. its orbital speed

5. What feature(s) of this spectrum indicate(s) that Mars appears red in color?
   a. the wavelength of the peak labeled 3
   b. the wavelength of the peak labeled 6
   c. the fact that the intensity of region 4 is higher than that of region 2
   d. the fact that the peak labeled 3 is higher than the peak labeled 6

exercises and problems

MasteringAstronomy®   For instructor-assigned homework and other learning materials, go to MasteringAstronomy®.

Review Questions

1. Define *wavelength, frequency,* and *speed* for light waves. If light has a long wavelength, what can you say about its frequency? Explain.
2. What is a *photon*? In what way is a photon like a particle? In what way is it like a wave?
3. List the different forms of light in order from lowest to highest energy. Is the order the same from lowest to highest frequency? from shortest to longest wavelength?
4. Briefly describe the structure and size of an atom. How big is the *nucleus* compared to the entire atom?
5. Define *atomic number* and *atomic mass number.* Under what conditions are two atoms different *isotopes* of the same element?
6. What is *electrical charge*? Will an electron and a proton attract or repel one another? How about two electrons?
7. What are the four major ways in which light and matter can interact? Give an example of each from everyday life.
8. Describe the conditions that lead to each of the three basic types of spectra. Which type is the Sun's spectrum, and why?
9. Why do atoms emit or absorb light of specific wavelengths? How does this fact allow us to determine the chemical composition of a distant object?
10. Describe two ways in which the thermal radiation spectrum of an 8000 K star would differ from that of a 4000 K star.
11. Describe the *Doppler effect* for light and what we can learn from it. What does it mean to say that radio waves are *blueshifted*?
12. What are the two key properties of a telescope, and why is each important? Also distinguish between *refracting* and *reflecting* telescopes.
13. List at least three ways Earth's atmosphere can hinder astronomical observations.

14. Briefly describe how adaptive optics and interferometry can improve astronomical observations.

Test Your Understanding

◐ Does It Make Sense?

Decide whether the statement makes sense (or is clearly true) or does not make sense (or is clearly false). Explain clearly; not all of these have definitive answers, so your explanation is more important than your chosen answer.

15. If you could view a spectrum of the light reflecting off a blue sweatshirt, you'd find the entire rainbow of color (looking the same as a spectrum of white light).
16. Because of their higher frequency, X rays must travel through space faster than radio waves.
17. Two isotopes of the element rubidium differ in their number of protons.
18. If the Sun's surface became much hotter (while the Sun's size remained the same), the Sun would emit more ultraviolet light but less visible light than it currently emits.
19. If you could see infrared light, you would see a glow from the backs of your eyelids when you closed your eyes.
20. If you had X-ray vision, then you could read this entire book without turning any pages.
21. If a distant galaxy has a substantial redshift (as viewed from our galaxy), then anyone living in that galaxy would see a substantial redshift in a spectrum of the Milky Way Galaxy.
22. Thanks to adaptive optics, telescopes on the ground can now make ultraviolet images of the cosmos.

23. Thanks to interferometry, a properly spaced set of 10-meter radio telescopes can achieve the angular resolution of a single 100-kilometer radio telescope.

24. If you lived on the Moon, you'd never see stars twinkle.

Quick Quiz

Choose the best answer to each of the following. Explain your reasoning with one or more complete sentences.

25. Why is a sunflower yellow? (a) It emits yellow light. (b) It absorbs yellow light. (c) It reflects yellow light.

26. Compared to red light, blue light has higher frequency and (a) higher energy and shorter wavelength. (b) higher energy and longer wavelength. (c) lower energy and shorter wavelength.

27. Radio waves are (a) a form of sound. (b) a form of light. (c) a type of spectrum.

28. Compared to an atom as a whole, an atomic nucleus is (a) very tiny but has most of the mass. (b) quite large and has most of the mass. (c) very tiny and has very little mass.

29. Some nitrogen atoms have seven neutrons and some have eight neutrons; these two forms of nitrogen are (a) ions of each other. (b) phases of each other. (c) isotopes of each other.

30. The set of spectral lines that we see in a star's spectrum depends on the star's (a) atomic structure. (b) chemical composition. (c) rotation rate.

31. A star whose spectrum peaks in the infrared is (a) cooler than our Sun. (b) hotter than our Sun. (c) larger than our Sun.

32. A spectral line that appears at a wavelength of 321 nm in the laboratory appears at a wavelength of 328 nm in the spectrum of a distant object. We say that the object's spectrum is (a) redshifted. (b) blueshifted. (c) whiteshifted.

33. How much greater is the light-collecting area of a 6-meter telescope than that of a 3-meter telescope? (a) two times (b) four times (c) six times

34. The Hubble Space Telescope obtains higher-resolution images than most ground-based telescopes because it is (a) larger. (b) closer to the stars. (c) above Earth's atmosphere.

Process of Science

35. *Elements in Space.* Astronomers claim that objects throughout the universe are made of the same chemical elements that exist here on Earth. Given that most of these objects are so far away that we can never hope to visit them, why are astronomers so confident that the objects are made from the same set of chemical elements, rather than completely different substances?

36. *Newton's Prisms.* Look back at the brief discussion in this chapter of how Newton demonstrated that the colors seen when sunlight passes through a prism come from the light itself rather than from the prism. Suppose you wanted to test Newton's findings. Assuming you have two prisms and a white screen, describe how you would arrange the prisms to duplicate Newton's discovery.

Group Work Exercise

37. *Which Telescope Would You Use?* **Roles:** *Scribe* (takes notes on the group's activities), *Proposer* (proposes explanations to the group), *Skeptic* (points out weaknesses in proposed explanations), *Moderator* (leads group discussion and makes sure everyone contributes). **Activity:** Your job is to choose a telescope for observing matter around a black hole; assume that the matter is emitting photons at

all wavelengths. Rank the following four telescopes from best to worst for this observing task. Explain your rankings.

a. an X-ray telescope, 2 meters in diameter, located at the South Pole

b. an infrared telescope, 2 meters in diameter, on a spacecraft in orbit around Earth and observing at a wavelength of 2 micrometers (2×10^{-6} m)

c. an infrared telescope, 10 meters in diameter, equipped with adaptive optics, located on Mauna Kea in Hawaii and observing at a wavelength of 10 micrometers (10^{-5} m)

d. a radio telescope, 300 meters in diameter, located in Puerto Rico

Investigate Further

Short-Answer/Essay Questions

38. *Atomic Terminology Practice I.*

a. The most common form of iron has 26 protons and 30 neutrons. For a neutral atom of this form of iron, state the atomic number, atomic mass number, and number of electrons.

b. Consider the following three atoms: Atom 1 has seven protons and eight neutrons; atom 2 has eight protons and seven neutrons; atom 3 has eight protons and eight neutrons. Which two are *isotopes* of the same element?

c. Oxygen has atomic number 8. How many times must an oxygen atom be ionized to create an O^{+5} ion? How many electrons are in an O^{+5} ion?

39. *Atomic Terminology Practice II.*

a. What are the atomic number and atomic mass number of fluorine atoms with 9 protons and 10 neutrons? If we could add a proton to a fluorine nucleus, would the result still be fluorine? What if we added a neutron to a fluorine nucleus? Explain.

b. The most common isotope of gold has atomic number 79 and atomic mass number 197. How many protons and neutrons does the gold nucleus contain? If it is electrically neutral, how many electrons does it have? If it is triply ionized, how many electrons does it have?

c. Uranium has atomic number 92. Its most common isotope is ^{238}U, but the form used in nuclear bombs and nuclear power plants is ^{235}U. How many neutrons are in each of these two isotopes of uranium?

40. *Energy Level Transitions.* The following labeled transitions represent an electron moving between energy levels in hydrogen. Answer each of the following questions and explain your answers.

a. Which transition could represent an atom that *absorbs* a photon with 10.2 eV of energy?

b. Which transition could represent an atom that *emits* a photon with 10.2 eV of energy?

c. Which transition represents an electron that is breaking free of the atom?

d. Which transition, as shown, is *not* possible?

e. Would transition A represent emission or absorption of light? How would the wavelength of the emitted or absorbed photon compare to that of the photon involved in transition C? Explain.

41. *Orion Nebula.* Viewed through a telescope, much of the Orion Nebula looks like a glowing cloud of gas. What type of spectrum would you expect to see from the glowing parts of the nebula? Why?

42. *The Doppler Effect.* In hydrogen, the transition from level 2 to level 1 has a rest wavelength of 121.6 nm. Suppose you see this line at a wavelength of 120.5 nm in Star A, at 121.2 nm in Star B, at 121.9 nm in Star C, and at 122.9 nm in Star D. Which stars are coming toward us? Which are moving away? Which star is moving fastest relative to us? Explain your answers without doing any calculations.

43. *Spectral Summary.* Clearly explain how studying an object's spectrum can allow us to determine each of the following properties of the object.

a. The object's surface chemical composition

b. The object's surface temperature

c. Whether the object is a low-density cloud of gas or something more substantial

d. The speed at which the object is moving toward or away from us

44. *Image Resolution.* What happens if you take a photograph from a newspaper, magazine, or book and blow it up to a larger size? Can you see more detail than you could before? Explain clearly, and relate your answer to the concepts of magnification and angular resolution in astronomical observations.

45. *Telescope Technology.* Suppose you were building a space-based observatory consisting of five individual telescopes. Which would be the best way to use these telescopes: as five individual telescopes with adaptive optics, or as five telescopes linked together for interferometry but without adaptive optics? Explain your reasoning clearly.

46. *Project: Twinkling Stars.* Using a star chart, identify 5–10 bright stars that should be visible in the early evening. On a clear night, observe each of these stars for a few minutes. Note the date and time, and for each star record the following information: approximate altitude and direction in your sky, brightness compared to other stars, color, and how much the star twinkles compared to other stars. Study your record. Can you draw any conclusions about how brightness and position in your sky affect twinkling?

Quantitative Problems

Be sure to show all calculations clearly and state your final answers in complete sentences.

47. *Thermal Radiation Laws.*

a. Find the emitted power per square meter and wavelength of peak intensity for a 3000 K object that emits thermal radiation.

b. Find the emitted power per square meter and wavelength of peak intensity for a 50,000 K object that emits thermal radiation.

48. *Hotter Sun.* Suppose the surface temperature of the Sun were about 12,000 K, rather than 6000 K.

a. How much more thermal radiation would the Sun emit?

b. What would happen to the Sun's wavelength of peak intensity?

c. Do you think it would still be possible to have life on Earth? Explain.

49. *Doppler Calculations.* In hydrogen, the transition from level 2 to level 1 has a rest wavelength of 121.6 nm. Find the speed and direction (toward or away from us) for a star in which this line appears at wavelength

a. 120.5 nm.

b. 121.2 nm.

c. 121.9 nm.

d. 122.9 nm.

50. *Hubble's Field of View.* Large telescopes often have small fields of view. For example, the Hubble Space Telescope's (HST's) advanced camera has a field of view that is roughly square and about 0.06° on a side.

a. Calculate the angular area of the HST's field of view in square degrees.

b. The angular area of the entire sky is about 41,250 square degrees. How many pictures would the HST have to take with its camera to obtain a complete picture of the entire sky?

Discussion Questions

51. *The Changing Limitations of Science.* In 1835, French philosopher Auguste Comte stated that science would never allow us to learn the composition of stars. Although spectral lines had been seen in the Sun's spectrum at that time, it wasn't until the mid–19th century that scientists recognized (primarily through the work of Foucault and Kirchhoff) that spectral lines give clear information about chemical composition. Why might our present knowledge have seemed unattainable in 1835? Discuss how new discoveries can change the apparent limitations of science. Today, other questions seem beyond the reach of science, such as the question of how life began on Earth. Do you think such questions will ever be answerable through science? Defend your opinion.

52. *Science and Technology Funding.* Technological innovation clearly drives scientific discovery in astronomy, but the reverse is also true. For example, Newton made his discoveries in part because he wanted to explain the motions of the planets, but his discoveries have had far-reaching effects on our civilization. Congress often must decide between funding programs with purely scientific purposes ("basic research") and funding programs designed to develop new technologies. If you were a member of Congress, how would you try to allocate spending for basic research and technology? Why?

53. *Your Microwave Oven.* A *microwave oven* emits microwaves that have just the right wavelength needed to cause energy level changes in water molecules. Use this fact to explain how a microwave oven cooks your food. Why doesn't a microwave oven make a plastic dish get hot? Why do some clay dishes get hot in the microwave? Why do dishes that aren't themselves heated by the microwave oven sometimes still get hot when you heat food on them? (*Note:* It's not a good idea to put empty dishes in a microwave.)

Web Projects

54. *Kids and Light.* Visit one of the many websites designed to teach middle and high school students about light. Read the content, and try the activities. If you were a teacher, would you find the site useful for your students? Why or why not? Write a one-page summary of your conclusions.

55. *Major Ground-Based Observatories.* Take a virtual tour of one of the world's major astronomical observatories. Write a short report on why the observatory is useful to astronomy.

56. *Space Observatory.* Visit the website of a major space observatory, either existing or under development. Write a short report about the observatory, including its purpose, its orbit, and how it operates.

57. *Really Big Telescopes.* Learn about one of the projects to build a very large telescope (such as the Giant Magellan Telescope, the Thirty Meter Telescope, the European Extremely Large Telescope, or the High Definition Space Telescope). Write a short report about the telescope's current status and potential capabilities.

TABLE 6.1 The Planetary Data[a]

Photo	Planet	Relative Size	Average Distance from Sun (AU)	Average Equatorial Radius (km)	Mass (Earth=1)	Average Density (g/cm³)	Orbital Period	Rotation Period	Axis Tilt	Average Surface (or Cloud-Top) Temperature[b]	Composition	Known Moons (2016)	Rings?
	Mercury	.	0.387	2440	0.055	5.43	87.9 days	58.6 days	0.0°	700 K (day) 100 K (night)	Rocks, metals	0	No
	Venus	●	0.723	6051	0.82	5.24	225 days	243 days	177.3°	740 K	Rocks, metals	0	No
	Earth	●	1.00	6378	1.00	5.52	1.00 year	23.93 hours	23.5°	290 K	Rocks, metals	1	No
	Mars	.	1.52	3397	0.11	3.93	1.88 years	24.6 hours	25.2°	220 K	Rocks, metals	2	No
	Jupiter	⬤	5.20	71,492	318	1.33	11.9 years	9.93 hours	3.1°	125 K	H, He, hydrogen compounds[c]	67	Yes
	Saturn	⬤	9.54	60,268	95.2	0.70	29.4 years	10.6 hours	26.7°	95 K	H, He, hydrogen compounds[c]	62	Yes
	Uranus	●	19.2	25,559	14.5	1.32	83.8 years	17.2 hours	97.9°	60 K	H, He, hydrogen compounds[c]	27	Yes
	Neptune	●	30.1	24,764	17.1	1.64	165 years	16.1 hours	29.6°	60 K	H, He, hydrogen compounds[c]	14	Yes
	Pluto	.	39.5	1185	0.0022	1.9	248 years	6.39 days	112.5°	44 K	Ices, rock	5	No
	Eris	.	67.7	1168	0.0028	2.3	557 years	1.08 days	78°	43 K	Ices, rock	1	No

[a]Including the dwarf planets Pluto and Eris; Appendix E gives a more complete list of planetary properties.

[b]Surface temperatures for all objects except Jupiter, Saturn, Uranus, and Neptune, for which cloud-top temperatures are listed.

[c]Includes water (H_2O), methane (CH_4), and ammonia (NH_3).

6.2 The Nebular Theory of Solar System Formation

Our major goal in this chapter is to understand the modern theory that we use to explain the origin of our solar system. To begin this process, let's investigate the criteria by which our theory can be judged.

◆ What features of our solar system provide clues to how it formed?

We have already seen that our solar system is not a random collection of worlds, but rather a family of worlds exhibiting many traits that would be difficult to attribute to coincidence. We could make a long list of such traits, but it is easier to develop a scientific theory by focusing on the more general structure of our solar system. For our purposes, four major features stand out, each corresponding to one of the numbered steps in Figure 6.1:

1. **Patterns of motion among large bodies.** The Sun, planets, and large moons generally orbit and rotate in a very organized way.

2. **Two major types of planets.** The eight planets[*] divide clearly into two groups: the small, rocky planets that are close together and close to the Sun, and the large, gas-rich planets that are farther apart and farther from the Sun.

3. **Asteroids and comets.** Between and beyond the planets, vast numbers of asteroids and comets orbit the Sun; some are large enough to qualify as dwarf planets. The locations, orbits, and compositions of these asteroids and comets follow distinct patterns.

4. **Exceptions to the rules.** The generally orderly solar system also has some notable exceptions. For example, among the inner planets only Earth has a large moon, and Uranus is tipped on its side. A successful theory must make allowances for exceptions even as it explains the general rules.

Because these four features are so important to our study of the solar system, let's investigate each of them in a little more detail.

Feature 1: Patterns of Motion Among Large Bodies   If you look back at Figure 6.1, you'll notice several clear patterns of motion among the large bodies of our solar system. (In this context, a "body" is simply an individual object such as the Sun, a planet, or a moon.) For example:

- All planetary orbits are nearly circular and lie nearly in the same plane.
- All planets orbit the Sun in the same direction: counterclockwise as viewed from high above Earth's North Pole.
- Most planets rotate in the same direction in which they orbit, with fairly small axis tilts. The Sun also rotates in this direction.
- Most of the solar system's large moons exhibit similar properties in their orbits around their planets, such as orbiting in their planet's equatorial plane in the same direction that the planet rotates.

---

[*]As this book goes to press, a search is on for a possible ninth planet orbiting far beyond Pluto. If this planet exists, it would have likely once orbited in the realm of the jovian planets, so most likely would have characteristics placing it in that group.

TABLE 6.2 Comparison of Terrestrial and Jovian Planets

Terrestrial Planets	Jovian Planets
Smaller size and mass	Larger size and mass
Higher density	Lower density
Made mostly of rock and metal	Made mostly of hydrogen, helium, and hydrogen compounds
Solid surface	No solid surface
Few (if any) moons and no rings	Rings and many moons
Closer to the Sun (and closer together), with warmer surfaces	Farther from the Sun (and farther apart), with cool temperatures at cloud tops

The Sun, planets, and large moons orbit and rotate in an organized way.

We consider these orderly patterns together as the first major feature of our solar system. As we'll see shortly, our theory of solar system formation explains these patterns as consequences of processes that occurred during the early stages of the birth of our solar system.

Feature 2: Two Types of Planets Our brief planetary tour showed that the four inner planets are quite different from the four outer planets. We say that these two groups represent two distinct planetary classes: *terrestrial* and *jovian*.

Terrestrial planets are small, rocky, and close to the Sun. Jovian planets are large, gas-rich, and far from the Sun.

The **terrestrial planets** (*terrestrial* means "Earth-like") are the four planets of the inner solar system: Mercury, Venus, Earth, and Mars. These planets are relatively small and dense, with rocky surfaces and an abundance of metals in their cores. They have few moons, if any, and no rings. We count our Moon as a fifth terrestrial world, because its history has been shaped by the same processes that have shaped the terrestrial planets.

The **jovian planets** (*jovian* means "Jupiter-like") are the four large planets of the outer solar system: Jupiter, Saturn, Uranus, and Neptune. The jovian planets are much larger in size and lower in average density than the terrestrial planets, and they have rings and many moons. They lack solid surfaces and are made mostly of hydrogen, helium, and **hydrogen compounds**—compounds containing hydrogen, such as water (H_2O), ammonia (NH_3), and methane (CH_4). Because these substances are gases under earthly conditions, the jovian planets are sometimes called "gas giants." Table 6.2 contrasts the general traits of the terrestrial and jovian planets.

Feature 3: Asteroids and Comets The third major feature of the solar system is the existence of vast numbers of small objects orbiting the Sun. These objects fall into two major groups: asteroids and comets.

Rocky asteroids and icy comets far outnumber the planets and their moons.

Asteroids are rocky bodies that orbit the Sun much like planets, but they are much smaller (Figure 6.12). Even the largest asteroids are much smaller than our Moon. Most known asteroids are found within the **asteroid belt** between the orbits of Mars and Jupiter (see Figure 6.1).

Comets are also small objects that orbit the Sun, but they are made largely of ices (such as water ice, ammonia ice, and methane ice) mixed with rock. You are probably familiar with the occasional appearance of comets in the inner solar system, where they may become visible to the naked eye with long, beautiful tails (Figure 6.13). These visitors, which may delight sky watchers for a few weeks or months, are actually quite rare among comets. The vast majority of comets never visit the inner solar system. Instead, they orbit the Sun in one of the two distinct regions shown as feature 3 in Figure 6.1. The first is a donut-shaped region beyond the orbit of Neptune that we call the **Kuiper belt** (*Kuiper* rhymes with *piper*). The Kuiper belt contains at least 100,000 icy objects that are more than 100 kilometers in diameter, of which Pluto and Eris are the largest known. The second cometary region, called the **Oort cloud** (*Oort* rhymes with *court*), is much farther from the Sun and may contain a trillion comets. These comets have orbits randomly inclined to the ecliptic plane, giving the Oort cloud a roughly spherical shape.

Feature 4: Exceptions to the Rules The fourth key feature of our solar system is that there are a few notable exceptions to the general rules.

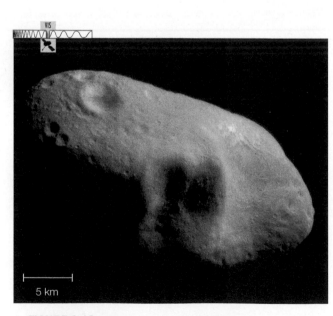

▲ **FIGURE 6.12**
The asteroid Eros (photographed from the *NEAR* spacecraft). Its appearance is probably typical of most asteroids. Eros is about 40 kilometers in length, and like other small objects in the solar system, it is not spherical.

For example, while most of the planets rotate in the same direction as they orbit, Uranus rotates nearly on its side, and Venus rotates "backward" (clockwise as viewed from high above Earth's North Pole). Similarly, while most large moons orbit their planets in the same direction as their planets rotate, many small moons have much more unusual orbits.

A successful theory of solar system formation must allow for exceptions to the general rules.

One of the most interesting exceptions concerns our own Moon. While the other terrestrial planets have either no moons (Mercury and Venus) or very tiny moons (Mars), Earth has one of the largest moons in the solar system.

◆ What is the nebular theory?

Historically, scientists have proposed more than one hypothesis about the origin of the solar system. But only one hypothesis has survived the test of time.

From Hypothesis to Theory   We generally trace the origins of our modern theory of solar system formation to around 1755, when German philosopher Immanuel Kant proposed that our solar system formed from the gravitational collapse of an interstellar cloud of gas. About 40 years later, French mathematician Pierre-Simon Laplace put forth the same idea independently. Because an interstellar cloud is usually called a *nebula* (Latin for "cloud"), this idea became known as the *nebular hypothesis*.

The nebular hypothesis remained popular throughout the 19th century. By the early 20th century, however, scientists had found a few aspects of our solar system that the hypothesis did not seem to explain well—at least in its original form as described by Kant and Laplace. While some scientists sought to modify the nebular hypothesis, others looked for alternative models of the solar system's birth.

During much of the first half of the 20th century, the nebular hypothesis faced stiff competition from a hypothesis proposing that the planets represent debris from a near-collision between the Sun and another star. According to this *close encounter hypothesis,* the planets formed from blobs of gas that had been gravitationally pulled out of the Sun during the near-collision.

Today, the close encounter hypothesis has been discarded. It began to lose favor when calculations showed that it could not account for either the observed orbital motions of the planets or the neat division of the planets into two major categories (terrestrial and jovian). Moreover, the close encounter hypothesis required a highly improbable event: a near-collision between our Sun and another star. Given the vast separation between star systems in our region of the galaxy, the chance of such an encounter is so small that it would be difficult to imagine it happening even once in order to form our solar system. It certainly could not account for the many other planetary systems that we have discovered in recent years.

The nebular theory holds that our solar system formed from the gravitational collapse of a great cloud of gas.

While the close encounter hypothesis was losing favor, new discoveries about the physics of planet formation led to modifications of the nebular hypothesis. Using more sophisticated models of the processes that occur in a collapsing cloud of gas, scientists found that the nebular hypothesis offered natural explanations for all four general features of our solar system. Indeed, so much evidence has accumulated in favor of the nebular hypothesis that it has achieved the status of a scientific *theory* [Section 3.4]—the **nebular theory** of our solar system's birth.

▲ **FIGURE 6.13**
Comet McNaught over Patagonia, Argentina, in 2007. The fuzzy patches above the comet tail are the Magellanic Clouds, satellite galaxies of the Milky Way.

rotate in this same direction as they formed—which is why most planets rotate the same way—though the small sizes of planets compared to the entire disk allowed some exceptions to arise. The fact that collisions in the disk tended to make orbits more circular explains why the planets in our solar system have nearly circular orbits.

see it for yourself You can demonstrate the development of orderly motion by sprinkling pepper into a bowl of water and stirring it quickly in random directions. The water molecules constantly collide with one another, so the motion of the pepper grains will tend to settle into a slow rotation representing the average of the original, random velocities. Try the experiment several times, stirring the water differently each time. Do the random motions ever cancel out exactly, resulting in no rotation at all? Explain how the experiment relates to what took place in the solar nebula.

Testing the Model The same processes should affect other collapsing gas clouds, so we can test our model by searching for disks around other forming stars. Observational evidence does indeed support our model of spinning, heating, and flattening.

Observations of spinning disks of gas around other stars support the idea that our solar system formed from a similar disk.

The heating that occurs in a collapsing cloud of gas means the gas should emit thermal radiation [Section 5.2], primarily in the infrared. We've detected infrared radiation from many nebulae where star systems appear to be forming. More direct evidence comes from flattened, spinning disks around other stars (Figure 6.17), some of

▼ **FIGURE 6.17**

These images show flattened, spinning disks of material around other stars.

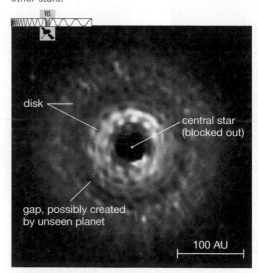

a This Hubble Space Telescope image shows a flattened, spinning disk around the star TW Hydrae. This particular disk also shows at least one circular "gap" in which material seems to have been cleared away, probably by a planet forming in the disk, which would have a gravitational attraction that would tend to sweep up material along its path.

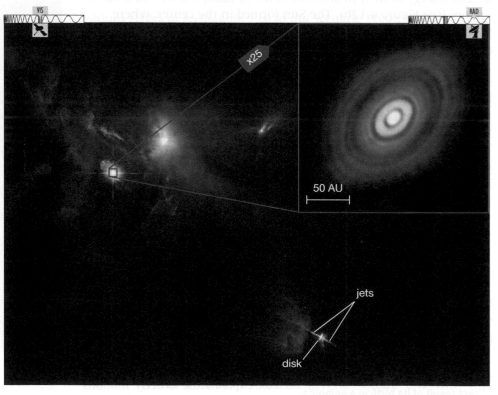

b The inset, from the Atacama Large Millimeter/submillimeter Array (ALMA), shows a disk around a star named HL Tauri; the concentric gaps in the disk are almost certainly regions being cleared as planets form. The disk diameter is about three times that of Neptune's orbit around the Sun. The background image, from the Hubble Space Telescope, shows the star-forming region in which this disk is located. Another disk, seen edge-on with jets extending outward, appears at lower right.

which appear to be ejecting jets of material perpendicular to their disks [Section 13.1]. These jets are thought to result from the flow of material from the disk onto the forming star, and they may influence the solar system formation processes.

Other support for the model comes from computer simulations of the formation process. A simulation begins with a set of data representing the conditions we observe in interstellar clouds. Then, with the aid of a computer, we apply the laws of physics to predict the changes that should occur over time. Computer simulations successfully reproduce most of the general characteristics of motion in our solar system, giving support to the nebular theory.

Additional evidence that our ideas about the formation of flattened disks are correct comes from many other structures in the universe. We expect flattening to occur anywhere orbiting particles can collide, which explains why we find so many cases of flat disks, including the disks of spiral galaxies like the Milky Way, the disks of planetary rings, and the *accretion disks* that surround neutron stars and black holes in close binary star systems [Section 14.2].

◆ Why are there two major types of planets?

The planets began to form after the solar nebula had collapsed into a flattened disk of perhaps 200 AU in diameter (about twice the present-day diameter of Pluto's orbit). The churning and mixing of gas in the solar nebula should have ensured that the nebula had the same composition throughout. How, then, did the terrestrial planets end up so different in composition from the jovian planets? The key clue comes from their locations: Terrestrial planets formed in the warm, inner regions of the swirling disk, while jovian planets formed in the colder, outer regions.

Condensation: Sowing the Seeds of Planets In the center of the collapsing solar nebula, gravity drew together enough material to form the Sun. In the surrounding disk, however, the gaseous material was too spread out for gravity alone to clump it together. Instead, material had to begin clumping in some other way and to grow in size until gravity could start pulling it together into planets. In essence, planet formation required the presence of "seeds"—solid bits of matter around which gravity could ultimately build planets.

Planet formation began around tiny "seeds" of solid metal, rock, or ice.

The basic process of seed formation was probably much like the formation of snowflakes in clouds on Earth: When the temperature is low enough, some atoms or molecules in a gas may bond and solidify. The general process in which solid (or liquid) particles form in a gas is called **condensation**—we say that the particles *condense* out of the gas. These particles start out microscopic in size, but they can grow larger with time.

Different materials condense at different temperatures. The ingredients of the solar nebula fell into four major categories (Table 6.3):

- **Hydrogen and helium gas (98% of the solar nebula's mass).** These gases never condense in interstellar space.
- **Hydrogen compounds (1.4% of the solar nebula).** Materials such as water (H_2O), methane (CH_4), and ammonia (NH_3) can solidify into **ices** at low temperatures (below about 150 K under the low pressure of the solar nebula).
- **Rock (0.4% of the solar nebula).** Rocky material is gaseous at high temperatures but condenses into solid form at temperatures below 500 K to 1300 K, depending on the type of rock.

TABLE 6.3 Materials in the Solar Nebula

A summary of the four types of materials present in the solar nebula. The squares represent the relative proportions of each type (by mass).

	Examples	Can condense at temperatures below	Relative abundance (by mass)
Hydrogen and Helium Gas	hydrogen, helium	do not condense in nebula	98%
Hydrogen Compounds	water (H_2O), methane (CH_4), ammonia (NH_3)	150 K	1.4%
Rock	various minerals	500–1300 K	0.4%
Metals	iron, nickel, aluminum	1000–1600 K	0.2%

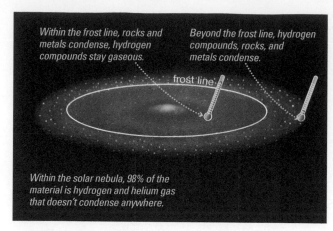

Within the frost line, rocks and metals condense, hydrogen compounds stay gaseous.

Beyond the frost line, hydrogen compounds, rocks, and metals condense.

frost line

Within the solar nebula, 98% of the material is hydrogen and helium gas that doesn't condense anywhere.

▲ **FIGURE 6.18**

Temperature differences in the solar nebula led to different kinds of condensed materials, sowing the seeds for two different kinds of planets.

- **Metals (0.2% of the solar nebula).** Metals such as iron, nickel, and aluminum are also gaseous at high temperatures but condense into solid form at temperatures below 1000 K to 1600 K (depending on the metal).

Because hydrogen and helium gas made up 98% of the solar nebula's mass and did not condense, the vast majority of the nebula remained gaseous at all times. However, other materials condensed wherever the temperature allowed (Figure 6.18). Close to the Sun, it was too hot for any material to condense. A little farther out (near Mercury's current orbit), it was cool enough for metals and some types of rock to condense into tiny solid particles, but other types of rock and all the hydrogen compounds remained gaseous. More types of rock could condense at the distances from the Sun where Venus, Earth, and Mars would form. In the region where the asteroid belt would eventually be located, temperatures were low enough to allow dark, carbon-rich minerals to condense along with minerals containing small amounts of water. It was cold enough for hydrogen compounds to condense into ices only beyond the **frost line,** which lay between the present-day orbits of Mars and Jupiter.

think about it Consider a region of the solar nebula in which the temperature was about 1300 K. What fraction of the material in this region was gaseous? What were the solid particles made of? Answer the same questions for a region with a temperature of 100 K. Was the 100 K region closer to or farther from the Sun? Explain.

The frost line marked the key transition between the warm inner regions of the solar system where terrestrial planets formed and the cool outer regions where jovian planets formed. Inside the frost line, only metal and rock could condense into solid "seeds." Beyond the frost line, the solid seeds were built of ice along with metal and rock. Moreover, because hydrogen compounds were nearly three times as abundant in the nebula as metal and rock combined (see Table 6.3), the total amount of solid material was far greater beyond the frost line than within it. The stage was set for the birth of two types of planets: planets born from seeds of metal and rock in the inner solar system and planets born from seeds of ice (as well as metal and rock) in the outer solar system.

The solid seeds contained only metal and rock in the inner solar system, but also included ices in the outer solar system.

Building the Terrestrial Planets From this point, the story of the inner solar system seems fairly clear: The solid seeds of metal and rock in the inner solar system ultimately grew into the terrestrial planets we see today, but these planets ended up relatively small in size because rock and metal made up such a small amount of the material in the solar nebula.

The process by which small "seeds" grew into planets is called **accretion** (Figure 6.19). Accretion began with the microscopic solid particles that condensed from the gas of the solar nebula. These particles orbited the forming Sun with the same orderly, circular paths as the gas from which they condensed. Individual particles therefore moved at nearly the same speed as neighboring particles, so "collisions" were more like gentle touches. Although the particles were far too small to attract

The terrestrial planets were made from metal and rock that condensed in the inner solar system.

Early in the accretion process, there are many relatively large planetesimals on crisscrossing orbits.

As time passes, a few planetesimals grow larger by accreting smaller ones, while others shatter in collisions.

Ultimately, only the largest planetesimals avoid shattering and grow into full-fledged planets.

Not to scale!

▲ FIGURE 6.19
These diagrams show how planetesimals gradually accrete into terrestrial planets.

each other gravitationally at this point, they were able to move together through electrostatic forces—the same "static electricity" that makes hair stick to a comb. Small particles thereby began to combine into larger ones. As the particles grew in mass, they began to attract each other through gravity, accelerating their growth into boulders large enough to count as **planetesimals,** which means "pieces of planets."

The planetesimals grew rapidly at first. As they grew larger, they had both more surface area to make contact with other planetesimals and more gravity to attract them. Some planetesimals probably grew to hundreds of kilometers in size in only a few million years—a long time in human terms, but only about *one-thousandth* of the present age of the solar system. However, once the planetesimals reached these relatively large sizes, further growth became more difficult.

Gravitational encounters [Section 4.4] between planetesimals tended to alter their orbits, particularly those of the smaller ones. With different orbits crossing each other, collisions between planetesimals tended to occur at higher speeds and hence became more destructive. Such collisions tended to shatter planetesimals rather than help them grow. Only the largest planetesimals avoided being shattered and could grow into terrestrial planets.

Computer simulations support this model of the accretion process. Observational evidence comes from **meteorites,** rocks that have fallen to Earth from space. Meteorites that appear to be surviving fragments from the period of condensation contain metallic grains embedded in rocky minerals (Figure 6.20), just as we would expect if metal and rock condensed in the inner solar system. Meteorites thought to come from the outskirts of the asteroid belt contain abundant carbon-rich materials, and some contain water—again as we would expect for material that condensed in that region.

Making the Jovian Planets Accretion should have occurred similarly in the outer solar system, but condensation of ices meant both that there was more solid material and that this material contained ice in addition to metal and rock. The solid objects that reside in the outer solar system today, such as comets and the moons of the jovian planets, still show this ice-rich composition. However, the growth of icy planetesimals cannot be the whole story of jovian planet formation, because the jovian planets contain large amounts of hydrogen and helium gas.

▲ FIGURE 6.20
Shiny flakes of metal are clearly visible in this slice through a meteorite (a few centimeters across), mixed in among the rocky material. Such metallic flakes are just what we would expect to find if condensation really occurred in the solar nebula as described by the nebular theory.

As planetesimals accrete to form terrestrial planets in the inner solar system . . .

Sun

spinning disk around forming jovian planet

2 AU

. . . farther out, huge icy planetesimals gather hydrogen and helium to form jovian planets . . .

. . . while the disk forms large moons by condensation and accretion, and captures small moons.

▲ **FIGURE 6.21**

The young jovian planets were surrounded by disks of gas, much like the disk of the entire solar nebula but smaller in size. According to the leading model, the planets grew as large, ice-rich planetesimals captured hydrogen and helium gas from the solar nebula. This painting shows the gas and planetesimals surrounding one jovian planet in the larger solar nebula.

The leading model for jovian planet formation holds that the largest ice-rich planetesimals became sufficiently massive for their gravity to capture some of the hydrogen and helium gas that made up the vast majority of the surrounding solar nebula. This added gas made their gravity even stronger, allowing them to capture even more gas. Ultimately, the jovian planets accreted so much gas that they bore little resemblance to the icy seeds from which they grew.

The jovian planets began as large, icy planetesimals, which then captured hydrogen and helium gas from the solar nebula.

This model also explains most of the large moons of the jovian planets. The same processes of heating, spinning, and flattening that made the disk of the solar nebula should also have affected the gas drawn by gravity to the young jovian planets. Each jovian planet came to be surrounded by its own disk of gas, spinning in the same direction as the planet rotated (Figure 6.21). Moons that accreted from ice-rich planetesimals within these disks ended up with nearly circular orbits going in the same direction as their planet's rotation and lying close to their planet's equatorial plane.

Clearing the Nebula   The vast majority of the hydrogen and helium gas in the solar nebula never became part of any planet. So what happened to it? Apparently, it was cleared away by a combination of high-energy radiation (ultraviolet and X rays) from the young Sun and the *solar wind*— a stream of charged particles continually blown outward in all directions from the Sun. Observations show that stars tend to have much stronger winds and emit much more high-energy radiation when they are young, so the young Sun should have had a strong enough combination of radiation and wind to clear the solar system of its remaining gas.

The clearing of the gas sealed the compositional fate of the planets. If the gas had remained longer, it might have continued to cool until hydrogen compounds could have condensed into ices even in the inner solar system. In that case, the terrestrial planets might have accreted abundant ice, and perhaps hydrogen and helium gas as well, changing their basic nature. At the other extreme, if the gas had been blown out earlier, the raw materials of the planets might have been swept away

Remaining gas in the solar nebula was cleared away into space, ending the era of planet formation.

before the planets could fully form. Although these extreme scenarios did not occur in our solar system, they may sometimes occur around other stars. Planet formation may also sometimes be interrupted when radiation from hot, neighboring stars drives away material in a solar nebula.

◆ **Where did asteroids and comets come from?**

The process of planet formation also explains the origin of the many asteroids and comets in our solar system (including those large enough to qualify as dwarf planets): They are "leftovers" from the era of planet formation. Asteroids are the rocky leftover planetesimals of the inner solar system, while comets are the icy leftover planetesimals of the outer solar system. We'll see in Chapter 9 why most asteroids ended up in the asteroid belt while most comets ended up in either the Kuiper belt or the Oort cloud.

Rocky asteroids and icy comets are leftover planetesimals from the era of planet formation.

Evidence that asteroids and comets are leftover planetesimals comes from analysis of meteorites, spacecraft visits to comets and asteroids, and theoretical models of solar system formation. In fact, the nebular theory allowed scientists to predict the existence of comets in the Kuiper belt decades before any of them were discovered.

The asteroids and comets that exist today probably represent only a small fraction of the leftover planetesimals that roamed the young solar system. The rest are now gone. Some of these "lost" planetesimals may have been flung into deep space by gravitational encounters, but many others must have collided with the planets. When impacts occur on solid worlds, they leave behind **impact craters** as scars. Impacts have thereby transformed planetary landscapes and, in the case of Earth, have altered the course of evolution. For example, an impact is thought to have been responsible for the extinction of the dinosaurs [Section 9.5].

Although impacts occasionally still occur, the vast majority of these collisions occurred in the first few hundred million years of our solar system's history, during the period we call the **heavy bombardment.** Every world in our solar system must have been pelted by impacts during the heavy bombardment (Figure 6.22), and most of the craters on the Moon and other worlds date from this period.

Leftover planetesimals battered the planets during the solar system's first few hundred million years.

▲ **FIGURE 6.22**
Around 4 billion years ago, Earth, its Moon, and the other planets were heavily bombarded by leftover planetesimals. This painting shows the young Earth and Moon, with an impact in progress on Earth.

These early impacts, including many that occurred before the planets finished forming, probably played a key role in making our existence possible. The metal and rock planetesimals that built the terrestrial planets should not have contained water or other hydrogen compounds, because it was too hot for these compounds to condense in our region of the solar nebula. How, then, did Earth come to have the water that makes up our oceans and the gases that first formed our atmosphere? The likely answer is that water, along with other hydrogen compounds, was brought to Earth and other terrestrial planets by the impacts of water-bearing planetesimals that formed farther from the Sun, probably in what is now the outer region of the asteroid belt. Remarkably, the water we drink and the air we breathe probably once were part of planetesimals that accreted beyond the orbit of Mars.

◆ How do we explain the "exceptions to the rules"?

We have now explained all the major features of our solar system except the exceptions to the rules, including our surprisingly large Moon. We now suspect that most of these exceptions arose from collisions or close gravitational encounters.

Captured Moons We have explained the orbits of most large jovian planet moons by their formation in a disk that swirled around the forming planet. But how do we explain moons with less orderly orbits, such as those that go in the "wrong" direction (opposite their planet's rotation) or that have large inclinations to their planet's equator? These moons are probably leftover planetesimals that originally orbited the Sun but were then captured into planetary orbit.

It's not easy for a planet to capture a moon. An object cannot switch from an unbound orbit (for example, an asteroid whizzing by Jupiter) to a bound orbit (for example, a moon orbiting Jupiter) unless it somehow loses orbital energy [Section 4.4]. For the jovian planets, captures probably occurred when passing planetesimals lost energy to friction in the extended and relatively dense gas that surrounded these planets as they formed. The planetesimals would have been slowed by friction with the gas, just as artificial satellites in low orbits are slowed by drag from Earth's atmosphere. If friction reduced a passing planetesimal's orbital

a Phobos   **b** Deimos

▲ **FIGURE 6.23**

The two moons of Mars are probably captured asteroids. Phobos is only about 13 kilometers across, and Deimos is only about 8 kilometers across—making each of these two moons small enough to fit within the boundaries of a typical large city. (Images from the *Mars Reconnaissance* orbiter.)

energy enough, it could have become an orbiting moon. Because of the random nature of the capture process, captured moons would not necessarily orbit in the same direction as their planet or in its equatorial plane. Most of the small moons of the jovian planets are thought to have been captured in this way. Mars may have similarly captured its two small moons, Phobos and Deimos, at a time when the planet had a much more extended atmosphere than it does today (Figure 6.23).

The Giant Impact Formation of Our Moon Capture processes cannot explain our own Moon, because it is much too large to have been captured by a small planet like Earth. We can also rule out the possibility that our Moon formed simultaneously with Earth, because if both had formed together, they would have accreted from planetesimals of the same type and should therefore have approximately the same composition and density. But this is not the case: The Moon's density is considerably lower than Earth's, indicating that it has a very different average composition. So how did we get our Moon? Today, the leading hypothesis suggests that it formed as the result of a **giant impact** between Earth and a huge planetesimal.

According to models, a few leftover planetesimals may have been as large as Mars. If one of these Mars-size objects struck a young planet, the blow might have tilted the planet's axis, changed the planet's rotation rate, or completely shattered the planet. The giant impact hypothesis holds that a Mars-size object hit Earth at a speed and angle that blasted Earth's outer layers into space. According to computer simulations, this material could have collected into orbit around our planet, and accretion within this ring of debris could have formed the Moon (Figure 6.24).

Our Moon is probably the result of a giant impact that blasted Earth's outer layers into orbit, where the material accreted to form the Moon.

---

extraordinary claims   **A Giant Impact Made Our Moon**

In this chapter, you have seen that Earth's large moon is a notable "exception to the rules" of the nebular theory. But how did this exception arise? By the mid-20th century, four competing models had been suggested. The first held that the Moon formed along with Earth through the process of accretion. The second suggested that the Moon was born as an independent "planet" that was captured into Earth orbit. The third, or *fission* (splitting), model suggested that the young, molten Earth rotated so rapidly that it split into two pieces, with the smaller piece becoming the Moon. And a fourth suggested that the Moon had been formed by a giant impact between a wandering planetesimal and Earth. The first three models had weaknesses from the start: Accretion cannot account for the Moon's low density, capture is too difficult for a body as big as the Moon in comparison to Earth, and fission would require an unreasonable spin rate for Earth and an unknown mechanism to prevent the Moon from flying off into space after it split off. The fourth model seemed even weaker: Indeed, it was considered so outrageous at the time (it predated studies of how the planets grew through accretion) that it was completely forgotten by the scientific community.

The *Apollo* missions to the Moon (1969–1972) ruled out the first three models more conclusively based on study of Moon rocks returned to Earth. Fortunately, the *Apollo* Moon rocks also helped scientists understand the history of cratering on the Moon, leading to a clearer picture of how many large objects had roamed the early solar system. With this in mind, in 1974, astronomers William Hartmann and Donald Davis proposed the giant impact hypothesis, unaware that a similar idea had been suggested previously. They recognized that this idea could explain why the Moon's composition closely matches that of Earth's mantle, and argued that enough large bodies had roamed the young solar system for such an impact to have been likely. This story is a clear example of how an extraordinary claim that may at first seem completely unreasonable will eventually be reconsidered if enough evidence accumulates for it.

We cannot go back in time to collect direct evidence of a giant impact, so we may never be able to establish with certainty that such an impact really occurred. Nevertheless, simulations of the event provide strong support for the idea. Many questions still remain to be answered, including the precise nature and size of the impactor, but most scientists now think it very likely that the Moon did indeed form in this way.

Verdict: Likely correct, though it may never be possible to support the hypothesis beyond reasonable doubt.

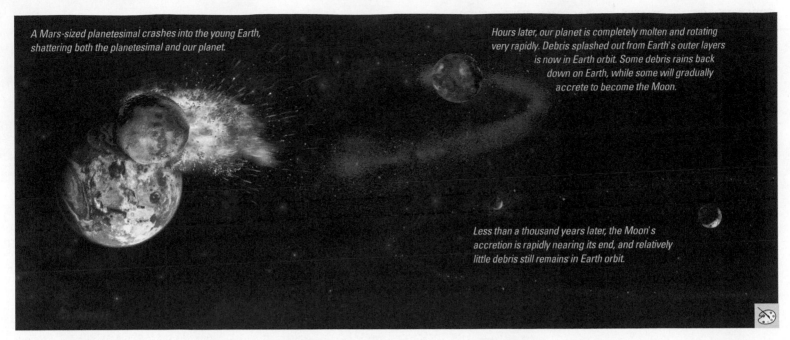

A Mars-sized planetesimal crashes into the young Earth, shattering both the planetesimal and our planet.

Hours later, our planet is completely molten and rotating very rapidly. Debris splashed out from Earth's outer layers is now in Earth orbit. Some debris rains back down on Earth, while some will gradually accrete to become the Moon.

Less than a thousand years later, the Moon's accretion is rapidly nearing its end, and relatively little debris still remains in Earth orbit.

▲ **FIGURE 6.24**

Artist's conception of the giant impact hypothesis for the formation of our Moon. The fact that ejected material came mostly from Earth's outer rocky layers explains why the Moon contains very little metal. The impact must have occurred more than 4.4 billion years ago, since that is the age of the oldest Moon rocks. As shown, the Moon formed quite close to a rapidly rotating Earth, but over billions of years, tidal forces have slowed Earth's rotation and moved the Moon's orbit outward (see Special Topic, page 99).

Strong support for the giant impact hypothesis comes from two features of the Moon's composition. First, the Moon's overall composition is quite similar to that of Earth's outer layers—just as we should expect if it were made from material blasted away from those layers. Second, the Moon has a much smaller proportion of easily vaporized ingredients (such as water) than Earth. This fact supports the hypothesis because the heat of the impact would have vaporized these ingredients. As gases, they would not have participated in the subsequent accretion of the Moon.

Other Exceptions Giant impacts may also explain other exceptions to the general trends. For example, Pluto's moon Charon likely formed in a giant impact similar to the one thought to have formed our Moon, and Mercury's surprisingly high density may be the result of a giant impact that blasted away its lower-density outer layers. Giant impacts could also have been responsible for tilting the axes of many planets (including Earth) and perhaps for tipping Uranus on its side. Venus's slow and backward rotation could also be the result of a giant impact, though some scientists suspect it is a consequence of processes attributable to Venus's thick atmosphere.

Although we cannot definitively explain these exceptions to the general rules, the overall lesson is clear: The chaotic processes that accompanied planet formation, including the many collisions that surely occurred, are *expected* to have led to at least a few exceptions. We conclude that the nebular theory successfully accounts for all four major features of our solar system. Figure 6.25 summarizes the theory.

6.4 The Age of the Solar System

The nebular theory seems to explain *how* our solar system was born. But *when* was it born, and how do we know? The answer is that the planets began to form through accretion just over 4½ billion years ago, a fact we learned by determining the age of the oldest rocks in the solar system.

FIGURE 6.25

A summary of the process by which our solar system formed, according to the nebular theory.

A large, diffuse interstellar gas cloud (solar nebula) contracts due to gravity.

Contraction of Solar Nebula: *As it contracts, the cloud heats, flattens, and spins faster, becoming a spinning disk of dust and gas.*

The Sun will be born in the center.

Planets will form in the disk.

Warm temperatures allow only metal/rock "seeds" to condense in inner solar system.

Condensation of Solid Particles: *Hydrogen and helium remain gaseous, but other materials can condense into solid "seeds" for building planets.*

Cold temperatures allow "seeds" to contain abundant ice in the outer solar system.

Terrestrial planets are built from metal and rock.

Accretion of Planetesimals: *Solid "seeds" collide and stick together. Larger ones attract others with their gravity, growing bigger still.*

The seeds of jovian planets grow large enough to attract hydrogen and helium gas, making them into giant, mostly gaseous planets; moons form in disks of dust and gas that surround the planets.

Clearing the Nebula: *The solar wind blows remaining gas into interstellar space.*

Terrestrial planets remain in the inner solar system.

Jovian planets remain in the outer solar system.

"Leftovers" from the formation process become asteroids (metal/rock) and comets (mostly ice).

Not to scale

◆ How do we know the age of the solar system?

The first step in understanding how we've measured the age of the solar system is to understand how we determine the ages of individual rocks.

Dating Rocks The method by which we measure a rock's age is called **radiometric dating,** and it relies on careful measurement of the proportions of various atoms and isotopes in the rock. The method works because some atoms undergo changes with time that allow us to determine how long they have been held in place within the rock's solid structure. In other words, the age of a rock is the time since its atoms became locked together in their present arrangement, which in most cases means the time *since the rock last solidified.*

Recall that each chemical element is uniquely characterized by the number of protons in its nucleus, and that different *isotopes* of the same element differ in their number of neutrons [Section 5.1]. A **radioactive** isotope has a nucleus prone to spontaneous change, or *decay,* such as breaking apart or having one of its protons turn into a neutron. This decay always occurs at the same, measurable rate for any particular radioactive isotope. Decay rates are usually stated in terms of a **half-life**—the length of time it would take for half the nuclei in a collection to decay.

Consider the radioactive isotope potassium-40 (19 protons and 21 neutrons), which decays when one of its protons turns into a neutron, changing the potassium-40 into argon-40. The half-life for this decay process is 1.25 billion years. (Potassium-40 also decays by other paths that we will not discuss.) Imagine a small piece of rock that contained 1 microgram of potassium-40 and no argon-40 when it solidified long ago. The half-life of 1.25 billion years means that half the original potassium-40 had decayed into argon-40 by the time the rock was 1.25 billion years old, so at that time the rock contained ½ microgram of potassium-40 and ½ microgram of argon-40. Half of this remaining potassium-40 had then decayed by the end of the next 1.25 billion years, so after 2.5 billion years the rock contained ¼ microgram of potassium-40 and ¾ microgram of argon-40. After three half-lives, or 3.75 billion years, only ⅛ microgram of potassium-40 remained, while ⅞ microgram had become argon-40. Figure 6.26 summarizes the gradual decrease in the amount of potassium-40 and the corresponding rise in the amount of argon-40.

We can determine the age of a rock through careful analysis of the proportions of various atoms and isotopes within it.

You can now see the essence of radiometric dating. Suppose you find a rock that contains equal numbers of atoms of potassium-40 and argon-40. If you assume that all the argon came from potassium decay (and if the rock shows no evidence of subsequent heating that could have allowed any argon to escape), then it must have taken precisely one half-life for the rock to end up with equal amounts of the two isotopes. You could therefore conclude that the rock is 1.25 billion years old. The only question is whether you are right in assuming that the rock lacked argon-40 when it formed. In this case, knowing a bit of "rock chemistry" helps. Potassium-40 is a natural ingredient of many minerals in rocks, but argon-40 is a gas that does not combine with other elements and did not condense in the solar nebula. If you find argon-40 gas trapped inside minerals, it must have come from radioactive decay of potassium-40.

Radiometric dating is possible with many other radioactive isotopes as well. In many cases, we can date a rock that contains more than one radioactive isotope, so agreement between the ages calculated from the different isotopes gives us confidence that we have dated the rock correctly.

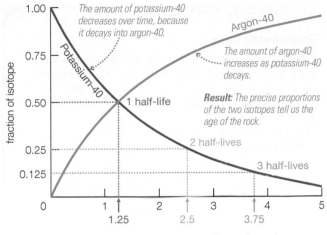

▲ **FIGURE 6.26**

Potassium-40 is radioactive, decaying into argon-40 with a half-life of 1.25 billion years. The red curve shows the decreasing amount of potassium-40, and the blue curve shows the increasing amount of argon-40. The remaining amount of potassium-40 drops in half with each successive half-life.

cosmic calculations 6.1

Radiometric Dating

From the definition of a half-life, it is possible to derive the following formula that allows you to calculate the age of a rock. To use the formula, you must measure the current amount of a radioactive substance in the rock and determine the original amount that was present long ago, which can often be done by measuring the abundance of the substance's decay products.

$$t = t_{half} \times \frac{\log_{10}\left(\frac{\text{current amount}}{\text{original amount}}\right)}{\log_{10}\left(\frac{1}{2}\right)}$$

where t is the time since the rock formed and t_{half} is the half-life of the radioactive substance; "$\log_{10}$" is the base-10 logarithm, which you can calculate with any scientific calculator.

Example: You chemically analyze a small sample of a meteorite. Potassium-40 and argon-40 are present in a ratio of 0.850 unit of potassium-40 atoms to 9.15 units of gaseous argon-40 atoms. (The units are unimportant, because only the relative amounts matter.) How old is the meteorite?

Solution: Because no argon gas could have been present in the meteorite when it formed, the 9.15 units of argon-40 must originally have been potassium-40. The sample must therefore have started with $0.850 + 9.15 = 10.0$ units of potassium-40 (the original amount), of which 0.85 unit remains (the current amount). The formula now reads

$$t = 1.25 \text{ billion yr} \times \frac{\log_{10}\left(\frac{0.850}{10.0}\right)}{\log_{10}\left(\frac{1}{2}\right)} = 4.45 \text{ billion yr}$$

This meteorite solidified about 4.45 billion years ago.

We can also check results from radiometric dating against those from other methods of measuring or estimating ages. For example, some fairly recent archaeological artifacts have original dates printed on them, and the dates agree with ages found by radiometric dating. We can validate the 4½-billion-year radiometric age for the solar system as a whole by comparing it to an age based on detailed study of the Sun. Theoretical models of the Sun, along with observations of other stars, show that stars slowly expand and brighten as they age. The model ages are not nearly as precise as radiometric ages, but they confirm that the Sun is between about 4 and 5 billion years old. Overall, the technique of radiometric dating has been checked in so many ways and relies on such basic scientific principles that there is no serious scientific debate about its validity.

Earth Rocks, Moon Rocks, and Meteorites Radiometric dating tells us how long it has been since a rock solidified, which is not the same as the age of a planet as a whole. For example, we find rocks of many different ages on Earth. Some rocks are quite young because they formed recently from molten lava, while the oldest Earth rocks date to about 4 billion years ago (some small mineral grains are older). Earth itself must be even older.

Moon rocks brought back by the *Apollo* astronauts date to as far back as 4.4 billion years ago. Although they are older than Earth rocks, these Moon rocks must still be younger than the Moon itself. The ages of these rocks also tell us that the giant impact thought to have created the Moon must have occurred more than 4.4 billion years ago.

To go all the way back to the origin of the solar system, we must find rocks that have not melted or vaporized since they first condensed in the solar nebula. Meteorites that have fallen to Earth are our source of such rocks. Many meteorites appear to have remained unchanged since they condensed and accreted in the early solar system. Careful analysis of radioactive isotopes in these meteorites shows that a significant number of them share the oldest time of formation, which is about 4.56 billion years ago, so this time must mark the beginning of accretion in the solar nebula. Because the planets apparently accreted within about 50 million (0.05 billion) years, Earth and the other planets formed by about 4.5 billion years ago.

Age dating of the oldest meteorites tells us that the solar system is about $4\frac{1}{2}$ billion years old.

the big picture | Putting Chapter 6 into Perspective

This chapter introduced the major features of our solar system and the current scientific theory of its formation. As you continue your study of the solar system, keep in mind the following "big picture" ideas:

- Our solar system is not a random collection of objects moving in random directions. Rather, it is highly organized, with clear patterns of motion and common traits among families of objects.

- We explain the origin of our solar system with the nebular theory, which holds that the solar system formed from the gravitational collapse of an interstellar gas cloud.

- Most of the general features of the solar system were determined by processes that occurred very early in the solar system's history.

- Our solar system is old—born about 4½ billion years ago—but it is still only about one-third as old as our 14-billion-year-old universe.

my cosmic perspective Events that happened more than 4 billion years ago may seem distant from our lives, but we wouldn't be here without them; they explain not only how our planet came to exist, but where life-sustaining water comes from, and how we came to have the Moon in our sky.

6.1 A Brief Tour of the Solar System

◆ What does the solar system look like?

The planets are tiny compared to the distances between them. Our solar system consists of the Sun, the planets and their moons, and vast numbers of asteroids and comets. Each world has its own unique character, but there are many clear patterns among the worlds.

6.2 The Nebular Theory of Solar System Formation

◆ What features of our solar system provide clues to how it formed?

Four major features provide clues: (1) The Sun, planets, and large moons generally rotate and orbit in a very organized way. (2) The planets divide clearly into two groups: **terrestrial** and **jovian.** (3) The solar system contains vast numbers of asteroids and comets. (4) There are some notable exceptions to these general patterns.

◆ What is the nebular theory?

The **nebular theory** holds that the solar system formed from the gravitational collapse of a great cloud of gas and dust, which itself was the product of recycling of gas through many generations of stars within our galaxy.

6.3 Explaining the Major Features of the Solar System

◆ What caused the orderly patterns of motion?

As the solar nebula collapsed under gravity, natural processes caused it to heat up, spin faster, and flatten out as it shrank. The orderly motions we observe today all came from the orderly motion of this spinning disk.

◆ Why are there two major types of planets?

The inner regions of the solar nebula were relatively hot, so only metal and rock could condense into tiny, solid grains; these grains accreted into larger **planetesimals** that ultimately merged to make the terrestrial planets. Beyond the **frost line,** cooler temperatures also allowed more abundant **hydrogen compounds** to condense into ice, building ice-rich planetesimals; some of these grew large enough for their gravity to draw in hydrogen and helium gas, forming the jovian planets.

◆ Where did asteroids and comets come from?

Asteroids are the rocky leftover planetesimals of the inner solar system, and comets are the ice-rich leftover planetesimals of the outer solar system. These objects still occasionally collide with planets or moons, but the vast majority of impacts occurred during the **heavy bombardment** in the solar system's first few hundred million years.

◆ How do we explain the "exceptions to the rules"?

Most of the exceptions probably arose from collisions or close encounters with leftover planetesimals. Our Moon is most likely the result of a **giant impact** between a Mars-size planetesimal and the young Earth.

6.4 The Age of the Solar System

◆ How do we know the age of the solar system?

We can determine the age of a rock through **radiometric dating,** which is based on knowing the **half-life** of various radioactive isotopes and carefully measuring the proportions of these isotopes and their decay products within a rock. The oldest rocks are meteorites, and their age tells us that the accretion began in the solar nebula about 4.56 billion years ago.

visual skills check

Check your understanding of some of the many types of visual information used in astronomy. For additional practice, try the Chapter 6 Visual Quiz at MasteringAstronomy®.

The graph shows the radioactive decay of uranium-235 to lead-207. (Uranium-235 also decays by another pathway, not shown.)

1. Compare the graph at the left to Figure 6.26, which shows the decay of potassium-40. Which element is more radioactive (undergoes radioactive decay more quickly)?
   a. uranium-235
   b. potassium-40
   c. Both are equally radioactive.

2. What fraction of the original uranium-235 should be left after 3.5 billion years?
   a. 1/2   b. 1/4
   c. 1/8   d. 1/32
   e. 1/64

3. You find a mysterious rock on the ground and determine that 60% of its uranium-235 has been converted into lead-207. What is the most likely origin of the rock, based on its radiometric age?
   a. It's older than our solar system, so it must have come from another solar system.
   b. It's a meteorite dating back to the formation of the solar system.
   c. It's a volcanic rock nearly a billion years old.
   d. It was just formed this year during the eruption of a nearby volcano.

exercises and problems

MasteringAstronomy® For instructor-assigned homework and other learning materials, go to MasteringAstronomy®.

Review Questions

1. Briefly describe the layout of the solar system as it would appear from beyond the orbit of Neptune.
2. For each of the objects in the solar system tour (pages 140–149), describe at least two features that you find interesting.
3. Briefly describe the four major features of our solar system that provide clues to how it formed.
4. What are the basic differences between *terrestrial* and *jovian* planets? Which planets fall into each group?
5. What is the *nebular theory,* and why is it widely accepted by scientists today?
6. What do we mean by the *solar nebula*? What was it made of, and where did it come from?
7. Describe three key processes that led the solar nebula to take the form of a spinning disk. What evidence supports this scenario?
8. Describe the four categories of materials in the solar nebula by their condensation properties and abundance. Which ingredients condensed inside and outside the *frost line*?
9. Briefly describe the process by which terrestrial planets are thought to have formed.
10. How was the formation of the jovian planets similar to that of the terrestrial planets? How was it different? Why did the jovian planets end up with many moons?
11. What are asteroids and comets, and how did they come to exist? How and why are they different?

12. What was the *heavy bombardment,* and when did it occur?
13. What is the leading hypothesis for the Moon's formation? What evidence supports this hypothesis?
14. Briefly explain the technique of *radiometric dating*. What is a *half-life*? How do we use radiometric dating to determine the age of the solar system?

Test Your Understanding

 Surprising Discoveries?

Suppose we found a solar system with the property described. (These are not real discoveries.) In light of what you've learned about the formation of our own solar system, decide whether the discovery should be considered reasonable or surprising. Explain your reasoning.

15. A solar system has five terrestrial planets in its inner solar system and three jovian planets in its outer solar system.
16. A solar system has four large jovian planets in its inner solar system and seven small terrestrial planets in its outer solar system.
17. A solar system has ten planets that all orbit the star in approximately the same plane. However, five planets orbit in one direction (e.g., counterclockwise), while the other five orbit in the opposite direction (e.g., clockwise).
18. A solar system has 12 planets that all orbit the star in the same direction and in nearly the same plane. The 15 largest moons in

this solar system orbit their planets in nearly the same direction and plane as well. However, several smaller moons have highly inclined orbits around their planets.

19. A solar system has six terrestrial planets and four jovian planets. Each of the six terrestrial planets has at least five moons, while the jovian planets have no moons at all.

20. A solar system has four Earth-size terrestrial planets. Each of the four planets has a single moon that is nearly identical in size to Earth's Moon.

21. A solar system has many rocky asteroids and many icy comets. However, most of the comets orbit in the inner solar system, while the asteroids orbit in far-flung regions much like the Kuiper belt and Oort cloud of our solar system.

22. A solar system has several planets similar in composition to the jovian planets of our solar system but similar in mass to the terrestrial planets of our solar system.

23. A solar system has several terrestrial planets and several larger planets made mostly of ice. (*Hint:* What would happen if the solar wind started earlier or later than in our solar system?)

24. Radiometric dating of the oldest meteorites from another solar system shows that they are a billion years younger than rocks from the terrestrial planets of the same system.

Quick Quiz

Choose the best answer to each of the following. Explain your reasoning with one or more complete sentences.

25. How many of the planets orbit the Sun in the same direction as Earth does? (a) a few (b) most (c) all

26. Planetary orbits in our solar system are (a) very eccentric (stretched-out) ellipses and in the same plane. (b) fairly circular and in the same plane. (c) fairly circular but oriented in every direction.

27. The solar nebula was 98% (a) rock and metal. (b) hydrogen compounds. (c) hydrogen and helium.

28. Which of the following did *not* occur during the collapse of the solar nebula? (a) spinning faster (b) heating up (c) concentrating denser materials nearer the Sun

29. What is Jupiter's main ingredient? (a) rock and metal (b) hydrogen compounds (c) hydrogen and helium

30. Which lists the major steps of solar system formation in the correct order? (a) collapse, accretion, condensation (b) collapse, condensation, accretion (c) accretion, condensation, collapse

31. Leftover ice-rich planetesimals are called (a) comets. (b) asteroids. (c) meteorites.

32. What's unusual about our Moon? (a) It's the only moon that orbits a terrestrial planet. (b) It's by far the largest moon in the solar system. (c) It's surprisingly large relative to the planet it orbits.

33. Are there any exceptions to the rule that planets rotate with small axis tilts and in the same direction as they orbit the Sun? (a) No (b) Venus is the only exception. (c) Venus and Uranus are exceptions.

34. About how old is the solar system? (a) 4.5 million years (b) 4.5 billion years (c) 4.5 trillion years

◐ Process of Science

35. *Explaining the Past.* Is it really possible for science to inform us about things that may have happened billions of years ago? To address this question, test the nebular theory against each of the three hallmarks of science discussed in Chapter 3. Be as detailed as possible in explaining whether the theory does or does not satisfy these hallmarks. Use your explanations to decide whether the theory can really tell us about how our solar system formed. Defend your opinion.

36. *Unanswered Questions.* As discussed in this chapter, the nebular theory answers many but not all questions about the origin of our solar system. Choose one important but unanswered question about the origin of our solar system and write two or three paragraphs in which you discuss how we might answer this question in the future. Be as specific as possible, focusing on the type of evidence necessary to answer the question and how the evidence could be gathered. What are the benefits of finding answers to this question?

Group Work Exercise

37. *A Cold Solar Nebula.* **Roles:** *Scribe* (takes notes on the group's activities), *Proposer* (proposes explanations to the group), *Skeptic* (points out weaknesses in proposed explanations), *Moderator* (leads group discussion and makes sure everyone contributes). **Activity:** In our solar system, the frost line was located between Mars and Jupiter, but study of other solar systems suggests that our solar system could have turned out differently. Consider a hypothetical scenario in which the solar nebula was not cleared away by the solar wind until the entire disk of gas had cooled to 50 K.
    a. Make a list of ingredients that will condense at 50 K.
    b. Make a list of ways in which the terrestrial planets might have turned out differently under this alternative formation scenario.
    c. Repeat part (b) for the jovian planets.
    d. Discuss the likelihood that your predicted changes would match the actual characteristics of this alternative solar system.
    e. Come up with additional "what if" scenarios, discussing various other ways in which the planets might have turned out differently.

Investigate Further

Short-Answer/Essay Questions

38. *True or False.* Decide whether each statement is true or false, and explain why.
    a. On average, Venus has the hottest surface temperature of any planet in the solar system.
    b. Our Moon is about the same size as moons of the other terrestrial planets.
    c. The weather conditions on Mars today are much different than they were in the distant past.
    d. Moons cannot have atmospheres, active volcanoes, or liquid water.
    e. Saturn is the only planet in the solar system with rings.
    f. Neptune orbits the Sun in the opposite direction of all the other planets.
    g. If Pluto were as large as the planet Mercury, we would classify it as a terrestrial planet.
    h. Asteroids are made of essentially the same materials as the terrestrial planets.
    i. When scientists say that our solar system is about 4½ billion years old, they are making a rough estimate based on guesswork about how long it should have taken planets to form.

1. How do light and matter interact? [Section 5.1]
2. What does the solar system look like? [Section 6.1]
3. Why are there two major types of planets? [Section 6.3]
4. Where did asteroids and comets come from? [Section 6.3]

It's easy to take for granted the qualities that make Earth so suitable for human life: a temperature neither boiling nor freezing, abundant water, a protective atmosphere, and a relatively stable environment. But we need look only as far as our neighboring terrestrial worlds to see how fortunate we are. The Moon is airless and barren, and Mercury is much the same. Venus is a searing hothouse, while Mars has an atmosphere so thin and cold that liquid water cannot last on its surface today.

How did the terrestrial worlds come to be so different, and why did Earth alone develop conditions that permit abundant life? We'll answer these questions by exploring key processes that have shaped Earth and the other terrestrial worlds over time. As we will see, the histories of the terrestrial worlds have been determined largely by properties endowed at their births.

7.1 Earth as a Planet

Earth's surface seems solid and steady, but every so often it offers us a reminder that nothing about it is permanent. If you live in Alaska or California, you've probably felt the ground shift beneath you in an earthquake. In Washington State, you may have witnessed the rumblings of Mount St. Helens. In Hawaii, a visit to the active Kilauea volcano will remind you that you are standing on mountains of volcanic rock protruding from the ocean floor.

Volcanoes and earthquakes are not the only processes acting to reshape Earth's surface. They are not even the most dramatic: Far greater change can occur on the rare occasions when an asteroid or a comet slams into Earth. More gradual processes can also have spectacular effects. The Colorado River causes only small changes in the landscape from year to year, but over millions of years its unrelenting flow carved the Grand Canyon. The Rocky Mountains were once twice as tall as they are today, but they have been cut down in size through tens of millions of years of erosion by wind, rain, and ice. Entire continents move slowly about, completely rearranging the map of Earth every few hundred million years.

Earth is not alone in having undergone tremendous change since its birth. The surfaces of all five terrestrial worlds—Mercury, Venus, Earth, the Moon, and Mars—must have looked quite similar when they were young, because all are made of rocky material and all were subjected to the impacts of the heavy bombardment [Section 6.3]. The great differences in their present-day appearances must therefore be the result of changes that have occurred through time.

Figure 7.1 shows global views of the terrestrial worlds to scale, along with sample surface views from orbit. Profound differences are immediately obvious. Mercury and the Moon still show the scars of their battering during the heavy bombardment. Venus is covered by a thick, cloudy atmosphere, but radar mapping reveals a surface dotted with volcanoes and other features indicating active geology. Mars has many features that appear to have been shaped by running water, but all are now dry. Earth has a diverse surface that reveals clear evidence of life.

Mercury

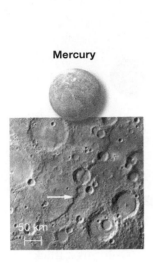

Heavily cratered Mercury has long steep cliffs (arrow).

50 km

Venus

Cloud-penetrating radar revealed this twin-peaked volcano on Venus.

100 km

Earth

A portion of Earth's surface as it appears without clouds.

100 km

Earth's Moon

The Moon's surface is heavily cratered in most places.

100 km

Mars

Mars has features that look like dry riverbeds; note the impact craters.

50 km

▲ **FIGURE 7.1**

Global views of the five terrestrial worlds to scale, along with sample close-ups viewed from orbit. All the images were taken with visible light except the Venus close-up, which is based on radar data.

Our primary goal in this chapter is to gain a deeper understanding of our own planet Earth by investigating how the terrestrial worlds came to be so different. We'll begin by examining the basic nature of our planet.

◆ Why is Earth geologically active?

All the terrestrial worlds have changed since their birth, but Earth is unique in the degree to which it continues to change today. We say that Earth is *geologically active*, meaning that its surface is continually being reshaped by volcanic eruptions, earthquakes, erosion, and other geological processes. Most geological activity is driven by processes that take place deep beneath the surface. Consequently, to understand why Earth is so much more geologically active than other worlds, we must examine what the terrestrial worlds are like inside.

Interior Structure We cannot see inside the terrestrial worlds, but a variety of clues tell us about their internal structures. For Earth, the most direct data come from *seismic waves*, vibrations that travel both through the interior and along the surface after an earthquake. We also have seismic data for the Moon, thanks to monitoring stations left behind by the *Apollo* astronauts, and the *Mars Insight* mission, scheduled for launch in 2018, includes a seismic station for Mars. We use less direct methods to study the interiors of other worlds. For example, comparing a world's overall average density to the density of its surface rock tells us how much more dense it must be inside, measurements of a world's gravity from spacecraft can tell us how mass is distributed inside it, studies of magnetic fields tell us about the interior layers in which these fields are generated, and volcanic rocks can tell us about interior composition.

Together, such studies have shown that all the terrestrial worlds have layered interiors. We divide these layers by density into three major categories:

- **Core:** The highest-density material, consisting primarily of metals such as nickel and iron, resides in a central core.

rocky crust
(lower density)

mantle
(medium density)

metal core
(highest density)

rigid lithosphere
(crust and
part of mantle)

lithosphere

lithosphere   lithosphere   lithosphere

Key: crust   mantle   ⊤ lithosphere   core

▲ **FIGURE 7.2**

Interior structures of the terrestrial worlds, shown to scale and in order of decreasing size. Color coding shows the core-mantle-crust layering by density; a dashed circle represents the inner boundary of the lithosphere, defined by strength of rock rather than by density. The thicknesses of the crust and the lithosphere of Venus and Earth are exaggerated to make them visible in this figure.

▲ **FIGURE 7.3**

Silly Putty stretches when pulled slowly but breaks cleanly when pulled rapidly. Rock behaves just the same, but on a longer time scale.

- **Mantle:** Rocky material of moderate density—mostly minerals that contain silicon, oxygen, and other elements—forms a thick mantle that surrounds the core.

- **Crust:** The lowest-density rock (which includes the familiar rocks of Earth's surface) forms a thin crust, essentially representing the world's outer skin.

Figure 7.2 shows these layers for the five terrestrial worlds. Although not shown in the figure, Earth's metallic core actually consists of two distinct regions: a solid *inner core* and a molten (liquid) *outer core*.

It's often more useful to categorize interior layers by rock strength instead of density. The idea that rock can vary in strength may seem surprising, but like all matter built of atoms, rock is mostly empty space; its apparent solidity arises from electrical bonds between its atoms and molecules [Section 5.1]. Although these bonds are strong, they can still break and re-form when subjected to heat or sustained stress, which means that even solid rock can slowly deform and flow over millions and billions of years. The long-term behavior of rock is much like that of Silly Putty, which breaks like a brittle solid when you pull it sharply but deforms and stretches when you pull it slowly (Figure 7.3). Also like Silly Putty, rock becomes softer and easier to deform when it is warmer.

see it for yourself Roll some room-temperature Silly Putty into a ball and measure its diameter. Put the ball on a table and gently place a heavy book on top of it. After 5 seconds, measure the height of the squashed ball. Repeat the experiment, but warm the Silly Putty in hot water before you start. Repeat again, but cool the Silly Putty in ice water before you start. How does temperature affect the rate of "squashing"? How does the experiment relate to planetary geology?

A planet's *lithosphere* is its outer layer of cool, rigid rock.

In terms of rock strength, Earth's outer layer consists of relatively cool and rigid rock, called the **lithosphere** (*lithos* is Greek for "stone"), that essentially "floats" on warmer, softer rock beneath. As shown by the dashed circles in Figure 7.2, the lithosphere encompasses the crust and part of the mantle of each world.

Differentiation and Internal Heat We can understand *why* the interiors are layered by thinking about what happens in a mixture of oil and water: Gravity pulls the denser water to the bottom, driving the less dense oil to the top. This process is called **differentiation,** because it

The terrestrial interiors were once hot enough to melt, allowing material to settle into layers of differing density.

results in layers made of *different* materials. The layered interiors of the terrestrial worlds tell us that they underwent differentiation at some time in the past, which means all these worlds must once have been hot enough inside for their interior rock and metal to melt. Dense metals like iron sank toward the center, driving less dense rocky material toward the surface.

Two major processes explain why all the terrestrial worlds once had hot interiors. First, as a planet formed through accretion [Section 6.3], the gravitational potential energy of incoming planetesimals was ultimately converted into thermal energy in the planet's interior. (The process of differentiation converted additional gravitational potential energy into thermal energy as denser materials sank to the core.) Second, the rock and metal that built the terrestrial worlds contained radioactive isotopes of elements such as uranium, potassium, and thorium. As these radioactive materials decay, they release heat directly into the planetary interiors, in essence converting some of the mass-energy ($E = mc^2$) of the radioactive

special topic — Seismic Waves

Seismic waves come in two basic types, analogous to the two ways you can generate waves in a Slinky (Figure 1). Pushing and pulling on one end of a Slinky (while someone holds the other end still) generates a wave in which the Slinky is bunched up in some places and stretched out in others. Waves like this in rock are called P waves. The *P* stands for *primary,* because these waves travel fastest and are the first to arrive after an earthquake, but it is easier to think of *P* as meaning *pressure* or *pushing.* P waves can travel through almost any material—whether solid, liquid, or gas—because molecules can always push on their neighbors no matter how weakly they are bound together. (Sound travels as a pressure wave quite similar to a P wave.)

Shaking a Slinky slightly up and down or side to side generates a different type of wave; in rock, such waves are called S waves. The *S* stands for *secondary* but is easier to remember as meaning *shear* or *side to side.* S waves travel only through solids, because the bonds between neighboring molecules in a liquid or gas are too weak to transmit up-and-down or sideways forces.

The speeds and directions of seismic waves depend on the composition, density, pressure, temperature, and phase (solid or liquid) of the material they pass through. For example, P waves reach the side of the world opposite an earthquake, but S waves do not. This tells us that a liquid layer has stopped the S waves, which is how we know that Earth has a liquid outer core (Figure 2). More careful analysis of seismic waves, combined with mathematical modeling, has allowed geologists to develop a detailed picture of Earth's interior structure.

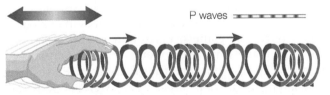

P waves

P waves result from compression and stretching in the direction of travel.

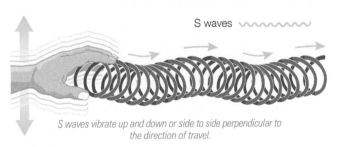

S waves

S waves vibrate up and down or side to side perpendicular to the direction of travel.

▲ **FIGURE 1**
Slinky examples demonstrating P and S waves.

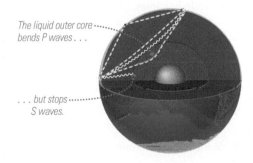

The liquid outer core bends P waves . . .

. . . but stops S waves.

▲ **FIGURE 2**
Because S waves do not reach the side of Earth opposite an earthquake, we infer that part of Earth's core is liquid.

Mantle convection: hot rock rises and cooler rock falls.

▲ **FIGURE 7.4**

Earth's hot interior allows the mantle to undergo convection, in which hot rock gradually rises upward while cool rock gradually falls. Arrows indicate the direction of flow in a portion of the mantle.

cosmic calculations 7.1

The Surface Area–to–Volume Ratio

The total amount of heat contained in a planet depends on its volume, but heat can escape into space only from the planet's *surface*. As heat escapes, more heat flows upward from the interior to replace it until the interior is no hotter than the surface. The time it takes a planet to lose its internal heat is related to the ratio of the *surface area* through which it loses heat to the *volume* that contains heat:

$$\text{surface area–to–volume ratio} = \frac{\text{surface area}}{\text{volume}}$$

A spherical planet (radius r) has surface area $4\pi r^2$ and volume $\frac{4}{3}\pi r^3$, so the ratio becomes

$$\underset{\text{(for a sphere)}}{\text{surface area–to–volume ratio}} = \frac{4\pi r^2}{\frac{4}{3}\pi r^3} = \frac{3}{r}$$

Because r appears in the denominator, we conclude that *larger objects have smaller surface area–to–volume ratios.*

Example: Compare the surface area–to–volume ratios of the Moon ($r_{\text{Moon}} = 1738$ km) and Earth ($r_{\text{Earth}} = 6378$ km).

Solution: We divide the two surface area–to–volume ratios:

$$\frac{\text{surface area–to–volume ratio (Moon)}}{\text{surface area–to–volume ratio (Earth)}} = \frac{3/r_{\text{Moon}}}{3/r_{\text{Earth}}} = \frac{r_{\text{Earth}}}{r_{\text{Moon}}}$$

$$= \frac{6378 \text{ km}}{1738 \text{ km}} = 3.7$$

The Moon's surface area–to–volume ratio is nearly four times as large as Earth's, which means the Moon would cool four times as fast if both worlds started with the same temperature and gained no additional heat.

nuclei to thermal energy. The amount of radioactive material declines with time as it decays, so this heat source supplied more heat when the planets were young than it does today.

The terrestrial interiors all retain at least some heat today, but the amount varies with size. Larger worlds tend to stay hot longer than smaller worlds for the same basic reason that a hot potato remains hot inside much longer than a hot pea.

see it for yourself It's easy to demonstrate that larger objects take longer to cool than smaller objects. The next time you eat something large and hot, cut off a small piece; notice how much more quickly the small piece cools than the rest of it. A similar experiment demonstrates the time it takes a cold object to warm up: Find two ice cubes of the same size. Crack one into small pieces, then compare the rates of melting. Explain your observations.

Internal Heat and Geological Activity Interior heat is the primary driver of geological activity. Temperature increases with depth inside a planet. If the interior is hot enough, the mantle can undergo **convection,** in which hot material gradually expands and cools as it rises upward, while cooler material from above gradually contracts and falls (Figure 7.4). Keep in mind that mantle convection primarily involves solid rock, which flows very slowly. At the typical rate of mantle convection on Earth—a few centimeters per year—it would take 100 million years for a piece of rock to be carried from the base of the mantle to the top.

Just as planetary size determines how long a planet stays hot, it is also the primary factor in the strength of mantle convection and lithospheric thickness. As a planet's interior cools, the rigid lithosphere grows thicker and convection occurs only deeper inside the planet. A thick lithosphere inhibits volcanic and tectonic activity, because any molten rock is too deeply buried to erupt to the surface and the strong lithosphere resists distortion by tectonic stresses. If the interior cools enough, convection may stop entirely, leaving the planet "geologically dead," with no eruptions or crustal movement.

> Larger planets retain internal heat much longer than smaller ones, and this heat drives geological activity.

We can now understand the differences in lithospheric thickness shown in Figure 7.2, which go along with differences in geological activity. As the largest terrestrial planets, Earth and Venus remain quite hot inside and therefore have thin lithospheres and substantial geological activity. (Venus may have a thicker lithosphere than Earth for reasons we will discuss later.) With their small sizes, Mercury and the Moon have lost so much heat that they now have very thick lithospheres (Mercury's looks thin on Figure 7.2, but extends nearly down to its large core) and little if any geological activity. Mars, intermediate in size, retains enough internal heat for limited geological activity.

The Magnetic Field Interior heat is also responsible for Earth's global **magnetic field.** You are probably familiar with the general pattern of the magnetic field created by an iron bar (Figure 7.5a). Earth's magnetic field is generated by a process more similar to that of an *electromagnet,* in which the magnetic field arises as a battery forces charged particles to move along a coiled wire (Figure 7.5b). Earth does not contain a battery, but charged particles move with the molten metal in its liquid outer core (Figure 7.5c). Internal heat causes the liquid metal to rise and fall (convection), while Earth's rotation twists and distorts the convection pattern. The result is that electrons in the molten metal move within the outer core in much the same way they move in an electromagnet, generating Earth's magnetic field.

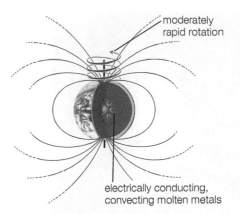

a This photo shows how a bar magnet influences iron filings (small black specks) around it. The *magnetic field lines* (red) represent this influence graphically.

b A similar magnetic field is created by an electromagnet, which is essentially a wire wrapped around a metal bar and attached to a battery. The field is created by the battery-forced motion of charged particles (electrons) along the wire.

c Earth's magnetic field also arises from the motion of charged particles. The charged particles move within Earth's liquid outer core, which is made of electrically conducting, convecting molten metals.

▲ **FIGURE 7.5**

Sources of magnetic fields.

The magnetic field is very important to life on Earth because it creates a **magnetosphere** that acts like a protective bubble surrounding our planet (Figure 7.6a), shielding Earth's surface from the energetic charged particles of the *solar wind* [Section 6.3]. These particles would otherwise strip away atmospheric gas and cause genetic damage to living organisms. The magnetosphere deflects most solar wind particles around our planet and channels the remaining particles toward the poles, where they can collide with atoms and molecules in our atmosphere and produce the beautiful lights of the **aurora** (Figure 7.6b).

Earth's magnetic field, generated by convection of molten metal in its outer core, creates a *magnetosphere* that protects our planet from the solar wind.

▼ **FIGURE 7.6**

Earth's magnetosphere acts like a protective bubble, shielding our planet from charged particles coming from the solar wind.

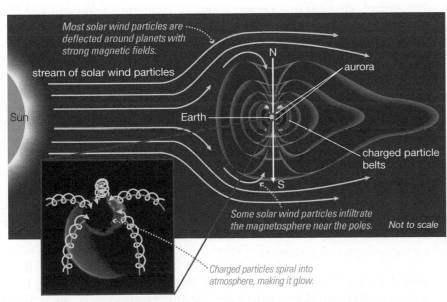

a This diagram shows how Earth's magnetosphere deflects solar wind particles. Some particles accumulate in charged particle belts encircling our planet. The inset is an ultraviolet image of a ring of auroras around the North Pole; the bright crescent at its left is part of the day side of Earth.

b This photograph shows the aurora near Yellowknife, Northwest Territories, Canada. In a video, you would see these lights dancing about in the sky.

▲ FIGURE 7.7
Artist's conception of the impact process.

None of the other terrestrial worlds have magnetic fields as strong as Earth's and they therefore lack protective magnetospheres. As we'll discuss later, this fact has profoundly affected the histories of Venus and Mars.

◆ What processes shape Earth's surface?

Although we find a huge variety of geological surface features on Earth and the other terrestrial worlds, nearly all of them can be explained by just four major geological processes:

- **Impact cratering:** the creation of bowl-shaped *impact craters* by asteroids or comets striking a planet's surface
- **Volcanism:** the eruption of molten rock, or *lava*, from a planet's interior onto its surface
- **Tectonics:** the disruption of a planet's surface by internal stresses
- **Erosion:** the wearing down or building up of geological features by wind, water, ice, and other phenomena of planetary weather

Nearly all geological features arise from impact cratering, volcanism, tectonics, or erosion. Note that impact cratering is the only one of the four processes with an external cause (impacts of objects from space). The other three are ultimately attributable to a planet's interior heat and represent what we usually define as *geological activity.*

Impact Cratering An impact crater forms when an asteroid or comet slams into a solid surface (Figure 7.7). An impacting object typically hits the surface at a speed between about 40,000 and 250,000 kilometers per hour. At such a tremendous speed, the impact releases enough energy to vaporize solid rock and blast out a *crater* (the Greek word for "cup"). Craters are usually circular, because an impact blasts out material in all directions, regardless of the incoming object's direction. Craters are typically about 10 times as wide as the objects that create them and about 10–20% as deep as they are wide. For example, an asteroid 1 kilometer in diameter will blast out a crater about 10 kilometers wide and 1–2 kilometers deep.

We have never witnessed a major impact on Earth, but geologists have identified more than 150 impact craters (Figure 7.8). While this may seem a substantial number, it is far smaller than the number of impact craters easily visible on the Moon, which leads to an important insight: Given their close proximity, we'd expect Earth and the Moon to have suffered similar numbers of impacts, so the relatively small number of craters on Earth suggests that Earth's craters have been erased with time by geological activity such as volcanic eruptions and erosion. This fact leads to a simple way to estimate the age of a world's surface, meaning the time since its current surface features formed.

We can estimate the geological age of any surface region from its number of impact craters, with more craters indicating an older surface. To understand the idea, recall that all the planets were battered by impacts during the heavy bombardment that ended almost 4 billion years ago [Section 6.3], but relatively few impacts have occurred since. In places where we see numerous craters, such as on much of the Moon's surface, we must be looking at a surface that has stayed virtually unchanged for at least 4 billion years. In contrast, when we see very few craters, as on Earth, we must be looking at a surface

▲ FIGURE 7.8
Meteor Crater in Arizona, made by an impact about 50,000 years ago, is one of the youngest of more than 150 known impact craters on Earth. It is more than a kilometer across and nearly 200 meters deep, implying the impact of an asteroid about 50 meters across.

200 m

that has undergone recent change. More detailed analysis (particularly of craters on the Moon) has allowed scientists to estimate the cratering rate throughout solar system history. As a result, scientists can estimate the age of a planetary surface just by photographing it from orbit and counting its craters.

Volcanism Volcanism occurs when underground molten rock finds a path to the surface (Figure 7.9). The "thickness" (or *viscosity*) of molten lava can vary, depending on the composition of the molten rock. Thick lava tends to make tall, steep volcanoes, while runny lava can make broad, flat lava plains. Earth is the most volcanically active of the terrestrial worlds, a fact traceable to its relatively large size, which has allowed it to retain internal heat.

Volcanic mountains are the most obvious result of volcanism, but volcanism has had a much more profound effect on our planet: It explains the existence of our atmosphere and oceans. Recall that Earth accreted from rocky and metallic planetesimals, while water and other ices were brought in by planetesimals from more distant reaches of the solar system [Section 6.3]. Water and gases became trapped beneath the surface in much the same way the gas in a carbonated beverage is trapped in a pressurized bottle. Volcanic eruptions later released some of this gas into the atmosphere in a process known as **outgassing** (Figure 7.10).

Earth's atmosphere and oceans were made from gases released from the interior by volcanic outgassing.

On Earth, the major gases released by outgassing have been water vapor (H_2O), carbon dioxide (CO_2), and nitrogen (N_2). Most of the outgassed water vapor condensed to form our oceans, and much of the nitrogen remains as the dominant ingredient (77%) of our atmosphere. We'll discuss how the atmosphere lost its carbon dioxide and gained its oxygen in Section 7.5.

Tectonics *Tectonics* refers to any surface reshaping that results from stretching, compression, or other forces acting on the lithosphere. Figure 7.11 shows two examples of tectonic features on Earth, one created as the surface is pushed upward by compression (the Himalayas) and the other created by surface stretching (the Red Sea).

Tectonic activity usually goes hand in hand with volcanism, because both require internal heat and therefore depend on planetary size. While tectonic activity has occurred on every terrestrial world, it has been particularly important on Earth, where the underlying mantle convection fractured the lithosphere into more than a dozen pieces, or *plates*. These plates move over, under, and around each other, leading to a special type of tectonics—**plate tectonics**—that appears to be unique to Earth in our solar system. We'll discuss plate tectonics further in Section 7.5.

Tectonics and volcanism both require internal heat and therefore depend on a planet's size.

Erosion Erosion begins with the breakdown and transport of surface rock through the action of ice, liquid, or gas. Familiar features of erosion include valleys carved by glacial ice, canyons carved by rivers, sand dunes shaped by wind, and river deltas made of sediments carried downstream (Figure 7.12). Note that while we usually associate erosion with breakdown, sand dunes and river deltas are examples of features built up by erosion. Indeed, erosion has built much of Earth's surface rock: Over long periods of time, erosion piled sediments into layers on the

molten rock in the crust

▲ **FIGURE 7.9**
Volcanism. The photo shows the eruption of an active volcano on the flanks of Kilauea on the Big Island of Hawaii. The inset shows the underlying process: Molten rock collects in a chamber from which it can erupt upward.

▲ **FIGURE 7.10**
This photo shows the eruption of Mount St. Helens (Washington State) on May 18, 1980. Note the tremendous outgassing that accompanied the eruption.

Internal stresses can cause compression in the crust . . .

. . . creating mountains like the Himalayas.

Internal stresses can also pull the crust apart . . .

. . . creating cracks and seas.

Earth's tallest mountain range, the Himalayas, created as India pushes into the rest of Asia.

The Red Sea, created as the Arabian Peninsula was torn away from Africa.

▲ **FIGURE 7.11**

Tectonic forces can produce a wide variety of features. Mountains created by tectonic compression and valleys or seas created by tectonic stretching are among the most common. Both images are satellite photos.

a The Colorado River has been carving the Grand Canyon for millions of years.

b Glaciers created Yosemite Valley during ice ages.

c Wind erosion wears away rocks and builds up sand dunes.

d This river delta is built from sediments worn away by wind and rain and then carried downstream.

▲ **FIGURE 7.12**

A few examples of erosion on Earth.

floors of oceans and seas, forming *sedimentary rock*. The layered rock of the Grand Canyon is an example, built up by erosion long before the Colorado River carved the canyon.

Erosion can both break down and build up geological features.

Erosion plays a far more important role on Earth than on any other terrestrial world, primarily because our planet has both strong winds and liquid water. Note that both winds and water are ultimately traceable to volcanic outgassing, which means that like volcanism and tectonics, erosion requires interior heat. However, interior heat alone is not enough. Venus lacks substantial erosion because it has weak winds and is too hot for liquid water, while water erosion no longer occurs on Mars because it is too cold.

◆ How does Earth's atmosphere affect the planet?

Most people are aware that the atmosphere supplies the oxygen we breathe, but Earth's atmosphere also affects our planet in several deeper ways. We've already discussed its role in weather and erosion. In addition, the atmosphere protects the surface from dangerous solar radiation and makes our planet warm enough for liquid water to exist.

As you study these effects, keep two other important ideas in mind. First, the atmosphere is a mix of gases; its overall composition is approximately 77% nitrogen (N_2) and 21% oxygen (O_2), with small amounts of argon, water vapor, carbon dioxide, and other gases. Second, the atmosphere is remarkably thin: Most of the air lies within 10 kilometers of the surface, which means it makes a layer around Earth equivalent to the thickness of a dollar bill laid over a standard globe.

Surface Protection The Sun emits the visible light that allows us to see, but it also emits dangerous ultraviolet and X-ray radiation. Our atmosphere protects us against this radiation by absorbing it high above the ground (Figure 7.13). We can understand how by considering interactions between air and different forms of light.

X rays can be absorbed by almost any atom or molecule. As a result, X rays from the Sun are absorbed where they first strike air, which is high in the atmosphere. No solar X rays reach the ground, which is why X-ray telescopes must be placed in space.

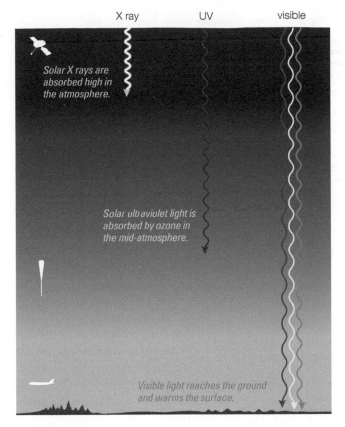

X ray　　　　UV　　　　visible

Solar X rays are absorbed high in the atmosphere.

Solar ultraviolet light is absorbed by ozone in the mid-atmosphere.

Visible light reaches the ground and warms the surface.

▲ **FIGURE 7.13**

This diagram summarizes how different forms of light from the Sun are affected by Earth's atmosphere.

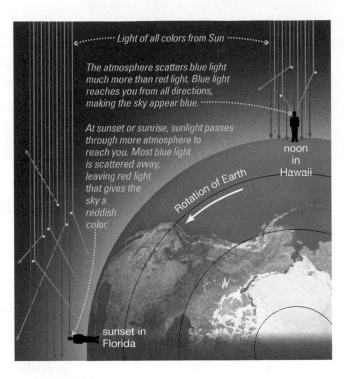

Light of all colors from Sun

The atmosphere scatters blue light much more than red light. Blue light reaches you from all directions, making the sky appear blue.

At sunset or sunrise, sunlight passes through more atmosphere to reach you. Most blue light is scattered away, leaving red light that gives the sky a reddish color.

noon in Hawaii

Rotation of Earth

sunset in Florida

▲ **FIGURE 7.14**

This diagram summarizes why the sky is blue and sunsets (and sunrises) are red.

Ultraviolet light is not so easily absorbed, because most gases are transparent to ultraviolet light. We owe our protection from ultraviolet light to a relatively rare gas, called **ozone** (O_3), that resides primarily in the middle layer of Earth's atmosphere (the *stratosphere*). Without this ultraviolet-absorbing ozone, life on land could not survive.

Solar X rays are absorbed by atoms and molecules high in the atmosphere, and ultraviolet radiation is absorbed by ozone in the middle atmosphere.

Visible light can pass through the atmosphere to the ground, making it the primary source of heat for Earth's surface, the energy source for photosynthesis, and the light that allows us to see. However, not all visible light photons take a straight path to the ground. Some are scattered randomly around the sky, which is why our sky is bright in the daytime. Without this scattering, our sky would look like the lunar sky does to an astronaut, with the Sun a very bright circle set against a black background. Scattering also explains the color of our sky (Figure 7.14). Visible light consists of all the colors of the rainbow, but the colors are not all scattered equally. Gas molecules scatter blue light (shorter wavelength and higher energy) so much more effectively than red light (longer wavelength and lower energy) that, for practical purposes, we can imagine that only the blue light gets scattered. When the Sun is overhead, this scattered blue light reaches our eyes from all directions, so the sky appears blue. At sunset or sunrise, when sunlight passes through more air on its way to our eyes, so much of the blue light is scattered away that we are left primarily with red light to color the sky.

common misconceptions

Why Is the Sky Blue?

If you ask around, you'll find a wide variety of misconceptions about why the sky is blue. Some people guess that the sky is blue because of light reflecting from the oceans, but that could not explain blue skies over inland areas. Others claim that "air is blue," a vague statement that is clearly wrong: If air molecules emitted blue light, then air would glow blue even in the dark; if they were blue because they reflected blue light and absorbed red light, then no red light could reach us at sunset. The real explanation for the blue sky is light scattering, as shown in Figure 7.14, which also explains our red sunsets.

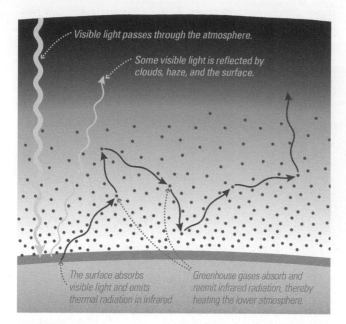

Visible light passes through the atmosphere.

Some visible light is reflected by clouds, haze, and the surface.

The surface absorbs visible light and emits thermal radiation in infrared.

Greenhouse gases absorb and reemit infrared radiation, thereby heating the lower atmosphere.

▲ **FIGURE 7.15**

The greenhouse effect. The lower atmosphere becomes warmer than it would be if it had no greenhouse gases such as water vapor, carbon dioxide, and methane.

TABLE 7.1	The Greenhouse Effect on Venus, Earth, and Mars		
World	Calculated "No Greenhouse" Average Surface Temperature	Actual Average Surface Temperature*	Greenhouse Warming
Venus	−40°C	470°C	510°C
Earth	−16°C	15°C	31°C
Mars	−56°C	−50°C	6°C

*The "no greenhouse" temperature is calculated by assuming no change to the atmosphere other than lack of greenhouse warming. For example, Venus has a lower "no greenhouse" temperature than Earth even though it is closer to the Sun, because the high reflectivity of its bright clouds means that it absorbs less sunlight than Earth.

The Greenhouse Effect Visible light warms Earth's surface, but not as much as you might guess. It's easy for scientists to calculate the temperature we'd expect for any world based on its distance from the Sun and the percentage of incoming sunlight that it absorbs (the rest is reflected).

The greenhouse effect keeps Earth's surface much warmer than it would be otherwise, allowing water to stay liquid over most of the surface.

These calculations give correct answers for airless worlds such as the Moon and Mercury, but underestimate the temperatures for worlds with atmospheres. The reason is that certain atmospheric gases can trap heat through what we call the **greenhouse effect.** Table 7.1 shows calculated "no greenhouse" temperatures for Venus, Earth, and Mars, along with actual temperatures. Note, for example, that Earth's temperature would be well below freezing without the greenhouse effect, which means this effect is crucial to the existence of life on Earth.

Figure 7.15 shows the basic idea behind the greenhouse effect. Some of the visible light that reaches the ground is reflected and some is absorbed. The absorbed energy must be returned to space—otherwise the ground would rapidly heat up—and planetary surfaces return energy by emitting infrared light (because planetary surface temperatures are in the range in which their thermal radiation peaks in the infrared [Section 5.2]). The greenhouse effect occurs when the atmosphere temporarily "traps" some of this infrared light, slowing its return to space.

Atmospheric gases that are particularly good at absorbing infrared light are called **greenhouse gases,** and they include water vapor (H_2O), carbon dioxide (CO_2), and methane (CH_4). A gas molecule that has absorbed a photon of infrared light then re-emits it in some random direction. This photon can then be absorbed by another gas molecule, which does the same thing. The net result is that greenhouse gases tend to slow the escape of infrared radiation from the lower atmosphere, while their molecular motions heat the surrounding air. In this way, the greenhouse effect makes the surface and the lower atmosphere warmer than they would be from sunlight alone. The more greenhouse gases present, the greater the degree of surface warming.

think about it Molecules made from two atoms of the same type—such as the N_2 and O_2 molecules that together make up 98% of Earth's atmosphere—are poor infrared absorbers. But imagine this were not the case. How would Earth be different if nitrogen and oxygen absorbed infrared light?

7.2 The Moon and Mercury: Geologically Dead

In the rest of this chapter, we will investigate the histories of the terrestrial worlds, with the goal of learning how and why Earth became unique. We'll start with the two worlds that have the simplest histories: the Moon and Mercury (Figure 7.16).

◆ Was there ever geological activity on the Moon or Mercury?

The simple histories of the Moon and Mercury are a direct consequence of their small sizes. Both lost most of their internal heat long ago, leaving them without any significant geological activity and without outgassing to supply atmospheric gas. Their small sizes also mean that their gravity is too weak to hold gas they may have gained in the past. This fact combined with the lack of outgassing explains why neither the Moon nor Mercury has a significant atmosphere.

The fact that these worlds have been "geologically dead" for billions of years explains why the major features of their surfaces are impact craters formed during the heavy bombardment. Nevertheless, we expect that both worlds should have had hot interiors early in their histories, and observations confirm that both have at least some volcanic and tectonic features.

Geological Features of the Moon The familiar face of the full moon shows that not all regions of the surface look the same (Figure 7.17). Some regions are heavily cratered while others, known as the **lunar maria,** look smooth and dark. Indeed, the maria (Latin for "seas") got their name because they look much like oceans when seen from afar. Today, we know that the maria are actually the sites of large impacts that were later flooded by lava.

Figure 7.18 shows how the maria probably formed. During the heavy bombardment, craters covered the Moon's entire surface. The largest impacts were violent enough to fracture the Moon's lithosphere beneath the huge craters they created. Although there was no molten rock to flood the craters immediately, the

The Moon's dark, smooth maria were made by floods of lava billions of years ago, when the Moon's interior was heated by radioactive decay.

ongoing decay of radioactive elements in the Moon's interior ultimately built up enough heat to cause mantle melting about 3 to 4 billion years ago. Molten rock then welled up through the cracks in the lithosphere, flooding the largest impact craters with lava. The maria are generally circular because they are flooded craters (and craters are almost always round), and they are dark because the lava consisted of dark, iron-rich rock. The relative lack of craters within the maria is a consequence of the fact that the lava floods occurred after the heavy bombardment subsided, and relatively few impacts have occurred since that time.

The Moon's era of geological activity is long gone. Today, the Moon is a desolate and nearly unchanging place (Figure 7.19a). The only ongoing geological change on the Moon is a very slow "sandblasting" of the surface by *micrometeorites,* sand-size particles from space—the same types of particles that burn up as meteors in Earth's atmosphere. The micrometeorites gradually pulverize the surface rock, which explains why the lunar surface is covered

Moon   Mercury

▲ **FIGURE 7.16**

Views of the Moon and Mercury, shown to scale. The Mercury photo is from *MESSENGER.*

▲ **FIGURE 7.17**

The familiar face of the full Moon shows numerous dark, smooth maria.

a This illustration shows the Mare Humorum region as it probably looked about 4 billion years ago, when it would have been completely covered in craters.

b Around that time, a huge impact excavated the crater that would later become Mare Humorum. The impact fractured the Moon's lithosphere and erased the many craters that had existed earlier.

c A few hundred million years later, heat from radioactive decay built up enough to melt the Moon's upper mantle. Molten lava welled up through the lithospheric cracks, flooding the impact crater.

d This photo shows Mare Humorum as it appears today, and the inset shows its location on the Moon.

▲ **FIGURE 7.18**

The lunar maria formed between 3 and 4 billion years ago, when molten lava flooded large craters that had formed hundreds of millions of years earlier. This sequence of diagrams represents the formation of Mare Humorum.

a An astronaut takes the Lunar Roving Vehicle for a spin during the final *Apollo* mission to the Moon (*Apollo 17*, December 1972).

b The *Apollo* astronauts left footprints, like this one, in the Moon's powdery "soil." Micrometeorites will eventually erase the footprints, but not for millions of years.

▲ **FIGURE 7.19**

The Moon today is geologically dead, but it can still tell us a lot about the history of our solar system.

by a layer of powdery "soil." You can see this powdery surface in photos from the *Apollo* missions to the Moon (Figure 7.19b). Pulverization by micrometeorites is a very slow process, so the rover tracks and astronaut footprints could remain for millions of years.

Humans have not returned to the Moon in the more than four decades since *Apollo*, but numerous robotic spacecraft have studied the Moon from orbit. These spacecraft have identified numerous small-scale features attesting to volcanic and tectonic activity when the Moon was young. They've also confirmed an important prediction: Water ice, presumably deposited by comet impacts over millions of years, resides in permanently shadowed craters near the lunar poles. Ice was first confirmed in 2009, when scientists sent the rocket from the *LCROSS* spacecraft crashing into a crater near the Moon's south pole so that they could study the debris splashed upward. Not long after, a radar sensor aboard India's *Chandrayaan-1* spacecraft detected ice deposits in similar craters near the Moon's north pole. There is apparently enough water ice to be useful to future colonists, at least if the colonies are built near the lunar poles.

think about it Do you think we should send humans back to the Moon? Why or why not?

Geological Features of Mercury Mercury's crater-covered surface looks so much like the Moon's that it's often difficult to tell them apart in surface photos. Nevertheless, these two worlds have a few important differences.

In many places, Mercury's craters are less crowded together than the craters in the most ancient regions of the Moon, suggesting that molten lava later covered up some of the craters that formed on Mercury during the heavy bombardment (Figure 7.20a). As on the Moon, these lava flows probably occurred when heat from radioactive decay accumulated enough to melt part of the mantle. The largest impact craters, called *basins* (Figure 7.20b), were made by impacts that released enough heat to fill the basins with molten rock. Many of these basins have few craters within them, indicating that they must have formed at a time when the heavy bombardment was already subsiding. However, Mercury does not appear to have any features formed by much later lava flows, like those of the lunar maria.

a A close-up view of Mercury's surface, showing impact craters and smooth regions where lava apparently covered up craters.

b The Rembrandt Basin, a large impact crater on Mercury.

c The light-colored "hollows" on this crater floor (shown with colors enhanced) are thought to have formed as easy-to-vaporize materials escaped over millions of years, causing the rock to crumble and make hollowed-out pits.

▲ **FIGURE 7.20**

MESSENGER images of geological features on Mercury.

Although there has been no more volcanism on Mercury for billions of years, its surface still displays one odd form of geological activity: Some crater floors appear to be releasing easily vaporized materials from the rock, causing the rock to crumble and make pits nicknamed "hollows" (see Figure 7.20c). The release of the vaporized gases leaves behind a light-colored coating, whose composition remains unknown. Spacecraft observations (by *MESSENGER*) also show evidence of water ice in permanently shadowed craters near Mercury's poles. As in polar craters on the moon, the ice probably came from impacts of comets.

Mercury's most surprising feature is a set of tremendous cliffs that appear to be distributed all over the planet. These cliffs have vertical faces up to 3 or more kilometers high and typically run for hundreds of kilometers across the surface. They probably formed when tectonic forces compressed the crust, causing the surface to crumple. Because crumpling would have shrunk the portions of the surface it affected, Mercury as a whole could not have stayed the same size unless other parts of the surface expanded. However, we find no evidence of large-scale "stretch marks" on Mercury. Can it be that the whole planet simply shrank?

Apparently so. Recall that in addition to being larger than the Moon, Mercury also has a surprisingly large iron core. Mercury therefore gained and retained more internal heat than the Moon, and this heat caused Mercury's core to swell in size. Later, as the core cooled, it contracted by perhaps as much as 20 kilometers in radius (Figure 7.21). The mantle and lithosphere must have contracted along with the core, generating the tectonic stresses that created the great cliffs. The contraction probably also closed off any remaining volcanic vents, ending Mercury's period of volcanism.

The planet Mercury appears to have shrunk long ago, leaving behind long, steep cliffs.

Mercury's core and mantle shrank . . .

Some portions of the crust were forced to slide under others.

Today we see long, steep cliffs created by this crustal movement.

Not to scale!

. . . causing Mercury's crust to contract.

a This diagram shows how Mercury's cliffs probably formed as the core shrank and the surface crumpled.

b This cliff extends about 100 kilometers in length, and its vertical face is as much as 2 kilometers tall. (Photo from *Mariner 10*.)

▲ **FIGURE 7.21**

Long cliffs on Mercury offer evidence that the entire planet shrank early in its history, perhaps by as much as 20 kilometers in radius.

7.3 Mars: A Victim of Planetary Freeze-Drying

Based on its size (see Figure 7.1), we expect Mars to be more geologically active than the Moon or Mercury but less active than Earth or Venus. Observations confirm this basic picture, though Mars's greater distance from the Sun—about 50% farther than Earth—has also played a role in its geological history.

Seasons on Mars

Here, Mars is farther from the Sun and moving more slowly in its orbit.

Here, Mars is closer to the Sun and moving faster in its orbit.

The northern hemisphere summer is long and cool . . .

. . . and the southern hemisphere winter is long and frigid.

The northern hemisphere winter is brief and mild . . .

. . . and the southern hemisphere summer is brief and warm.

▲ **FIGURE 7.22**

The ellipticity of Mars's orbit makes seasons more extreme (warmer summers and colder winters) in the southern hemisphere than in the northern hemisphere.

Mars bears many superficial similarities to Earth. Surface views might easily be mistaken for deserts or volcanic plains on Earth (see Figure 6.6), the Martian day is less than an hour longer than an Earth day, and Mars has polar caps that resemble Earth's, although they contain frozen carbon dioxide in addition to water ice. Mars even has Earth-like seasons as a result of having a similar axis tilt, though its more elliptical orbit puts it significantly closer to the Sun during southern hemisphere summer (and farther from the Sun during southern hemisphere winter), giving its southern hemisphere more extreme seasons (Figure 7.22). In fact, winds associated with seasonal changes sometimes lead to global dust storms that can change the appearance of Martian surface features in telescopic views from Earth. Such changes fooled astronomers of the past into thinking they were seeing seasonal changes in vegetation.

These similarities between Earth and Mars have long made the idea of life on Mars a staple of science fiction, but there are also very important differences. The Martian atmosphere is so thin that the atmospheric pressure is less than 1% of that on the surface of Earth; as a result, you could not survive without a spacesuit. The thin atmosphere also means a weak greenhouse effect, even though carbon dioxide is the main component of the atmosphere. This fact, combined with Mars's distance from the Sun, gives it a global average temperature of about −50°C (−58°F). The lack of oxygen means that Mars lacks an ozone layer, so much of the Sun's damaging ultraviolet radiation passes unhindered to the surface.

All in all, surface conditions on Mars today make it seem utterly inhospitable to life. However, careful study of Martian geology offers evidence that Mars had a warmer and wetter past. If so, it might have had conditions under which life could have arisen, and it's conceivable that such life could still survive under the surface. The search for past or present life is a major reason why we have sent more spacecraft to Mars than to any other planet.

extraordinary claims — Martians!

Have you ever wondered why people often speak of Martians but rarely of, say, Venusians or Jupiterians? The answer revolves around the extraordinary claim that Mars is home to an advanced civilization. The story begins with observations of Mars made in the late 18th century by brother and sister astronomers William and Caroline Herschel (best known for discovering the planet Uranus), who discovered superficial similarities with Earth that include similar axis tilt, day length, ice caps, and seasonal changes. Taking these resemblances to an unwarranted extreme, by 1784 William Herschel claimed Mars was populated by "inhabitants" who enjoyed circumstances "in many ways similar to our own."

The hypothetical Martians got a bigger break about a century later. In 1879, Italian astronomer Giovanni Schiaparelli reported seeing a network of linear features on Mars through his telescope. He named these features *canali*, by which he meant the Italian word for "channels," but it was frequently translated as "canals." Motivated by what sounded like evidence of intelligent life, wealthy American astronomer Percival Lowell built an observatory (still operating in Flagstaff, Arizona) for the study of Mars. He published his first maps of the canals barely a year later, and eventually mapped almost 200 canals. Besides claiming them to be the work of an advanced civilization, he also claimed they were needed to transport water from the polar caps to drying cities.

Lowell's claims generated great public interest, but his fellow scientists were far more skeptical. They did not see the canals through their own telescopes, and pointed out that Lowell's straight-line canals made no sense, because real canals would follow natural contours of topography (for example, to go around mountains). Nevertheless, much of the public didn't let go of the Martians until 1965, when NASA's *Mariner 4* spacecraft flew past Mars and sent back photos of a barren, cratered surface.

Even then, not everyone gave up. In the late 1970s, NASA's *Viking* orbiters snapped tens of thousands of photographs of Mars, and among them were a few that looked like artifacts of a civilization, including one that resembled a human face. The "face on Mars" became a cottage industry for those who still wished to believe in Martians, but higher-resolution images from later missions confirmed what every scientist already knew: The face and other supposed artifacts of civilization were nothing more than plays of light and shadow, along with the human tendency to see patterns where none exist. In the end, visions of Martian civilization proved to be no more real than the shapes that children see in clouds, or the patterns among stars that led our ancestors to see the mythical gods in the constellations.

Verdict: Rejected.

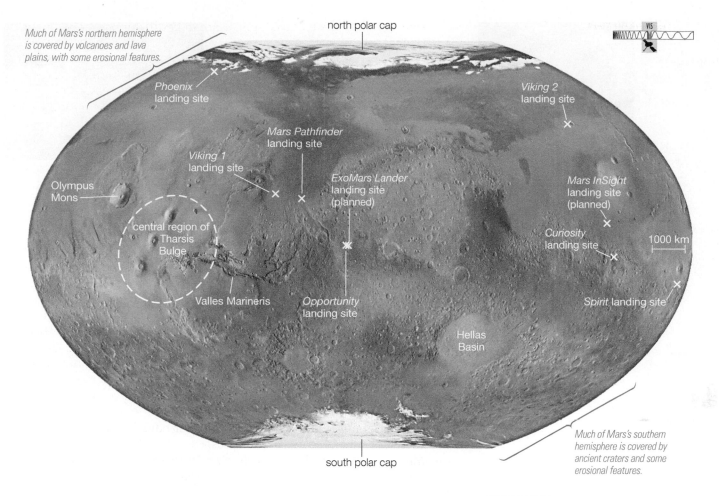

Much of Mars's northern hemisphere is covered by volcanoes and lava plains, with some erosional features.

north polar cap

VIS

Phoenix landing site

Viking 2 landing site

Mars Pathfinder landing site

Viking 1 landing site

ExoMars Lander landing site (planned)

Mars InSight landing site (planned)

Olympus Mons

central region of Tharsis Bulge

Curiosity landing site

1000 km

Valles Marineris

Opportunity landing site

Spirit landing site

Hellas Basin

Much of Mars's southern hemisphere is covered by ancient craters and some erosional features.

south polar cap

▲ **FIGURE 7.23**

This image showing the full surface of Mars is a composite made by combining more than 1000 images with more than 200 million altitude measurements from the *Mars Global Surveyor* mission. Several key geological features are labeled, and landing sites of Mars missions are marked. On the same scale, a map of Earth would be about twice as tall and twice as wide, giving it four times the area; however, because Earth's surface is about three-quarters ocean, both planets have nearly the same land area.

◆ What geological features tell us that water once flowed on Mars?

There are no lakes, rivers, or even puddles of liquid water on the surface of Mars today. We know this not only because we've photographed most of the surface in fairly high resolution but also because the surface conditions do not allow it. In most places and at most times, Mars is so cold that any liquid water would immediately freeze into ice. Even when the temperature rises above freezing, as it often does at midday near the equator, the air pressure is so low that liquid water would quickly evaporate. In other words, liquid water is *unstable* on Mars today: If you put on a spacesuit and took a cup of water outside your pressurized spaceship, the water would rapidly either freeze or boil away (or some combination of both). Nevertheless, Mars offers ample geological evidence of past water flows.

The Geology of Mars Figure 7.23 shows a map of the full surface of Mars. Aside from the polar caps, the most striking feature is the dramatic difference in terrain around different parts of the planet. Much of the southern hemisphere has relatively high elevation and is scarred by numerous large impact craters, including the large crater known as the Hellas Basin. In contrast, the northern plains show few impact craters and tend to be below the average Martian surface level. The differences in crater crowding tell us that the southern highlands are a much older

▲ FIGURE 7.24

Olympus Mons, photographed from orbit; note the tall cliff around its rim and the central volcanic crater from which lava erupted. The inset shows a 3-D perspective on this immense volcano.

▲ FIGURE 7.25

Valles Marineris is a huge valley on Mars created in part by tectonic stresses. The inset shows a perspective view looking north across the center of the canyon, obtained by *Mars Express*.

surface than the northern plains, which must have had their early craters erased by other geological processes.

Mars has clearly had active volcanism in the past, as it is dotted with towering volcanoes. One, called *Olympus Mons* (Figure 7.24), is the tallest known mountain in the solar system. Its peak stands about 26 kilometers above the average Martian surface level—about three times as high as Mount Everest stands above sea level on Earth—and its base is large enough to cover an area the size of Arizona. Much of the base is rimmed by a cliff that in places is 6 kilometers high. Several other large volcanoes are also found on or near the continent-size *Tharsis Bulge*, which was probably created by a long-lived plume of rising mantle material that pushed the surface upward and provided the molten rock for the eruptions that built the giant volcanoes.

> Mars has had active volcanism in the past, and its surface is dotted with numerous large volcanoes.

Mars also has tectonic features, of which the most prominent is a long, deep system of valleys called *Valles Marineris* (Figure 7.25). Valles Marineris extends almost a fifth of the way along the planet's equator. It is as long as the United States is wide and almost four times as deep as Earth's Grand Canyon. No one knows exactly how Valles Marineris formed, but its location suggests a link to the Tharsis Bulge. Perhaps it formed because of tectonic stresses accompanying the uplift of material that created Tharsis, cracking the surface and leaving the tall cliff walls of the valleys.

We have not witnessed any recent volcanic or tectonic activity on Mars, but Mars is not yet "geologically dead" like the Moon or Mercury. It probably still retains underground volcanic heat, and it is possible that some of its volcanoes may erupt again someday. Nevertheless, because of Mars's relatively small size, its interior is presumably cooling and its lithosphere thickening, and its era of geological activity will likely come to an end within a few billion years.

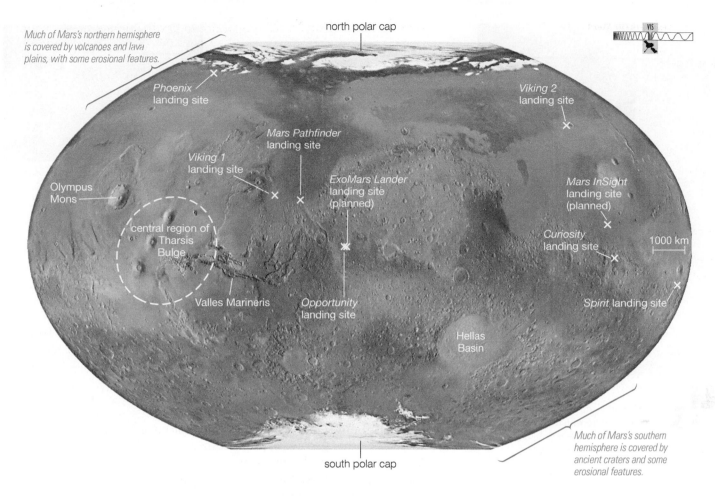

Much of Mars's northern hemisphere is covered by volcanoes and lava plains, with some erosional features.

north polar cap

VIS

Phoenix landing site

Viking 2 landing site

Mars Pathfinder landing site

Viking 1 landing site

ExoMars Lander landing site (planned)

Mars InSight landing site (planned)

Olympus Mons

central region of Tharsis Bulge

Curiosity landing site

1000 km

Valles Marineris

Opportunity landing site

Spirit landing site

Hellas Basin

south polar cap

Much of Mars's southern hemisphere is covered by ancient craters and some erosional features.

▲ **FIGURE 7.23**
This image showing the full surface of Mars is a composite made by combining more than 1000 images with more than 200 million altitude measurements from the *Mars Global Surveyor* mission. Several key geological features are labeled, and landing sites of Mars missions are marked. On the same scale, a map of Earth would be about twice as tall and twice as wide, giving it four times the area; however, because Earth's surface is about three-quarters ocean, both planets have nearly the same land area.

◆ What geological features tell us that water once flowed on Mars?

There are no lakes, rivers, or even puddles of liquid water on the surface of Mars today. We know this not only because we've photographed most of the surface in fairly high resolution but also because the surface conditions do not allow it. In most places and at most times, Mars is so cold that any liquid water would immediately freeze into ice. Even when the temperature rises above freezing, as it often does at midday near the equator, the air pressure is so low that liquid water would quickly evaporate. In other words, liquid water is *unstable* on Mars today: If you put on a spacesuit and took a cup of water outside your pressurized spaceship, the water would rapidly either freeze or boil away (or some combination of both). Nevertheless, Mars offers ample geological evidence of past water flows.

The Geology of Mars   Figure 7.23 shows a map of the full surface of Mars. Aside from the polar caps, the most striking feature is the dramatic difference in terrain around different parts of the planet. Much of the southern hemisphere has relatively high elevation and is scarred by numerous large impact craters, including the large crater known as the Hellas Basin. In contrast, the northern plains show few impact craters and tend to be below the average Martian surface level. The differences in crater crowding tell us that the southern highlands are a much older

▲ **FIGURE 7.24**

Olympus Mons, photographed from orbit; note the tall cliff around its rim and the central volcanic crater from which lava erupted. The inset shows a 3-D perspective on this immense volcano.

50 km

20 km

200 km

▲ **FIGURE 7.25**

Valles Marineris is a huge valley on Mars created in part by tectonic stresses. The inset shows a perspective view looking north across the center of the canyon, obtained by *Mars Express*.

surface than the northern plains, which must have had their early craters erased by other geological processes.

Mars has clearly had active volcanism in the past, as it is dotted with towering volcanoes. One, called *Olympus Mons* (Figure 7.24), is the tallest known mountain in the solar system. Its peak stands about 26 kilometers above the average Martian surface level—about three times as high as Mount Everest stands above sea level on Earth—and its base is large enough to cover an area the size of Arizona. Much of the base is rimmed by a cliff that in places is 6 kilometers high. Several other large volcanoes are also found on or near the continent-size *Tharsis Bulge*, which was probably created by a long-lived plume of rising mantle material that pushed the surface upward and provided the molten rock for the eruptions that built the giant volcanoes.

> Mars has had active volcanism in the past, and its surface is dotted with numerous large volcanoes.

Mars also has tectonic features, of which the most prominent is a long, deep system of valleys called *Valles Marineris* (Figure 7.25). Valles Marineris extends almost a fifth of the way along the planet's equator. It is as long as the United States is wide and almost four times as deep as Earth's Grand Canyon. No one knows exactly how Valles Marineris formed, but its location suggests a link to the Tharsis Bulge. Perhaps it formed because of tectonic stresses accompanying the uplift of material that created Tharsis, cracking the surface and leaving the tall cliff walls of the valleys.

We have not witnessed any recent volcanic or tectonic activity on Mars, but Mars is not yet "geologically dead" like the Moon or Mercury. It probably still retains underground volcanic heat, and it is possible that some of its volcanoes may erupt again someday. Nevertheless, because of Mars's relatively small size, its interior is presumably cooling and its lithosphere thickening, and its era of geological activity will likely come to an end within a few billion years.

Ancient Water Flows Strong evidence that Mars had flowing water in the distant past comes from both orbital and surface studies. For example, Figure 7.26 shows a dry riverbed that was almost certainly carved by running water, although we cannot yet say whether the water came

Dried-up riverbeds and other geological features show that water flowed on Mars in the distant past.

from runoff after rainfall, from erosion by water-rich debris flows, or from an underground source. Regardless of the specific mechanism, the water apparently stopped flowing long ago. Notice that a few impact craters lie on top of the channels. Based on counts of impact craters in and near the river channels, it must have been at least 2–3 billion years since water last flowed through them.

Other orbital evidence also argues for rain and surface water in the Martian past. Figure 7.27a shows a broad region of the ancient, heavily cratered southern highlands. Notice the indistinct rims of many large craters and the relative lack of small craters. Both facts argue for ancient rainfall, which would have eroded crater rims and erased small craters altogether. Figure 7.27b shows a three-dimensional perspective of the surface that suggests water once flowed between two ancient crater lakes. Figure 7.27c shows what looks like a river delta where water flowed into an ancient crater; spectra indicate clay minerals on the crater floor, which were probably deposited by sediments flowing down the river. Thousands of other orbital images show additional evidence of water erosion.

Surface studies further strengthen the case for past water. In 2004, the robotic rovers *Spirit* and *Opportunity* landed on nearly opposite sides of Mars (see Figure 7.23). The twin rovers carried cameras, instruments to identify rock composition, and a grinder to expose fresh rock for analysis. The rovers long outlasted their design lifetime of 3 months, with *Opportunity* still going as this book was being written, more than 12 years

▲ **FIGURE 7.26**

This photo, taken by the *Mars Express* orbiter, shows what appears to be a dried-up meandering riverbed, now filled with windblown dust. The small impact craters scattered about the site allow scientists to estimate how long ago the water flowed.

▼ **FIGURE 7.27**

More evidence of past water on Mars.

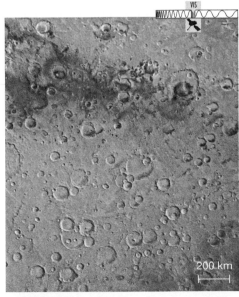

a This photo shows a broad region of the southern highlands on Mars. The eroded rims of large craters and the relative lack of small craters suggest erosion by rainfall.

landing site of *Spirit* rover

100 km

b This computer-generated perspective view shows how a Martian valley forms a natural passage between two possible ancient lakes (shaded blue). Vertical relief is exaggerated 14 times to reveal the topography.

portion of crater wall

river delta deposits

1 km

c Combined visible/infrared image of an ancient river delta that formed where water flowing down a valley emptied into a lake filling a large crater (portions of the crater wall are identified). Clay minerals are identified in green.

▲ FIGURE 7.38

This photo from one of the former Soviet Union's *Venera* landers shows Venus's surface; part of the lander is in the foreground, with sky in the background. Many volcanic rocks are visible, hardly affected by erosion despite their presumed age of about 750 million years (the age of the entire surface).

10 cm

erosion (Figure 7.38). We can trace the lack of erosion on Venus to two facts. First, Venus is far too hot for any type of rain or snow on its surface. Second, Venus has virtually no wind or weather because its slow rotation—once every 243 days—means that its atmosphere barely stirs the surface.

The Absence of Plate Tectonics   We can easily explain the lack of erosion on Venus, but another "missing feature" of its geology is more surprising: Venus shows no evidence of Earth-like plate tectonics. As we'll discuss in the next section, plate tectonics shapes nearly all of Earth's major geological features, including mid-ocean ridges, deep ocean trenches, and long mountain ranges. Venus lacks any similar features.

Instead, Venus shows evidence of a very different type of global geological change. On Earth, plate tectonics resculpts the surface gradually, so different regions have different ages. In contrast, Venus's relatively few impact craters are distributed fairly uniformly over the entire planet, suggesting that the surface is about the same age everywhere. Crater counts suggest a surface age of about 750 million years, leading us to conclude that the entire surface was somehow "repaved" at that time.

The absence of present-day plate tectonics on Venus is a major mystery, though scientists have a few ideas that might explain it. Earth's lithosphere was broken into plates by forces due to the underlying mantle convection. The lack of plate tectonics on Venus therefore suggests either that it has weaker mantle convection or that its lithosphere resists fracturing. The first possi-

Venus's lack of Earth-like plate tectonics poses a scientific mystery, but may arise because Venus has a thicker and stronger lithosphere than Earth.

bility seems unlikely, because Venus's similarity to Earth in size and density lead us to expect it to have a similar level of mantle convection. Most scientists therefore suspect that Venus's lithosphere resists fracturing into plates because it is thicker and stronger than Earth's.

Even if a thicker and stronger lithosphere explains the lack of plate tectonics on Venus, we are still left with the question of why the lithospheres of Venus and Earth should differ. One possible answer invokes Venus's high surface temperature. Venus is so hot that any water in its crust and mantle has probably been baked out over time. Water tends to soften and lubricate rock, so its loss would have thickened and strengthened Venus's lithosphere. If this hypothesis is correct, then Venus might have had plate tectonics if it had not become so hot in the first place.

◆ Why is Venus so hot?

It's tempting to attribute Venus's high surface temperature solely to the fact that it is closer than Earth to the Sun, but Venus's clouds reflect so much sunlight back to space that its surface actually absorbs less sunlight than Earth. As a result, Venus would be quite cold without its strong greenhouse effect: Calculations show that its average surface temperature would be a frigid −40°C (−40°F) in that case, while its actual temperature is about 470°C (880°F). The real question is why Venus has such a strong greenhouse effect.

The simple answer is that Venus has a huge amount of carbon dioxide in its atmosphere—nearly 200,000 times as much as in Earth's atmosphere. However, a deeper question still remains. Given their similar sizes and compositions, we expect Venus and

Venus's thick carbon dioxide atmosphere creates the extremely strong greenhouse effect that makes Venus so hot.

Earth to have had similar levels of volcanic outgassing, and the released gas ought to have had about the same composition on both worlds. Why, then, is Venus's atmosphere so different from Earth's?

The Fate of Outgassed Water and Carbon Dioxide We expect that huge amounts of water and carbon dioxide should have been outgassed into the atmospheres of both Venus and Earth. Venus's atmosphere does indeed have huge amounts of carbon dioxide, but it has virtually no water. Earth's atmosphere has very little of either gas. We conclude that Venus must have somehow lost its outgassed water, while Earth has lost both water vapor and carbon dioxide. But where did these gases go?

We can easily account for both missing gases on Earth. The huge amount of water vapor released into our atmosphere condensed into rain, forming our oceans. In other words, the water is still here, but mostly in liquid rather than gaseous form. The huge amount of carbon dioxide released into our atmosphere is also still here, but in solid form:

Earth has as much carbon dioxide as Venus, but it is mostly locked away in rocks rather than in our atmosphere.

Carbon dioxide dissolves in water, where it can undergo chemical reactions to make **carbonate rocks** (rocks rich in carbon and oxygen) such as limestone. Earth has about 170,000 times as much carbon dioxide locked up in rocks as in its atmosphere—which means that Earth does indeed have almost as much total carbon dioxide as Venus. Of course, the fact that Earth's carbon dioxide is mostly in rocks rather than in the atmosphere makes all the difference in the world: If this carbon dioxide were in our atmosphere, our planet would be nearly as hot as Venus and certainly uninhabitable.

We are left with the question of what happened to Venus's water. Venus has no oceans and little atmospheric water, and as noted earlier, any water in its crust and mantle was probably baked out long ago. This absence of water explains why Venus retains so much carbon dioxide in its atmosphere: Without oceans, carbon dioxide cannot

Venus retains carbon dioxide in its atmosphere because it lacks oceans to dissolve the carbon dioxide and lock it away in rock.

dissolve or become locked away in carbonate rocks. If it is true that a huge amount of water was outgassed on Venus, the water molecules have somehow disappeared.

The leading hypothesis for the disappearance of Venus's water invokes one of the same processes thought to have removed water from Mars. Ultraviolet light from the Sun breaks apart water molecules in Venus's atmosphere. The hydrogen atoms then escape to space, ensuring that the water molecules can never re-form. The oxygen from the water molecules is lost to a combination of chemical reactions with surface rocks and stripping by the solar wind; Venus's lack of magnetic field leaves its atmosphere vulnerable to the solar wind.

Acting over billions of years, the breakdown of water molecules and the escape of hydrogen can easily explain the loss of an ocean's worth of water from Venus—as long as the water was in the atmosphere rather than in liquid oceans. Our quest to understand Venus's high temperature thereby leads to one more question: Why didn't Venus end up with oceans like Earth, which would have prevented its water from being lost to space?

The Runaway Greenhouse Effect To understand why Venus does not have oceans, let's consider what would happen if we could magically move Earth to the orbit of Venus (Figure 7.39).

If Earth moved to Venus's orbit

More intense sunlight . . .

. . . would raise surface temperature by about 30°C.

Higher temperature increases evaporation, and warmer air holds more water vapor.

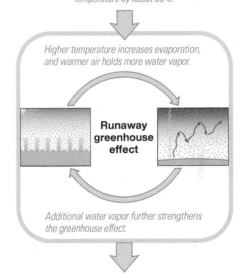

Runaway greenhouse effect

Additional water vapor further strengthens the greenhouse effect.

Result: Oceans evaporate and carbonate rocks decompose, releasing CO$_2$ . . .

. . . making Earth hotter than Venus.

▲ **FIGURE 7.39**
This diagram shows how, if Earth were placed at Venus's distance from the Sun, the runaway greenhouse effect would cause the oceans to evaporate completely.

The greater intensity of sunlight would almost immediately raise Earth's global average temperature by about 30°C, from its current 15°C to about 45°C (113°F). Although this is still well below the boiling point of water, the higher temperature would lead to increased evaporation of water from the oceans. The higher temperature would also allow the atmosphere to hold more water vapor before the vapor condensed to make rain. The combination of more evaporation and greater atmospheric capacity for water vapor would substantially increase the total amount of water vapor in Earth's atmosphere. Now, remember that water vapor, like carbon dioxide, is a greenhouse gas. The added water vapor would therefore strengthen the greenhouse effect, driving temperatures a little higher. The higher temperatures, in turn, would lead to even more ocean evaporation and more water vapor in the atmosphere—strengthening the greenhouse effect even further. In other words, we'd have a positive feedback loop in which each little bit of additional water vapor in the atmosphere would mean higher temperature and even more water vapor. The process would career rapidly out of control as a **runaway greenhouse effect.**

The runaway process would cause Earth to heat up until the oceans completely evaporated and the carbonate rocks released all their carbon dioxide back into the atmosphere. By the time the process was complete, temperatures on our "moved Earth" would be even higher than they are on Venus today, thanks to the combined greenhouse effects of carbon dioxide and water vapor in the atmosphere. The water vapor would then gradually disappear, as ultraviolet light broke water molecules apart and the hydrogen escaped to space. In short, moving Earth to Venus's orbit would essentially turn our planet into another Venus.

We have arrived at a simple explanation of why Venus is so much hotter than Earth. Even though Venus is only about 30% closer to the Sun than Earth, this difference was enough to be critical. On Earth, it was cool enough for water to rain down to make oceans. The oceans then dissolved carbon dioxide and chemical reactions locked it away in carbonate rocks, leaving our atmosphere with only enough greenhouse gases to make our planet pleasantly warm. On Venus, the greater intensity of sunlight made it just enough warmer that oceans either never formed or soon evaporated, leaving Venus with a thick atmosphere full of greenhouse gases.

Venus is too close to the Sun to have liquid water oceans. Without water to dissolve carbon dioxide gas, Venus was doomed to its runaway greenhouse effect.

The next time you see Venus shining brightly as the morning or evening "star," consider the radically different path it has taken from that taken by Earth—and thank your lucky star. If Earth had formed a bit closer to the Sun or if the Sun had been slightly hotter, our planet might have suffered the same greenhouse-baked fate.

think about it We've seen that moving Earth to Venus's orbit would cause our planet to become Venus-like. If we could somehow move Venus to Earth's orbit, would it become Earth-like? Why or why not?

7.5 Earth as a Living Planet

Now that we have discussed general features of terrestrial planet geology and atmospheres, along with a brief overview of the histories of the other terrestrial worlds, we are ready to explore our own planet Earth in more detail. In this section, we'll discuss the features of Earth that make it so hospitable to life, the ways in which human activity may be affecting this hospitability, and general lessons about what may make some worlds habitable and others not.

◆ What unique features of Earth are important for life?

If you think about all we've learned about the terrestrial worlds, you can probably identify a number of features that are unique to Earth. Four unique features turn out to be particularly important to life on Earth:

- **Surface liquid water:** Earth has a surface temperature and atmospheric pressure that allow liquid water to be stable on its surface.
- **Atmospheric oxygen:** Earth has atmospheric oxygen and an ozone layer.
- **Plate tectonics:** Earth's surface is shaped largely by this distinctive type of tectonics.
- **Climate stability:** Earth's climate has remained stable enough for liquid water to persist for billions of years.

Our Unique Oceans and Atmosphere The first and second items in our list—abundant liquid water and atmospheric oxygen—are clearly important to our existence. Life as we know it requires water [Section 19.1], and animal life requires oxygen. We have already explained the origin of Earth's water: Water vapor outgassed from volcanoes rained down on the surface to make the oceans and neither froze nor evaporated thanks to our moderate greenhouse effect and distance from the Sun. But where did the oxygen in our atmosphere come from?

Oxygen (O_2) is not a product of volcanic outgassing. In fact, no geological process can explain how oxygen came to make up such a large fraction (21%) of Earth's atmosphere. Moreover, oxygen is a highly reactive gas that would disappear from the atmosphere in just a few million years if it were not continuously resupplied. Fire, rust, and the discoloration of freshly cut fruits and vegetables are everyday examples of chemical reactions that remove oxygen from the atmosphere. Similar reactions between oxygen and surface materials give rise to the reddish appearance of much of Earth's rock and clay. So we must explain not only how oxygen got into Earth's atmosphere in the first place, but also how the amount of oxygen remains relatively steady even though chemical reactions remove it rapidly from the atmosphere.

The answer to the oxygen mystery is life itself (Figure 7.40). Plants and many microorganisms release oxygen through photosynthesis. Photosynthesis takes in CO_2 and releases O_2 (while the carbon becomes incorporated into living tissues).

Without life, Earth would lack atmospheric oxygen and an ozone layer. Virtually all Earth's oxygen was originally released into the atmosphere by photosynthetic life. Today, photosynthetic organisms return oxygen to the atmosphere in approximate balance with the rate at which animals and chemical reactions consume it, which is why the oxygen concentration remains relatively steady. This oxygen is also what makes possible Earth's protective ozone layer, since ozone (O_3) is produced from ordinary oxygen (O_2).

think about it Suppose that, somehow, all photosynthetic life (such as plants) died out. What would happen to the oxygen in our atmosphere? Could animals, including us, still survive?

Photosynthetic life in oceans creates O_2.

O_2 + UV creates O_3 (ozone).

O_3 layer makes surface safe for living things.

Photosynthetic life on land adds O_2.

▲ **FIGURE 7.40**
The origin of oxygen and ozone in Earth's atmosphere can be traced to life.

▲ FIGURE 7.45

Average global temperatures from 1880 through 2015. Notice the clear global warming trend of the past few decades. (Data from the National Climate Data Center.)

increased CO_2 concentration strengthens the greenhouse effect and warms the planet back up.

We can now see why plate tectonics is so intimately connected to our existence. Plate tectonics is a crucial part of the CO_2 cycle; without plate tectonics, Earth would lack a mechanism for self-regulating its climate, and Earth might then have undergone changes as dramatic as those that occurred on Venus and Mars. Note, however, that the role of plate tectonics also means that this climate regulation occurs only on long time scales of hundreds of thousands to millions of years. It therefore has no effect on short-term changes, such as those we will discuss next.

◆ How is human activity changing our planet?

Our planet may regulate its own climate quite effectively over long time scales, but fossil and geological evidence tells us that substantial and rapid swings in global climate can occur on shorter ones. For example, Earth cycles in and out of ice ages on geologically short time scales of tens of thousands of years, and in some cases the geological evidence indicates that the climate warmed several degrees Celsius in just decades. Past climate changes have obviously been due to natural causes, but Earth is now undergoing climate change for a new reason: Human activity is rapidly increasing the atmospheric concentration of greenhouse gases, particularly of carbon dioxide. Effects of this increase in greenhouse gas concentration are apparent already: Global average temperatures have risen by about 0.85°C (1.5°F) in the past century (Figure 7.45). This **global warming** is one of the most important issues of our time.

Global Warming Global warming has been a hot political issue, both because some people debate its cause and because efforts to slow or stop the warming would require finding new energy sources and making other changes that could dramatically affect the world's economy. However, a major research effort has gradually added to our understanding of the potential threat, particularly in the past two decades. The case linking global warming with human activity rests on three basic facts:

Human activity is rapidly increasing the atmospheric concentrations of greenhouse gases, causing the global average temperature to rise.

1. The greenhouse effect is a simple and well-understood scientific model. We can be confident in our understanding of it because it so successfully explains the observed surface temperatures of other planets. Given this basic model, there is no doubt that a rising concentration of greenhouse gases would make our planet warm up more than it would otherwise; the only debate is about how soon and how much.

2. Human activity such as the burning of fossil fuels is clearly increasing the amounts of greenhouse gases in the atmosphere. Observations show that the atmospheric concentration of carbon dioxide is now about 40% higher than it was before the industrial revolution began or at any other time during the past million years, and it is continuing to rise rapidly (Figure 7.46). We can be confident that the rise is a result of human activity, because the atmosphere is becoming enriched in molecules of CO_2 carrying the distinct ratio of isotopes present in fossil fuels.

3. Climate models that ignore human activity fail to match the observed rise in global temperatures. In contrast, climate models that

common misconceptions

The Greenhouse Effect Is Bad

The greenhouse effect is often in the news, usually in discussions about environmental problems, but in itself the greenhouse effect is not a bad thing. In fact, we could not exist without it, since it is responsible for keeping our planet warm enough for liquid water to flow in the oceans and on the surface. The "no greenhouse" temperature of Earth is well below freezing. Why, then, is the greenhouse effect discussed as an environmental problem? The reason is that human activity is adding more greenhouse gases to the atmosphere—and scientists agree that the additional gases are changing Earth's climate. While the greenhouse effect makes Earth livable, it is also responsible for the searing 470°C temperature of Venus—proving that it's possible to have too much of a good thing.

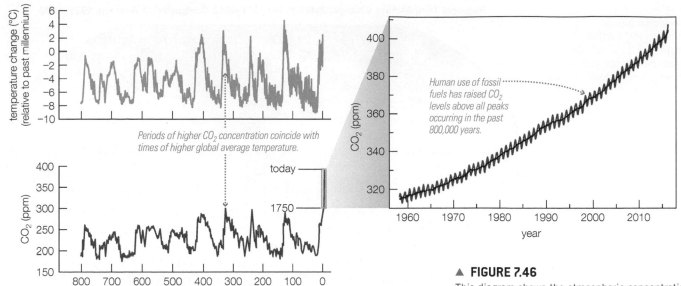

▲ **FIGURE 7.46**

This diagram shows the atmospheric concentration of carbon dioxide and global average temperature over the past 800,000 years. Data for the past few decades come from direct measurements; earlier data come from studies of air bubbles trapped in Antarctic ice (ice core samples). The CO_2 concentration is measured in parts per million (ppm), which is the number of CO_2 molecules among every 1 million air molecules.

include the enhanced greenhouse effect from human production of greenhouse gases match the observed temperature trend quite well (Figure 7.47), providing additional support for the idea that global warming results from human activity.

These facts offer convincing evidence that we humans are now tinkering with the climate in a way that may cause major changes not just in the distant future, but in our own lifetimes. The same models that convince scientists of the reality of human-induced global warming tell us that if current trends in the greenhouse gas concentration continue—that is, if we do nothing to slow our emissions of carbon dioxide and other greenhouse gases—the warming trend will continue to accelerate. By the end of this century, the global average temperature would be 2°C–5°C (4°F–10°F) higher than it is now, giving our children and grandchildren the warmest climate that any generation of *Homo sapiens* has ever experienced.

think about it Based on the rate of rise in the CO_2 concentration shown in Figure 7.46, how long will it be until we reach a doubling of the pre-industrial-age concentration of 280 ppm? Discuss the implications of your answer.

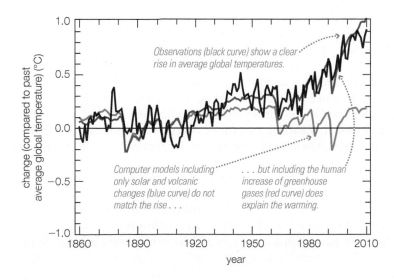

◄ **FIGURE 7.47**

This graph compares observed temperature changes (black curve) with the predictions of climate models that include only natural factors, such as changes in the brightness of the Sun and effects of volcanoes (blue curve) and models that also include the human contribution to increasing greenhouse gas concentration (red curve). Only the red curve matches the observations well. (The red and blue model curves are averages of many scientists' independent models of global warming, which generally agree with each other within 0.1°C–0.2°C.)

This map shows how regional average temperatures for the period 2011–2015 compare to the averages from 1951–1980. Notice the large regional differences, and the particularly large warming in north polar regions.

< −0.2   −0.2 to 0.2   0.2 to 0.5   0.5 to 1.0   1.0 to 2.0   > 2.0

temperature difference (°C)

Consequences of Global Warming A temperature increase of a few degrees might not sound so bad, but small changes in *average* temperature can lead to much more dramatic changes in climate patterns. Figure 7.48 compares recent regional temperatures to the averages from 1951–1980. Notice that almost all regions of the world are now significantly warmer than they were a few decades ago, but some regions warmed much more than others. This is what we mean by "climate change"—the idea that regional effects can be very different from the global average. Models suggest that regional climate changes will be further amplified as the global average temperature continues to increase.

The consequences of global warming are not simply hotter weather. Changes in rainfall patterns are also expected; for example, many scientists suspect that recent drought and wildfires in the United States and Canada are a result of the changing climate, in which case we can expect these regions to experience more periods of prolonged drought and more wildfires in the future. The warmer weather is also causing spring to arrive earlier, which can further contribute to drier summers and wildfire risk. Moreover, the general warming of the atmosphere means more total energy in the atmosphere and increased evaporation from the oceans, leading to more intense storms—perhaps including more frequent or more severe hurricanes. The same phenomena can also increase the severity of winter storms, leading to the somewhat surprising fact that global warming can cause more severe winter blizzards, a pattern that we may already be seeing in recent winters in the eastern United States.

Global warming is also expected to cause a rise in sea level. The oceans expand very slightly as they warm, an effect that has already caused sea level to rise about 20 centimeters in the past century and is expected to cause a rise of another 30 centimeters by about 2100. Melting ice may have a much greater effect. While the melting of ice in the

Arctic Ocean does not alter sea level—it is already floating—melting of landlocked ice does. Recent data suggest a surprisingly rapid change in Greenland's ice sheet, leading some scientists to worry that ice melt could cause sea level to rise as much as several *meters*—enough to flood much of Florida—by the end of this century. The oceans are also suffering in another way. Some of the carbon dioxide released into the atmosphere by human activity (roughly 30% of it) ends up dissolving in the oceans, where it undergoes chemical reactions that make the oceans more acidic. This "ocean acidification" has been tied to the demise of many coral reefs around the world and to less productive fisheries, and even reduces the ability of the oceans to absorb more carbon dioxide.

Figure 7.49 summarizes the evidence for and consequences of global warming. Fortunately, most scientists believe that we still have time to avert the most serious consequences of global warming, provided we dramatically and rapidly curtail our greenhouse gas emissions. The most obvious way to cut back on these emissions is to improve energy efficiency. For example, doubling the average gas mileage of cars would immediately cut automobile-related carbon dioxide emissions in half. Other tactics could include replacing fossil fuels with alternative energy sources—such as biofuel, solar, wind, or nuclear energy—or finding ways to capture and bury the carbon dioxide from the fossil fuels that we still use. The key idea to keep in mind is that global warming is a problem of our own making, and it is therefore up to us to find a way to solve it.

think about it If you were a political leader, how would *you* deal with the threat of global warming?

---

extraordinary claims Human Activity Can Change the Climate

The topic of global warming and associated climate changes is so commonplace in today's news that it's tempting to think of it as a relatively new idea. But the first clear claim that human emissions of carbon dioxide might change the climate dates back to 1896, when Swedish scientist Svante Arrhenius was contemplating possible causes of ice ages, which had recently been identified in the geological record.

The greenhouse effect of gases like carbon dioxide and water vapor had already been discovered, and Arrhenius decided to check whether changes in the carbon dioxide concentration might trigger ice ages. Calculating how a change in carbon dioxide concentration will change the temperature requires complex calculations of the many feedbacks involved. Today scientists do such calculations with detailed computer models, but Arrhenius had only pencil and paper. Nevertheless, after months of tedious calculations, he concluded that a 50% drop in the carbon dioxide concentration would cause Earth's temperature to drop about 5°C—which was indeed enough to bring about an ice age—while doubling it would cause a rise of about 5°C. Moreover, with the help of a colleague, he made an astonishing discovery: Human activities such as the burning of coal were already adding about as much carbon dioxide to the atmosphere each year as volcanoes. This insight led Arrhenius to make an extraordinary claim: Human activity might eventually raise the carbon dioxide concentration enough to cause significant global warming.

Arrhenius was not particularly concerned by his prediction, because he did not think we could add carbon dioxide fast enough for a doubling to occur in less than several centuries. But the rate of carbon dioxide emissions grew rapidly. In 1958, scientist Charles David Keeling began making the measurements shown in Figure 7.46 (the graph is often called the *Keeling curve* in his honor). These measurements, along with measurements of isotope ratios that show the added carbon dioxide comes from human activity, leave no doubt that we are causing a substantial rise in the carbon dioxide concentration.

The only question that remained was whether this increase would really cause global warming, as Arrhenius had predicted. As discussed in the chapter, modern computer models do an excellent job of reproducing past climate, and while there are uncertainties in the precise values, these models generally agree with Arrhenius's prediction that a doubling of the carbon dioxide concentration should cause the global average temperature to rise by a few degrees Celsius. This fact, along with data showing that global warming is already well under way, explain why Arrhenius's extraordinary claim is now well accepted by the vast majority of scientists.

Verdict: Strongly supported.

The Role of Planetary Size

Small Terrestrial Planets

Interior cools rapidly . . .

. . . so that tectonic and volcanic activity cease after a billion years or so. Many ancient craters therefore remain. . . . . . .

Lack of volcanism means little outgassing, and low gravity allows gas to escape more easily; no atmosphere means no erosion.

Large Terrestrial Planets

Warm interior causes mantle convection . . .

. . . leading to ongoing tectonic and volcanic activity; most ancient craters have been erased.

Outgassing produces an atmosphere and strong gravity holds it, so that erosion is possible.

Core may be molten, producing a magnetic field if rotation is fast enough, and a magnetosphere that can shield an atmosphere from the solar wind.

The Role of Distance from the Sun

Planets Close to the Sun

Surface is too hot for rain, snow, or ice, so little erosion occurs.

Sun

High atmospheric temperature allows gas to escape more easily.

Planets at Intermediate Distances from the Sun

Moderate surface temperatures can allow for oceans, rain, snow, and ice, leading to substantial erosion.

Gravity can more easily hold atmospheric gases.

Planets Far from the Sun

Low surface temperatures can allow for ice and snow, but no rain or oceans, limiting erosion.

Atmosphere may exist, but gases can more easily condense to make surface ice.

▲ **FIGURE 7.50**

This illustration shows how a terrestrial world's size and distance from the Sun help determine its geological history and whether it has conditions suitable for life. Earth is habitable because it is large enough and at a suitably moderate distance from the Sun.

◆ What makes a planet habitable?

We have discussed the features of our planet that have made it habitable for a great variety of life, including us. But why is Earth the only terrestrial world that has these features?

Our comparative study of the terrestrial worlds tells us there are two primary answers, both summarized in Figure 7.50. First, Earth is habitable because it is large enough to have remained geologically active since its birth, so that outgassing could release the water and gases that formed our atmosphere and oceans. In addition, the core has remained hot enough that Earth has retained a global magnetic field, which generates a magnetosphere that protects our atmosphere from the solar wind. Second, we are located at a distance from the Sun at which outgassed water vapor was able to

> Earth is habitable because it is large enough to remain geologically active and located at a distance from the Sun where oceans were able to form.

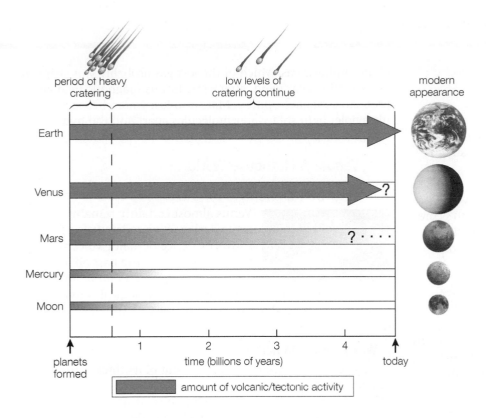

This diagram summarizes the geological histories of the terrestrial worlds. The brackets along the top indicate that impact cratering has affected all worlds similarly. The arrows represent volcanic and tectonic activity. A thicker and darker arrow means more volcanic/tectonic activity, and the arrow length tells us how long this activity persisted. Notice the trend's relationship to planetary size: Earth remains active to this day; Venus has also been active, though we are uncertain whether it remains so; Mars has had an intermediate level of activity and might still have low-level volcanism; Mercury and the Moon have had very little volcanic/tectonic activity. Erosion is not shown, because it has played a significant role only on Earth (ongoing) and on Mars (in the past and at low levels today).

condense and rain down to form oceans, making possible the carbon dioxide cycle that regulates our climate.

Figure 7.51 shows the trends we've seen for the terrestrial planets in our solar system, which should make sense as you examine the role of planetary size. In principle, these lessons mean we can now predict the geological and atmospheric properties of terrestrial worlds around other stars. Only a suitably large terrestrial planet located at an intermediate distance from its star is likely to have conditions under which life could thrive. We will discuss these conditions—along with possibilities for life—further in Chapter 19.

the big picture   Putting Chapter 7 into Perspective

In this chapter, we have explored the histories of the terrestrial worlds. As you think about the details you have learned, keep the following "big picture" ideas in mind:

- The terrestrial worlds all looked much the same when they were born, so their present-day differences are a result of geological processes that occurred in the ensuing 4½ billion years.

- The primary factor in a terrestrial world's geological history is its size: Only a relatively large world can retain internal heat long enough for ongoing geological activity. However, distance from the Sun also plays an important role in determining whether temperatures will allow for liquid water.

- Although distance from the Sun helps determine surface temperature, the strength of the greenhouse effect can play an even bigger role. Humans are currently altering the balance of greenhouse gases in Earth's atmosphere, with potentially dire consequences.

- The histories of Venus and Mars show that a stable climate like Earth's is more the exception than the rule. The stable climate that makes our existence possible is a direct consequence of our planet's unique geology, including its plate tectonics and carbon dioxide cycle.

my cosmic perspective   Our presence on Earth has been made possible both by the obvious "hazards" of a geologically active planet, and the less visible mechanisms that render Earth's climate stable.

7.1 Earth as a Planet

◆ **Why is Earth geologically active?**

Internal heat drives geological activity, and Earth retains internal heat because of its relatively large size for a terrestrial world. This heat causes mantle **convection** and keeps Earth's **lithosphere** thin, ensuring active surface geology. It also keeps part of Earth's core melted, and circulation of this molten metal creates Earth's magnetic field.

◆ **What processes shape Earth's surface?**

The four major geological processes are **impact cratering, volcanism, tectonics,** and **erosion.** Earth has experienced many impacts, but most craters have been erased by other processes. We owe the existence of our atmosphere and oceans to volcanic **outgassing.** A special type of tectonics—**plate tectonics**—shapes much of Earth's surface. Ice, water, and wind drive rampant erosion on our planet.

◆ **How does Earth's atmosphere affect the planet?**

Two crucial effects are: (1) protecting the surface from dangerous solar radiation—ultraviolet is absorbed by ozone and X rays are absorbed high in the atmosphere; and (2) the **greenhouse effect,** without which Earth's surface temperature would be below freezing.

7.2 The Moon and Mercury: Geologically Dead

◆ **Was there ever geological activity on the Moon or Mercury?**

Both the Moon and Mercury had limited volcanism and tectonics when they were young. However, because of their small sizes, their interiors long ago cooled too much for ongoing geological activity.

7.3 Mars: A Victim of Planetary Freeze-Drying

◆ **What geological features tell us that water once flowed on Mars?**

Dry riverbeds, eroded craters, and studies of Martian minerals all show that water once flowed on Mars, though any periods of rainfall seem to have ended at least 3 billion years ago. Mars today still has water ice underground and in its polar caps and could possibly have pockets of underground liquid water.

◆ **Why did Mars change?**

Mars's atmosphere must once have been thicker with a stronger greenhouse effect, so Mars must have lost a great deal of atmospheric gas. Much of the lost gas probably was stripped away by the solar wind, after Mars lost its magnetic field and protective magnetosphere. Mars also lost water, because solar ultraviolet light split water molecules apart and the hydrogen escaped to space.

7.4 Venus: A Hothouse World

◆ **Is Venus geologically active?**

Venus almost certainly remains geologically active today. Its surface shows evidence of major volcanic or tectonic activity in the past billion years, and it should retain nearly as much internal heat as Earth. However, geological activity on Venus differs from that on Earth in at least two key ways: lack of erosion and lack of plate tectonics.

◆ **Why is Venus so hot?**

Venus's extreme surface heat is a result of its thick, carbon dioxide atmosphere, which creates a very strong greenhouse effect. The reason Venus has such a thick atmosphere is its distance from the Sun: It was too close to develop liquid oceans like those on Earth, where most of the outgassed carbon dioxide dissolved in water and became locked away in **carbonate rock.** Carbon dioxide remained in Venus's atmosphere, creating a **runaway greenhouse effect.**

7.5 Earth as a Living Planet

◆ **What unique features of Earth are important for life?**

Unique features of Earth on which we depend for survival are (1) surface liquid water, made possible by Earth's moderate temperature; (2) atmospheric oxygen, a product of photosynthetic life; (3) plate tectonics, driven by internal heat; and (4) climate stability, a result of the **carbon dioxide cycle,** which in turn requires plate tectonics.

◆ **How is human activity changing our planet?**

The global average temperature has risen about 0.8°C over the past hundred years, accompanied by an even larger rise in the atmospheric CO_2 concentration—a result of fossil fuel burning and other human activity. The current CO_2 concentration is higher than at any time in the past million years, and strong evidence indicates that this higher concentration is indeed the cause of **global warming.**

◆ **What makes a planet habitable?**

We can trace Earth's habitability to its relatively large size and its distance from the Sun. Its size maintains the internal heat that allowed volcanic outgassing to lead to our oceans and atmosphere, and also drives the plate tectonics that helps regulate our climate through the carbon dioxide cycle. Earth's distance from the Sun is neither too close nor too far, thereby allowing liquid water to exist on its surface.

Refer to this image of Mercury from *MESSENGER* to answer the following questions.

1. Label 1a lies on the rim of a large crater, and 1b lies on the rim of a smaller one. Which crater must have formed first?
   a. crater 1a
   b. crater 1b
   c. cannot be determined

2. The region around 2b has far fewer craters than the region around 2c. The crater floor at 2a is also flat and smooth, without many smaller craters on it. Why are regions 2a and 2b so smooth?
   a. Few small craters ever formed in these regions.
   b. Erosion erased craters that once existed in these regions.
   c. Lava flows covered craters that once existed in these regions.

3. A tectonic ridge appears to connect points 3a and 3b, crossing several craters. From its appearance, we can conclude that it must have formed
   a. before the area was cratered.
   b. after the area was cratered.
   c. at the same time the area was cratered.

4. Using your answers from questions 1–3, list the following features in order from oldest to youngest:
   a. the tectonic ridge from 3a to 3b
   b. crater 1a
   c. the smooth floor of crater 1b

MasteringAstronomy®   For instructor-assigned homework and other learning materials, go to MasteringAstronomy®.

Review Questions

1. Describe the core-mantle-crust structures of the terrestrial worlds. What is a *lithosphere*? What is *differentiation*?
2. Why did the terrestrial worlds undergo *differentiation*? Why have larger worlds retained more internal heat than smaller ones?
3. Why does Earth have a global *magnetic field*? What is the *magnetosphere*?
4. Define the four major geological processes, giving examples of features on Earth shaped by each process.
5. How do crater counts tell us the age of a surface? Explain why the Moon has so many more craters than Earth.
6. What is *outgassing*, and how did it lead to the existence of Earth's atmosphere and oceans?
7. Describe the key ways in which the atmosphere affects Earth. What is the *greenhouse effect*, and how does it work?
8. Briefly summarize the geological histories of the Moon and Mercury. How did the lunar maria form? How are Mercury's great cliffs thought to have formed?
9. Choose at least three features on the global map of Mars (Figure 7.23), and explain the nature and likely origin of each.
10. Explain why liquid water is not stable on Mars today, but why we nonetheless think it flowed there in the distant past.
11. Describe the leading hypothesis for how Mars lost much of its atmosphere some 3 billion years ago, and identify the role played by Mars's size.

12. Describe the basic geology of Venus. Why is it surprising that Venus lacks plate tectonics? What might explain this lack?

13. What do we mean by a *runaway greenhouse effect*? Explain why this process occurred on Venus but not on Earth.

14. Describe four ways in which Earth is unique among the terrestrial worlds, and how each is important to life.

15. Describe the conveyor-like action of *plate tectonics*, and how it changes the arrangement of the continents with time.

16. What is the *carbon dioxide cycle*, and why is it so crucial to life on Earth?

17. Briefly summarize the evidence linking human activity to *global warming*. What are its potential consequences?

18. Based on Figure 7.50, summarize the roles of planetary size and distance from the Sun in explaining the histories of the terrestrial worlds.

Test Your Understanding

Surprising Discoveries?

Suppose we were to make the following discoveries. (These are not real discoveries.) In light of your understanding of planetary geology, decide whether the discovery should be considered reasonable or surprising. Explain your reasoning clearly, if possible tracing your logic back to basic planetary properties of size or distance from the Sun; because not all of these have definitive answers, your explanation is more important than your chosen answer.

19. New photographs reveal sand dunes on Mercury.

20. A new orbiter observes a volcanic eruption on Venus.

21. Radiometric dating of rocks brought back from one lunar crater shows it formed only 10 million years ago.

22. A new orbital photograph of Mars shows a crater bottom filled with a lake of liquid water.

23. Clear-cutting in the Amazon rain forest on Earth exposes terrain that is as heavily cratered as the Moon.

24. Drilling into the Martian surface, a robotic spacecraft discovers liquid water a few meters beneath the slopes of a Martian volcano.

25. Seismic studies on Earth reveal a "lost continent" that held great human cities just a few thousand years ago but is now buried beneath the Atlantic seafloor.

26. We find a planet in another solar system that has an Earth-like atmosphere with plentiful oxygen but no life of any kind.

27. We find a planet in another solar system that has Earth-like plate tectonics; the planet is the size of the Moon and orbits 1 AU from its star.

28. We find evidence that during dinosaur times, when Earth had no polar ice caps, the atmosphere had more carbon dioxide than it does today.

Quick Quiz

Choose the best answer to each of the following. Explain your reasoning with one or more complete sentences.

29. Which heat source continues to contribute to Earth's *internal* heat? (a) accretion (b) radioactive decay (c) sunlight

30. In general, what kind of terrestrial planet would you expect to have the thickest lithosphere? (a) a large planet (b) a small planet (c) a planet located far from the Sun

31. Which of a planet's fundamental properties has the greatest effect on its level of volcanic and tectonic activity? (a) size (b) distance from the Sun (c) rotation rate

32. Which describes our understanding of flowing water on Mars? (a) It was never important. (b) It was important once, but no longer. (c) It is a major process on the Martian surface today.

33. What do we conclude if a planet has few impact craters of any size? (a) The planet was never bombarded by asteroids or comets. (b) Its atmosphere stopped impactors of all sizes. (c) Geological processes have erased craters.

34. How many of the five terrestrial worlds are considered "geologically dead"? (a) none (b) two (c) four

35. Which terrestrial world has the most atmospheric gas? (a) Venus (b) Earth (c) Mars

36. Which of the following is a strong greenhouse gas? (a) nitrogen (b) carbon dioxide (c) oxygen

37. The oxygen in Earth's atmosphere was released by (a) volcanic outgassing. (b) the CO_2 cycle. (c) life.

38. Where is most of the CO_2 that has outgassed from Earth's volcanoes? (a) in the atmosphere (b) escaped to space (c) locked up in rocks

Process of Science

39. *What Is Predictable?* Briefly explain why much of a planet's geological history is destined from its birth, and discuss the level of detail that is predictable. For example, was Mars's general level of volcanism predictable? Could we have predicted a mountain as tall as Olympus Mons or a canyon as long as Valles Marineris? Explain.

40. *Science with Consequences.* A small, vocal group of people still dispute that humans are causing global warming. Do some research to find the basis of their claims. Then defend or refute their findings based on your own studies and your understanding of the hallmarks of science discussed in Chapter 3.

41. *Unanswered Questions.* Choose one important but unanswered question about Mars's past, and write two or three paragraphs discussing how we might answer this question in the future. Be as specific as possible, focusing on the type of evidence necessary to answer the question and on how the evidence could be gathered. What are the benefits of finding answers to this question?

Group Work Exercise

42. *Are We Causing Global Warming?* **Roles:** *Scribe* (takes notes on the group's activities), *Advocate* (argues in favor of the claim that human activity is causing global warming), *Skeptic* (points out weaknesses in the arguments made by the *Advocate*), *Moderator* (leads group discussion and makes sure everyone contributes). **Activity:**

    a. Work together to make a list of scientific observations that have been proposed as evidence that humans are causing global warming. Your list should include, but not be limited to, the evidence in Figures 7.45–7.49.

    b. *Advocate* presents the case that humans are causing global warming, drawing on the evidence from part (a).

    c. *Skeptic* attempts to refute *Advocate*'s case using scientific arguments.

    d. After hearing these arguments, *Moderator* and *Scribe* decide whose arguments were more persuasive and explain their reasoning.

    e. Each person in the group writes up a summary of the discussion.

Investigate Further

Short-Answer/Essay Questions

43. *Miniature Mars.* Suppose Mars had turned out to be significantly smaller than its current size—say, the size of our Moon. How would this have affected the number of geological features due to each of the four major geological processes? Do you think Mars would still be a good candidate for harboring extraterrestrial life? Summarize your answers in two or three paragraphs.

44. *Two Paths Diverged.* Briefly explain how the different atmospheric properties of Earth and Venus can be explained by the fundamental properties of size and distance from the Sun.

45. *Change in Formation Properties.* Consider either Earth's size or its distance from the Sun, and suppose that it had been different (for example, smaller size or greater distance). Describe how this change might have affected Earth's subsequent history and the possibility of life on Earth.

46. *Experiment: Planetary Cooling in a Freezer.* Fill two small plastic containers of similar shape but different size with cold water and put both into the freezer at the same time. Every hour or so, record the time and your estimate of the thickness of the "lithosphere" (the frozen layer) in each container. How long does it take the water in each container to freeze completely? Describe the relevance of your experiment to planetary geology. Extra credit: Plot your results on a graph with time on the *x*-axis and lithospheric thickness on the *y*-axis. What is the ratio of the two freezing times?

47. *Amateur Astronomy: Observing the Moon.* Any amateur telescope has a resolution adequate to identify geological features on the Moon. The light highlands and dark maria should be evident, and shadowing is visible near the line between night and day. Try to observe the Moon near the first- or third-quarter phase. Sketch or photograph the Moon at low magnification, and then zoom in on a region of interest. Again sketch or photograph your field of view, label its features, and identify the geological process that created them. Look for craters, volcanic plains, and tectonic features. Estimate the size of each feature by comparing it to the size of the whole Moon (radius = 1738 kilometers).

48. *Global Warming.* What, if anything, do you think we should be doing to alleviate the threat of global warming? Write a one-page editorial defending your opinion.

Quantitative Problems

Be sure to show all calculations clearly and state your final answers in complete sentences.

49. *Surface Area–to–Volume Ratio.* Compare the surface area–to–volume ratios of
    a. the Moon and Mars.
    b. Earth and Venus.
    In each case, use your answer to discuss differences in internal heat on the two worlds.

50. *Doubling Your Size.* Just as the surface area–to–volume ratio depends on size, so can other properties. To see how, suppose that your size suddenly doubled; that is, your height, width, and depth all doubled. (For example, if you are 5 feet tall, you would become 10 feet tall.)
    a. By what factor has your waist size increased?
    b. How much more material will be required for your clothes? (*Hint:* Clothes cover the *surface area* of your body.)
    c. By what factor has your weight increased? (*Hint:* Weight depends on the *volume* of your body.)
    d. The pressure on your weight-bearing joints depends on how much *weight* is supported by the *surface area* of each joint. How has this pressure changed?

51. *Plate Tectonics.* Typical motions of one plate relative to another are 1 centimeter per year. At this rate, how long would it take for two continents 3000 kilometers apart to collide? What are the global consequences of motions like this?

52. *Planet Berth.* Imagine a planet, which we'll call *Berth*, orbiting a star identical to the Sun at a distance of 1 AU. Assume that Berth has eight times as much mass as Earth and is twice as large as Earth in diameter.
    a. How does Berth's density compare to Earth's?
    b. How does Berth's surface area compare to Earth's?
    c. Based on your answers to (a) and (b), discuss how Berth's geological history is likely to have differed from Earth's.

Discussion Questions

53. *Worth the Effort?* Politicians often debate whether planetary missions are worth the expense involved. If you were in Congress, would you support more or fewer missions? Why?

54. *Lucky Earth.* The climate histories of Venus and Mars make it clear that it's not "easy" to get a pleasant climate like that of Earth. How does this affect your opinion about whether Earth-like planets might exist around other stars? Explain.

55. *Terraforming Mars.* Some people have suggested that we might be able to carry out planetwide engineering of Mars that would cause its climate to warm and its atmosphere to thicken. This type of planet engineering is called *terraforming*, because its objective is to make a planet more Earth-like and therefore easier for humans to live on. Discuss possible ways to terraform Mars. Do any of these ideas seem practical? Do they seem like good ideas? Defend your opinions.

Web Projects

56. *"Coolest" Surface Photo.* Visit the Astronomy Picture of the Day website, and search for past images of the terrestrial worlds. After looking at many of the images, choose the one you think is the "coolest." Make a printout, write a short description of what it shows, and explain what you like about it.

57. *Planetary Mission.* Choose a current mission that is studying one of the terrestrial worlds, visit its website, and write a brief summary of its goals, current status, and most important discoveries to date.

58. *Mars Colonization.* Visit the website of a group that advocates human colonization of Mars, such as the Mars Society. Learn about the challenges of human survival on Mars and about prospects for terraforming Mars. Do you think colonization of Mars is a good idea? Write a short essay describing what you've learned and defend your opinions.

Earth

Jupiter
Distance from Sun = 5.20 AU
Mass = $318M_{Earth}$
Density = 1.33 g/cm^3
Composition: mostly H, He

Saturn
Distance from Sun = 9.54 AU
Mass = $95M_{Earth}$
Density = 0.71 g/cm^3
Composition: mostly H, He

Uranus
Distance from Sun = 19.2 AU
Mass = $14M_{Earth}$
Density = 1.24 g/cm^3
Composition: H compounds,
rock, H and He

Neptune
Distance from Sun = 30.1 AU
Mass = $17M_{Earth}$
Density = 1.67 g/cm^3
Composition: H compounds,
rock, H and He

▲ **FIGURE 8.1**
Jupiter, Saturn, Uranus, and Neptune, shown to scale with Earth
for comparison.

compounds were so much more abundant than metal and rock, some of the ice-rich planetesimals of the outer solar system grew to great size. Once these planetesimals became sufficiently massive, their grav-

The jovian planets are made mostly of hydrogen, helium, and hydrogen compounds, and differ primarily in their relative proportions of hydrogen compounds.

ity allowed them to draw in the hydrogen and helium gas that surrounded them. Models suggest that all four jovian planets grew from ice-rich planetesimals of about the same mass—roughly 10 times the mass of Earth—but they captured different amounts of hydrogen and helium gas from the surrounding solar nebula.

Jupiter and Saturn captured so much hydrogen and helium gas that these gases now make up the vast majority of their masses. The ice-rich planetesimals from which they grew now represent only about 3% of Jupiter's mass and about 10% of Saturn's mass. Uranus and Neptune pulled in much less gas from the solar nebula, so hydrogen and helium make up less than half of their total masses.

Why did the different planets capture different amounts of gas? The answer probably lies in their distances from the Sun as they formed. The solid particles that condensed farther from the Sun should have been

The jovian planets farther from the Sun took longer to form and captured less hydrogen and helium gas, explaining why Uranus and Neptune have larger proportions of hydrogen compounds, rock, and metal.

more widely spread out than those that condensed nearer to the Sun, which means it would have taken longer for them to accrete into large, icy planetesimals. As the nearest jovian planet to the Sun, Jupiter would have been the first to get a planetesimal large enough for its gravity to start drawing in gas, followed by Saturn, Uranus, and Neptune. Because all the planets stopped accreting gas at the same time—when the solar wind blew all the remaining gas into interstellar space—the more distant planets had less time to capture gas and ended up smaller in size. Similar processes, played out to different extents in different planetary systems, may explain much of the wider variety of planetary types that scientists have discovered among planets around other stars [Section 10.2].

Density Differences Figure 8.1 shows that Saturn is considerably less dense than Uranus or Neptune. This should make sense, because the hydrogen compounds, rock, and metal that make up Uranus and Neptune are normally much more dense than hydrogen or helium gas. However, by the same logic we'd expect Jupiter to be even less dense than Saturn—but it's not.

think about it Saturn's average density of 0.71 g/cm³ is less than that of water. As a result, it is sometimes said that Saturn could float on a giant ocean. Suppose there really were a gigantic planet with a gigantic ocean and we put Saturn on the ocean's surface. Would it float? If not, what would happen?

We can understand Jupiter's surprisingly high density by thinking about how massive planets are affected by their own gravity. Building a planet of hydrogen and helium is a bit like making one out of fluffy pillows. Imagine assembling a planet pillow by pillow. As each new pillow is added, those on the bottom are compressed more by those above. As the lower pillows are forced closer together, their mutual gravitational attraction increases, compressing them even further. At first the stack grows substantially with each pillow, but eventually the growth slows until adding pillows barely increases the height of the stack (Figure 8.2a).

This analogy explains why Jupiter is only slightly larger than Saturn in radius even though it is more than three times as massive. The extra mass of Jupiter compresses its interior to a much higher density. More precise calculations show that Jupiter's radius is almost the maximum possible radius for a jovian planet. If much more gas were added to Jupiter, its weight would actually compress the interior enough to make the planet *smaller* rather than larger (Figure 8.2b). Some extrasolar planets that are larger in mass than Jupiter are therefore smaller in size.

see it for yourself Measure the thickness of your pillow; then put it at the bottom of a stack of other pillows, folded blankets, or clothing. How much has the pillow been compressed by the stack above it? Insert your hand between the different layers to feel the pressure differences—and imagine the kind of pressures and compression you'd find in a stack tens of thousands of kilometers tall!

Jovian Planet Interiors The jovian planets are often called "gas giants," making it sound as if they were entirely gaseous like air on Earth. However, while it is true that they are made mostly of materials that would be gases on Earth, the high pressures in jovian interiors compress these materials to different forms. Let's first consider Jupiter's interior.

Jupiter's lack of a solid surface makes it tempting to think of the planet as "all atmosphere," but you could not fly through Jupiter's interior in the way airplanes fly through air. A spacecraft plunging into Jupiter would find increasingly higher temperatures and pressures as it descended. The *Galileo* spacecraft dropped a scientific probe into Jupiter in 1995 that collected measurements for about an hour before the ever-increasing pressures and temperatures destroyed it. The probe provided valuable data about Jupiter's atmosphere but didn't last long enough to sample the interior: It survived to a depth of only about 200 kilometers, or about 0.3% of Jupiter's radius.

Computer models tell us that Jupiter has fairly distinct interior layers (Figure 8.3). The layers do not differ much in composition—all except the core are mostly hydrogen and helium. Instead they differ in the phase

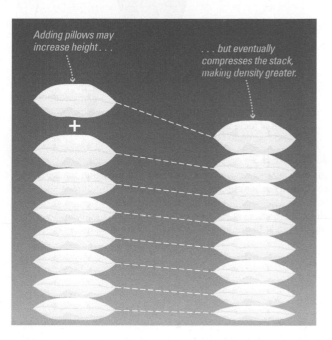

Adding pillows may increase height . . .

. . . but eventually compresses the stack, making density greater.

a Adding pillows to a stack may increase its height at first but eventually compresses the stack, making its density greater.

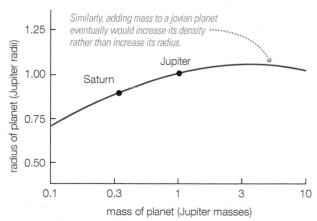

Similarly, adding mass to a jovian planet eventually would increase its density rather than increase its radius.

b This graph shows how radius depends on mass for a hydrogen/helium planet. Notice that Jupiter is only slightly larger in radius than Saturn, despite being three times as massive. Gravitational compression of a planet much more massive than Jupiter would actually make its radius smaller.

▲ **FIGURE 8.2**

The relationship between mass and radius for a planet made of hydrogen and helium.

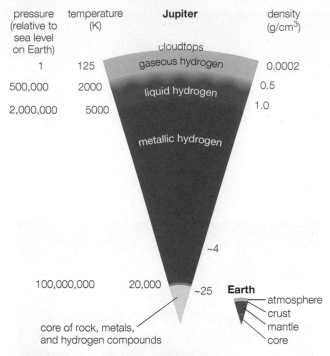

pressure (relative to sea level on Earth)	temperature (K)	Jupiter	density (g/cm³)
		cloudtops	
1	125	gaseous hydrogen	0.0002
500,000	2000	liquid hydrogen	0.5
2,000,000	5000		1.0
		metallic hydrogen	
			~4
100,000,000	20,000		~25

core of rock, metals, and hydrogen compounds

Earth — atmosphere — crust — mantle — core

▲ **FIGURE 8.3**

Jupiter's interior structure, labeled with the pressure, temperature, and density at various depths. Earth's interior structure is shown to scale for comparison. (The thicknesses of Earth's crust and atmosphere are exaggerated.) Note that Jupiter's core is only slightly larger than Earth but is about 10 times as massive.

▼ **FIGURE 8.4**

These diagrams compare the interior structures of the jovian planets, shown approximately to scale. All four planets have cores of rock, metal, and hydrogen compounds, with masses about 10 times the mass of Earth. They differ primarily in the depth of the hydrogen/helium layers that surround their cores. The cores of Uranus and Neptune are differentiated into separate layers of rock/metal and hydrogen compounds.

If you plunged below Jupiter's clouds, you'd never encounter a solid surface—just ever denser and hotter hydrogen/helium compressed into bizarre liquid and metallic phases.

(such as liquid or gas) of their hydrogen. The outer layer is the only region in which conditions are moderate enough for hydrogen to remain in its familiar, gaseous form. This layer makes up about the outer 10% of Jupiter and represents what we usually think of as Jupiter's atmosphere. As we look deeper, the high pressures compress the hydrogen into liquid form in the next 10% of Jupiter's depth, and below that the temperatures and pressures become so extreme that hydrogen is forced into a compact, liquid metallic (electrically conducting) form. Finally, the models tell us that Jupiter's core is a mix of hydrogen compounds, rock, and metal, but compressed to such extremes of temperature and density that this mix bears little resemblance to familiar solids or liquids.

We can extend the ideas from Jupiter to the other jovian planets. Because all four jovian planets have cores of about the same mass, their interiors differ mainly in the hydrogen/helium layers that surround their cores (Figure 8.4). Remember that while the outer layers are named for the phase of their hydrogen, they also contain helium and hydrogen compounds.

Saturn has the same basic layering as Jupiter, but its lower mass makes the weight of the overlying layers less than on Jupiter. As a result, we must look deeper into Saturn to find each level where pressure changes hydrogen from one phase to another. Uranus and Neptune have somewhat different layering because their internal pressures never become high enough to form liquid or metallic hydrogen, so they have only a thick layer of gaseous hydrogen surrounding their cores. Models suggest that their core mix of hydrogen compounds, rock, and metal may be liquid, making for very odd "oceans" buried deep inside Uranus and Neptune; the cores may also be differentiated so that hydrogen compounds reside in an outer core above an inner core of rock and metal.

Magnetic Fields   Recall that Earth has a global magnetic field generated by the movements of charged particles in our planet's outer core of molten metal [Section 7.1]. The jovian planets also have global magnetic fields generated by motions of charged particles deep in their interiors.

Jupiter's magnetic field is by far the strongest—some 20,000 times as strong as Earth's. This strong field, generated in Jupiter's thick layer of metallic hydrogen, creates an enormous magnetosphere that begins to deflect the solar wind some 3 million kilometers in front of Jupiter (Figure 8.5). If we could see Jupiter's magnetosphere, it would be larger than the full moon in our sky. Gases escaping from volcanoes on Jupiter's moon Io feed vast numbers of particles into the magnetosphere, where they become ionized and form a donut-shaped charged particle belt (called the *Io torus*) that

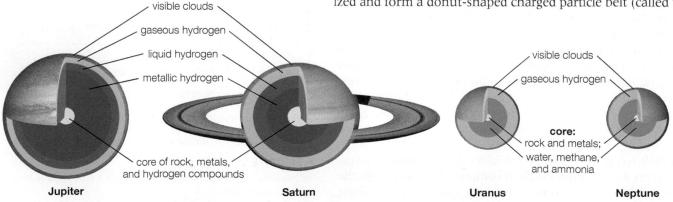

visible clouds
gaseous hydrogen
liquid hydrogen
metallic hydrogen
core of rock, metals, and hydrogen compounds

visible clouds
gaseous hydrogen
core:
rock and metals;
water, methane, and ammonia

Jupiter   **Saturn**   **Uranus**   **Neptune**

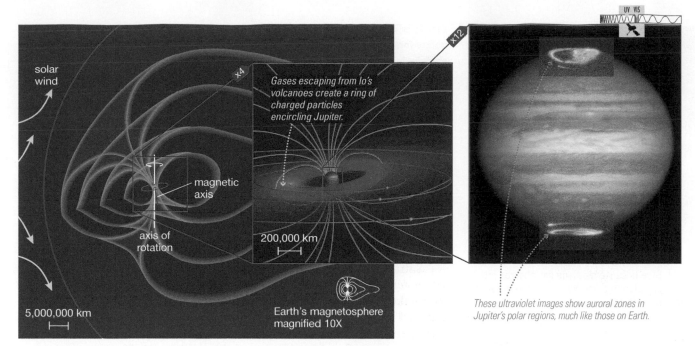

solar
wind

magnetic
axis

axis of
rotation

Gases escaping from Io's volcanoes create a ring of charged particles encircling Jupiter.

200,000 km

5,000,000 km

Earth's magnetosphere
magnified 10X

These ultraviolet images show auroral zones in Jupiter's polar regions, much like those on Earth.

▲ **FIGURE 8.5**

Jupiter's strong magnetic field gives it an enormous magnetosphere. Gases escaping from Io feed the donut-shaped Io torus, and particles entering Jupiter's atmosphere near its magnetic poles contribute to auroras on Jupiter. The image at the right is a composite of ultraviolet images of the polar regions overlaid on a visible image of the whole planet, all taken by the Hubble Space Telescope.

approximately traces Io's orbit. The particles also create belts of intense radiation and contribute to auroras on Jupiter.

think about it The *Juno* mission entered Jupiter orbit in July 2016 to study Jupiter's interior, atmosphere, and magnetosphere. Find and briefly describe its major discoveries to date.

The other jovian planets also have magnetic fields and magnetospheres, but theirs are much weaker than Jupiter's (although still much stronger than Earth's). Saturn's magnetic field is weaker than Jupiter's because it has a thinner layer of electrically conducting metallic hydrogen. Uranus and Neptune, smaller still, have no metallic hydrogen at all. Their relatively weak magnetic fields must be generated in their core "oceans" of hydrogen compounds, rock, and metal.

◆ **What is the weather like on jovian planets?**

Jovian atmospheres have dynamic winds and weather, with colorful clouds and enormous storms. Weather on these planets is driven not only by energy from the Sun (as on the terrestrial planets), but also by heat generated within the planets themselves. All but Uranus generate a great deal of internal heat. No one knows the precise source of the internal heat on jovian planets, but it probably comes from the conversion of gravitational potential energy to thermal energy inside them. The best guesses are that this conversion comes from a slow but imperceptible contraction in overall size, or from ongoing differentiation as heavier materials continue to sink toward the core.

Clouds and Colors Many mysteries remain about the colors of the jovian planets, but clouds play a major role. Earth's clouds look white from space because they are made of water that reflects the white light of the Sun. The jovian planets have clouds of several different types, and some of these reflect light of other colors.

cold enough for ammonia to condense to form clouds

cold enough for ammonium hydrosulfide to condense to form clouds

cold enough for water to condense to form clouds

altitude relative to cloud tops (km)

▲ **FIGURE 8.6**

This diagram shows the temperature structure of Jupiter's atmosphere. Jupiter has at least three distinct cloud layers because different atmospheric gases condense at different temperatures and hence at different altitudes. The tops of the ammonia clouds are usually considered the zero altitude for Jupiter, which is why lower altitudes are negative.

Light of all colors comes from the Sun.

Methane gas absorbs red light and transmits blue light . . .

. . . and methane clouds reflect the blue light back into space.

methane gas mixed with hydrogen

methane clouds

▲ **FIGURE 8.7**

Neptune and Uranus look blue because methane gas absorbs red light but transmits blue light. Clouds of methane snowflakes reflect the transmitted blue light back to space.

Clouds of different compositions and colors form at different altitudes in each jovian planet's atmosphere.

Clouds form when a gas condenses to make tiny liquid droplets or solid flakes. Water vapor is the only gas that can condense to form clouds in Earth's atmosphere, but Jupiter's atmosphere has three major types of clouds, each of which forms at different altitudes. Looking from the bottom up in Figure 8.6, Jupiter's lowest cloud layer occurs about 100 kilometers below the highest cloudtops. At this depth, temperatures are nearly Earth-like and water can condense to form clouds. The temperature drops as you go higher, and about 50 kilometers above the water clouds it is cold enough for a gas called ammonium hydrosulfide (NH_4SH) to condense into clouds. These ammonium hydrosulfide clouds reflect brown and red light, producing many of the dark colors of Jupiter. Higher still, the temperature is so cold that ammonia (NH_3) condenses to make an upper layer of white clouds.

Saturn has the same set of three cloud layers as Jupiter, but Saturn's lower temperatures (due to both its greater distance from the Sun and its weaker gravity) mean these layers occur deeper in Saturn's atmosphere. This fact probably explains Saturn's more subdued colors: Less light penetrates to the depths at which Saturn's clouds are found, and the light they reflect is more obscured by the atmosphere above them.

Uranus and Neptune are so cold that any cloud layers similar to those of Jupiter or Saturn would be buried too deep in their atmospheres for us to see. However, the cold temperatures allow some of their abundant methane gas to condense into clouds. Methane gas also absorbs red light, allowing only blue light to penetrate to the level at which the methane clouds form. The methane clouds reflect this blue light upward, giving these two planets their blue colors (Figure 8.7).

Global Winds and Storms   One of the most striking visual features of the jovian planets is the striped appearance of Jupiter. The stripes represent alternating bands of rising and falling air, and their colors arise from the clouds that we see. Bands of rising air are white because the rising air condenses and forms white ammonia clouds at high altitudes (see Figure 8.6). Bands of falling air do not contain ammonia clouds, allowing us to see the reddish-brown ammonium hydrosulfide clouds that lie at lower altitudes. The fact that these bands wrap around Jupiter is a consequence of the same effect

▼ **FIGURE 8.8**

Wind patterns on both Earth and Jupiter arise from the way planetary rotation affects moving air.

a This photograph shows how storms circulate around low-pressure regions (L) on Earth. Earth's rotation causes this circulation, which is in opposite directions in the two hemispheres.

reddish brown bands of falling air

white bands of rising air

b Jupiter's faster rotation and larger size essentially stretch out its circulation patterns into planet-wide bands of fast-moving air.

(called the *Coriolis effect*) that makes storms around low-pressure regions on Earth circulate counterclockwise in the Northern Hemisphere and clockwise in the Southern Hemisphere (Figure 8.8a). Jupiter's faster rotation and larger size make this effect much stronger, in essence stretching the circulation east-west to the point that it wraps all the way around the planet (Figure 8.8b). Jupiter therefore has very high east-west wind speeds—sometimes more than 400 kilometers per hour (250 miles per hour).

Jovian planets also show numerous storms, the most famous being Jupiter's **Great Red Spot,** which is more than twice as wide as Earth. The Great Red Spot is somewhat like a hurricane on Earth, except that its winds circulate around a high- rather than low-pressure region (Figure 8.9). It is also extremely long-lived compared to storms on Earth: Astronomers have seen it throughout the three centuries during which telescopes have been powerful enough to detect it. No one knows why the Great Red Spot has lasted so long. However, storms on Earth tend to lose their strength when they pass over land. Perhaps Jupiter's biggest storms last for centuries simply because there's no solid surface effect to sap their energy. Two other long-lived storms have recently been observed to undergo a mysterious change, turning from white to red. The more recent one was torn apart by the Great Red Spot as it passed nearby (Figure 8.10a).

The rapid rotation of the jovian planets helps drive strong winds, creating their banded appearances and sometimes giving rise to huge storms.

The other jovian planets also have dramatic weather patterns (Figure 8.10b–d). As on Jupiter, Saturn's rapid rotation creates alternating bands of rising and falling air, along with rapid east-west winds. In fact, Saturn's winds are even faster than Jupiter's—a surprise that scientists have yet to explain. Neptune's atmosphere is also banded, and we have seen a high-pressure storm, called the Great Dark Spot, similar to Jupiter's Great Red Spot. However, the Great Dark Spot did not last as long; it disappeared from view just 6 years after its discovery. Uranus had a more subdued appearance when *Voyager 2* flew past it in 1986, but now seems to have more frequent storms, probably due to the slow but dramatic change of seasons caused by its extreme axis tilt and 84-year orbit around the Sun.

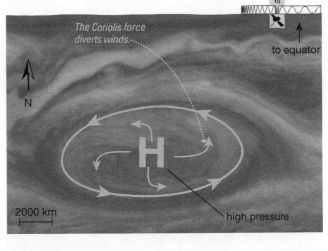

▲ **FIGURE 8.9**

This photograph shows Jupiter's Great Red Spot, a huge, high-pressure storm that is large enough to swallow two or three Earths. The overlaid diagram shows a weather map of the region.

▼ **FIGURE 8.10**

Selected views of weather patterns on the four jovian planets.

a This Hubble Space Telescope image shows Jupiter's southern hemisphere with the Great Red Spot, "Baby Red" (to its left), and "Red Jr." (below). Baby Red was torn apart by the Great Red Spot a few days later.

b Saturn's atmosphere, photographed by *Voyager 1*. Its banded appearance is very similar to that of Jupiter.

c This infrared image of Uranus from the Keck Telescope shows several storms (the bright blotches) and Uranus's thin rings (red).

d Neptune's atmosphere, viewed from *Voyager 2*, shows bands and occasional strong storms. The large storm (white arrow) was called the Great Dark Spot.

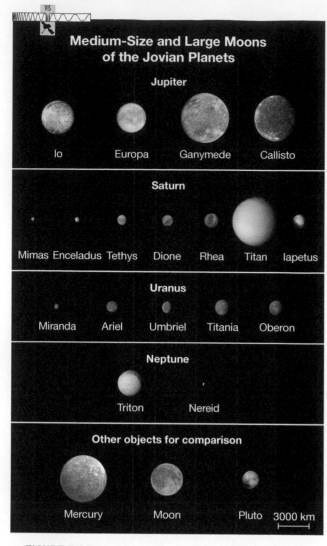

Medium-Size and Large Moons of the Jovian Planets

Jupiter

Io   Europa   Ganymede   Callisto

Saturn

Mimas Enceladus Tethys Dione Rhea Titan Iapetus

Uranus

Miranda Ariel Umbriel Titania Oberon

Neptune

Triton   Nereid

Other objects for comparison

Mercury   Moon   Pluto   3000 km

▲ **FIGURE 8.11**

The medium-size and large moons of the jovian planets, with sizes (but not distances) shown to scale. Mercury, the Moon, and Pluto are included for comparison.

8.2 A Wealth of Worlds: Satellites of Ice and Rock

The jovian planets are majestic and fascinating, but they are only the beginning of our exploration of jovian planet *systems*. Each of the four jovian systems includes numerous moons and a set of rings. The total mass of all the moons and rings put together is minuscule compared to that of any one of the jovian planets, but the remarkable diversity of these satellites makes up for their lack of size.

◆ What kinds of moons orbit the jovian planets?

We now know of at least 170 moons orbiting the jovian planets. Jupiter and Saturn have the most, each with more than 60 known moons. It's helpful to organize these moons into three groups by size: small moons less than about 300 kilometers in diameter, medium-size moons ranging from about 300 to 1500 kilometers in diameter, and large moons more than 1500 kilometers in diameter. These categories are useful because size relates to geological activity. In general, larger moons are more likely to show evidence of past or present geological activity.

Figure 8.11 shows a montage of all the medium-size and large moons. These moons resemble the terrestrial planets in many ways. Each is spherical with a solid surface and its own unique geology. Some possess atmospheres, hot interiors, and even magnetic fields. The two largest—Jupiter's moon Ganymede and Saturn's moon Titan—are larger than the planet Mercury, while four others (Jupiter's moons Io, Europa, and Callisto and Neptune's moon Triton) are larger than the largest known dwarf planets, Pluto and Eris. However, these moons differ from terrestrial worlds in their compositions: Because they formed in the cold outer solar system, most of them contain substantial amounts of ice in addition to metal and rock.

Most of the medium-size and large moons probably formed by accretion within the disks of gas surrounding individual jovian planets [Section 6.3]. That explains why their orbits are almost circular and lie close to the equatorial plane of their parent planet, and also why these moons orbit in the same direction in which their planet rotates. In contrast, many small moons are probably captured asteroids or comets, and therefore do not follow any particular orbital patterns; many even orbit backward relative to their planet's rotation.

A few jovian moons rival the smallest planets in size and geological interest, while vast numbers of smaller moons are captured asteroids and comets.

The small moons have irregular shapes, much like potatoes (Figure 8.12), because their gravities are too weak to force their rigid material into spheres. We do not expect these moons to have any significant geological activity, so they are essentially just chunks of ice and rock held captive by the gravity of their parent planet.

◆ Why are Jupiter's Galilean moons geologically active?

We now embark on a brief tour of the most interesting moons of the jovian planets. Our first stop is Jupiter, where the four *Galilean*

Calypso (22 km) Pandora (84 km) Telesto (24 km) Hyperion (180 km) Phoebe (220 km) Janus (180 km)

▲ **FIGURE 8.12**
These photos from the *Cassini* spacecraft show six of Saturn's smaller moons. All are much smaller than the smallest moons shown in Figure 8.11. Their irregular shapes are due to their small size, which makes their gravities too weak to force them into spheres. The sizes in parentheses represent approximate lengths along their longest axes.

moons (discovered by Galileo [Section 3.3]) are each large enough that they would count as planets or dwarf planets if they orbited the Sun (Figure 8.13).

Io: The Volcano World For anyone who thinks of moons as barren, geologically dead places like our own Moon, Io shatters the stereotype. Io is by far the most volcanically active world in our solar system. Large volcanoes pockmark its entire surface (Figure 8.14), and eruptions are so frequent that they have buried virtually every impact crater. Io probably also has tectonic activity, because tectonics and volcanism generally go hand in hand. However, debris from volcanic eruptions has probably buried most tectonic features.

Io's active volcanoes tell us that it must be quite hot inside. However, Io is only about the size of our geologically dead Moon, so it should have

▼ **FIGURE 8.13**
This set of photos, taken by the *Galileo* spacecraft, shows global views of the four Galilean moons as we know them today. Sizes are shown to scale. (Io is about the size of Earth's Moon.)

1000 km

Io Europa Ganymede Callisto

This close-up shows the glow of intensely hot lava from a volcanic eruption.

50 km

500 km

x50

jets of SO₂ gas

SO₂ frost

Basalt lava flow

10 km

An 80-km-high gas plume was created when hot lava flowed over sulfur dioxide frost, causing it to sublimate explosively into gas.

Three large plumes lit by the Sun blanket the surface in sulfur-rich snow . . .

. . . while many more eruptions are visible on Io's night side glowing in the infrared.

a Most of the black, brown, and red spots on Io's surface are recently active volcanic features. White and yellow areas are sulfur dioxide (SO_2) and sulfur deposits, respectively, from volcanic gases. (Photographs from the *Galileo* spacecraft; some colors slightly enhanced or altered.)

b Two views of Io's volcanoes taken by *New Horizons* on its way to Pluto.

▲ **FIGURE 8.14**

Io is the most volcanically active body in the solar system.

long ago lost any heat from its birth and is too small for radioactivity to provide much ongoing heat. How, then, can Io be so hot inside? The only possible answer is that some other ongoing process must be heating Io's interior. Scientists have identified this process and call it **tidal heating,** because it arises from effects of tidal forces exerted by Jupiter.

Just as Earth exerts a tidal force that causes the Moon to keep the same face toward us at all times [Section 4.4], a tidal force from Jupiter makes Io keep the same face toward Jupiter as it orbits. But Jupiter's mass makes this tidal force far larger than the tidal force that Earth exerts on the Moon. Moreover, Io's orbit is slightly elliptical, so its orbital speed and distance from Jupiter vary. This variation means that the strength and direction of the tidal force change slightly as Io moves through each orbit, which in turn changes the size and orientation of Io's tidal bulges (Figure 8.15a). The result is that Io is continuously being

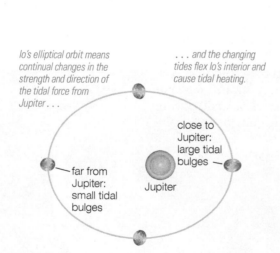

Io's elliptical orbit means continual changes in the strength and direction of the tidal force from Jupiter . . .

. . . and the changing tides flex Io's interior and cause tidal heating.

close to Jupiter: large tidal bulges

far from Jupiter: small tidal bulges

Jupiter

a Tidal heating arises because Io's elliptical orbit (exaggerated in this diagram) causes varying tides.

1 Ganymede orbit (7 days)

= 2 Europa orbits

= 4 Io orbits

Io

Jupiter

Europa

Ganymede

Io, Europa, and Ganymede share an orbital resonance that returns them to the positions shown about every 7 days . . .

. . . and the recurring gravitational tugs make all three orbits slightly elliptical (not shown).

b Io's orbit is elliptical because of the orbital resonance Io shares with Europa and Ganymede.

▲ **FIGURE 8.15**

These diagrams explain the cause of Io's tidal heating. Tidal heating has a weaker effect on Europa and Ganymede, because they are farther from Jupiter and tidal forces weaken with distance.

Tidal stresses cause parts of Europa's icy crust to slowly slide past each other.

Frictional heating expands ice here, forming the ridge . . .

. . . and may melt ice here, collapsing the ridge center.

Europa's surface has very few impact craters and appears visibly cracked.

Close-up photos show double-ridged cracks, best explained by an icy crust moving upon a soft or liquid layer below.

▲ **FIGURE 8.16**
Europa's icy crust probably hides a deep, liquid water ocean beneath its surface. These photos are from the *Galileo* spacecraft; colors are enhanced in the global view.

flexed in different directions, which generates friction inside it. The flexing heats the interior in the same way that flexing warms Silly Putty. Tidal heating generates tremendous heat on Io, and calculations show that this heat can explain Io's incredible volcanic activity.

see it for yourself Pry apart the overlapping ends of a paper clip, and hold one end in each hand. Flex the ends apart and together until the paper clip breaks. Lightly touch the broken end to your finger or lips—can you feel the warmth produced by flexing? How is this heating similar to the tidal heating of Io?

However, we are still left with a deeper question: Why is Io's orbit slightly elliptical, when almost all other large satellites have nearly circular orbits? The answer lies in an interesting dance executed by Io and its neighboring moons (Figure 8.15b). During the time Ganymede takes to complete one orbit of Jupiter, Europa completes exactly two orbits and Io completes exactly four orbits. The three moons therefore line up periodically, and the gravitational tugs they exert on one another add up over time. Because the tugs are always in the same direction with each alignment, they tend to stretch out the orbits, making them slightly elliptical. The effect is much like that of pushing a child on a swing. If timed properly, a series of small pushes can add up to a *resonance* that causes the child to swing quite high. For the three moons, the **orbital resonance** that makes their orbits elliptical comes from the small gravitational tugs that repeat at each alignment.

Orbital resonances among the Galilean moons make Io's orbit slightly elliptical, leading to tidal heating that explains Io's volcanic activity.

Europa: The Water World? Europa's surface is made almost entirely of water ice, with very few impact craters and extensive cracks (Figure 8.16). These features represent clear signs of ongoing geological activity, presumably involving flows of either liquid water or ice that is soft enough to undergo convection. The driver for this activity is the same type of tidal heating that drives Io's volcanoes, except it is weaker because of Europa's greater distance from Jupiter. Still, calculations suggest that Europa should have enough tidal heating to melt a subsurface layer of ice into liquid water.

These facts led scientists to suspect that Europa may hide a deep ocean of liquid water between its rocky mantle and its icy crust (Figure 8.17). Data

Europa may have a 100-km-thick ocean under an icy crust.

Tides or upwelling warm ice may sometimes create lakes within the ice, causing the crust above to crack . . .

. . . explaining surface terrain that looks like a jumble of icebergs suspended in a place where liquid or slushy water froze.

10 km

▲ **FIGURE 8.17**

This diagram shows the leading model of Europa's interior structure. There is little doubt that the H_2O layer is real, but some questions remain about whether the material beneath the icy crust is liquid water, relatively warm convecting ice, or some of each.

collected by the *Galileo* spacecraft support this hypothesis in two primary ways. First, many surface features are difficult to explain unless there is a subsurface ocean. Second, Europa has a magnetic field that changes in a way that suggests it is generated in a liquid layer of electrically conducting material, and a salty ocean would fit the bill.

Tidal heating may create a deep ocean of liquid water beneath Europa's icy crust.

If it really exists, Europa's liquid ocean may be more than 100 kilometers deep and contain more than twice as much liquid water as all of Earth's oceans combined. It is this possibility—along with the likelihood that the seafloor is dotted with undersea volcanoes—that makes scientists wonder whether Europa might harbor life, a possibility we will discuss in Chapter 19.

Ganymede and Callisto Jupiter's two other large moons, Ganymede and Callisto, also show intriguing geology. Like Europa, both have surfaces of water ice.

Ganymede, the largest moon in the solar system, appears to have a dual personality (Figure 8.18). Some regions are dark and densely cratered, suggesting that they look much the same today as they did billions of years ago. Other regions are light-colored with very few craters, suggesting that liquid water has recently erupted and refrozen. Moreover, magnetic field data indicate that Ganymede, like Europa, could have a subsurface ocean of liquid water. If so, we'd need to explain the source of the heat that melts Ganymede's subsurface ice. Ganymede has some tidal heating, but calculations suggest that it is not strong enough to account for an ocean. Perhaps ongoing radioactive decay supplies enough additional heat to make an ocean. Or perhaps not—no one yet knows what secrets Ganymede hides.

Callisto, the outermost Galilean moon, looks most like what scientists originally expected for an outer solar system satellite: a heavily cratered iceball (Figure 8.19). The bright patches on its surface are impact craters. However, the surface also holds some surprises. Close-up images show a dark, powdery substance concentrated in low-lying areas, leaving ridges and crests bright white. The nature of this material and how it got there are unknown. Even more surprising, magnetic field data suggest that Callisto, too,

▲ FIGURE 8.18

Ganymede, the largest moon in the solar system, has both old and young regions on its surface of water ice. The dark regions are heavily cratered and must be billions of years old, while the light regions are younger landscapes where eruptions of water have presumably erased ancient craters; the long grooves in the light regions were probably formed by water erupting along surface cracks. Notice that the boundary between the two types of terrain can be quite sharp.

could hide a subsurface ocean. No one knows what might heat the interior of Callisto, since it does not participate in the orbital resonances of the other

> Tidal heating is weak on Ganymede and absent on Callisto, yet both moons show some evidence of subsurface oceans.

Galilean moons and therefore has no tidal heating at all. Nevertheless, the potential for an ocean raises the intriguing possibility that there could be oceans on three worlds orbiting Jupiter—with far more total water than we have here on Earth.

Callisto is heavily cratered, indicating an old surface that nonetheless may hide a deeply buried ocean.

Close-up photo shows a dark powder overlaying the low areas of the surface.

▲ FIGURE 8.19

Callisto, the outermost of the four Galilean moons, has a heavily cratered icy surface.

◆ What geological activity do we see on Titan and other moons?

Aside from the four Galilean moons, the rest of Jupiter's moons fall in the small category, for which we expect no geological activity. However, if you look back at Figure 8.11, you'll see that the remaining jovian planets have 14 more medium-size or large moons among them: seven for Saturn, five for Uranus, and two for Neptune. Thanks especially to the *Cassini* spacecraft, which began orbiting Saturn in 2004, we have learned that some of these moons have surprisingly active geology.

Titan Saturn's moon Titan is the second-largest moon in the solar system (after Ganymede). It is also unique among the moons of our solar system in having a thick atmosphere—so thick that we cannot see through it with visible light (Figure 8.20). Titan's reddish color comes from chemicals in its atmosphere much like those that make smog over cities on Earth. The atmosphere is more than 95% nitrogen, not that different from the 77% nitrogen content of Earth's atmosphere. However, the rest of Earth's atmosphere is mostly oxygen, while the rest of Titan's consists of argon and methane (CH_4), ethane (C_2H_6), and other hydrogen compounds.

▲ FIGURE 8.20

Titan, as photographed by the *Cassini* spacecraft, is enshrouded by a thick atmosphere with clouds and haze. *Cassini* was outfitted with filters designed to peer through the atmosphere at the near-infrared wavelengths of light that are least affected by the atmosphere. The inset shows sunlight reflecting off a lake of liquid methane in Titan's north polar region.

Titan's atmosphere is thought to be a product of methane and ammonia gas released from Titan's interior and surface. Some is released by vaporization of methane and ammonia ices, and some may be released volcanically. Solar ultraviolet light can split these gas molecules, releasing hydrogen atoms that escape to space and leaving highly reactive compounds containing carbon and nitrogen, which react to make the other ingredients of Titan's atmosphere. For example, the abundant molecular nitrogen is made after ultraviolet light breaks down ammonia (NH_3) molecules, and ethane is made from methane.

Methane and ethane are both greenhouse gases and therefore give Titan a greenhouse effect [Section 7.1] that makes it warmer than it would be otherwise. Still, because of its great distance from the Sun, its surface temperature is a frigid 93 K (−180°C). The surface pressure on Titan is about 1.5 times the sea level pressure on Earth, which would be fairly comfortable if not for the lack of oxygen and the cold temperatures.

A moon with a thick atmosphere would be intriguing enough, but we have at least two other reasons for special interest in Titan. First, its complex atmospheric chemistry produces numerous carbon compounds—the chemicals that are the basis of life. Second, although it is far too cold for

Titan has a thick atmosphere, leading to methane rain and surprising erosional geology.

liquid water to exist on Titan, conditions are right for methane or ethane rain, which creates rivers flowing into lakes and seas. These facts led NASA and the European Space Agency (ESA) to combine forces to explore Titan. In 2005, NASA's *Cassini* "mother ship" released the ESA-built probe called *Huygens* (pronounced "Hoy-guns"), which parachuted to the surface (Figure 8.21). During its descent, the probe photographed river valleys merging together, flowing down to what looks like an ancient shoreline. On landing, instruments on the probe discovered that the surface has a hard crust but is a bit squishy below, perhaps like sand with liquid mixed in, and photos showed "ice boulders" rounded by erosion. All these results support the idea of a wet climate—but wet with liquid methane rather than liquid water.

Subsequent *Cassini* observations taught us more about Titan. The brighter regions in the central image of Figure 8.21 are icy hills that may have been made by ice volcanoes. The dark valleys were probably created

▼ **FIGURE 8.21**

This sequence zooms in on the *Huygens* landing site on Titan. Left: a global view taken by the orbiting *Cassini* spacecraft. Center: an aerial view from the descending probe. Right: a surface view taken by the probe after landing; the "rocks," which are 10–20 centimeters across, are presumably made of water ice.

600 km   1 km   5 cm

when methane rain carried down "smog particles" that concentrated on river bottoms. The vast plains into which the valleys appear to empty are low-lying regions, but they do not appear to be liquid. Instead, they are probably covered by smog particles carried down by the rivers and then sculpted into vast dune fields by Titan's global winds. All in all, conditions in Titan's equatorial regions appear to be analogous to those in the desert southwest of the United States, where infrequent rainfall carves valleys and creates vast dry lakes called *playas* where the water evaporates or soaks into the ground. The polar regions of Titan, revealed by *Cassini* radar, contain numerous lakes of liquid methane or ethane (Figure 8.22). Images also reveal polar storm clouds and riverbeds leading into the lakes, suggesting that Titan has a methane/ethane cycle resembling the water cycle on Earth.

Perhaps the most astonishing result from the *Cassini/Huygens* mission is how familiar the landscape looks in this alien environment with unfamiliar materials. Instead of liquid water, Titan has liquid methane and ethane. Instead of rock, Titan has ice. Instead of molten lava, Titan has a slush of water ice mixed with ammonia. Instead of surface dirt, Titan's surface has smog-like particles that rain out of the sky and accumulate on the ground. The similarities between the physical processes that occur on Titan and Earth appear to be far more important in shaping the landscapes than the fact that the two worlds have very different compositions and temperatures.

think about it What other geological features might you expect on Titan, given its similarities to Earth? How might those features be different, given the differences in temperature and composition?

Saturn's Medium-Size Moons The *Cassini* mission also flew past other moons of Saturn. The six medium-size moons reveal complex histories (Figure 8.23).

Only Mimas, the smallest of these six moons, shows little evidence of past volcanism or tectonics. It is essentially a heavily cratered iceball, with one huge crater nicknamed "Darth Crater" because of Mimas's resemblance to the Death Star in the *Star Wars* movies. Most of Saturn's other medium-size moons also have heavily cratered surfaces, confirming that they lack global geological activity today. However, we find abundant evidence of past volcanism and/or tectonics. Smooth regions appear to be places where icy lava once flowed, and close-up views of the bright streaks (such as the long streaks visible on Dione) show them to be vast sets of tectonic cliffs running parallel to one another.

RADIO

▲ **FIGURE 8.22**
Radar image of Ligeia Mare near Titan's north pole, showing lakes of liquid methane or ethane at a temperature of −180°C. Most solid surfaces reflect radar well, and these regions are artificially shaded tan to suggest land. The liquid surfaces reflect radar poorly, and these regions are shaded blue and black to suggest lakes.

▼ **FIGURE 8.23**
Portraits taken by the *Cassini* spacecraft of Saturn's medium-size moons (not to scale). All but Mimas show evidence of past volcanism and/or tectonics.

VIS

Mimas (398 km) Enceladus (498 km) Tethys (1060 km) Dione (1118 km) Rhea (1528 km) Iapetus (1436 km)

▲ FIGURE 8.24

Saturn's moon Iapetus has a 10-kilometer-tall equatorial ridge (white arrow) that spans nearly half its circumference. The inset shows a portion of the ridge in perspective.

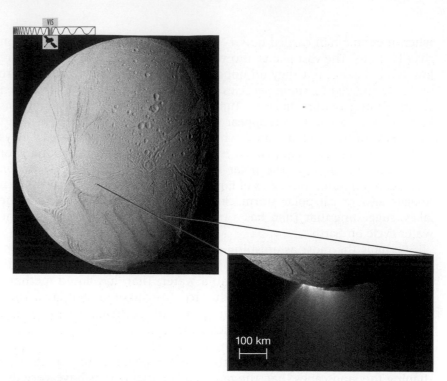

▲ FIGURE 8.25

Cassini photo of Saturn's moon Enceladus. The blue "tiger stripes" near the bottom of the main photo are regions of fresh ice that must have recently emerged from below. The colors are exaggerated; the image is a composite made at near-ultraviolet, visible, and near-infrared wavelengths. The inset shows Enceladus backlit by the Sun, with fountains of ice particles (and water vapor) clearly visible as they spray out of the south polar region.

Iapetus is particularly bizarre (Figure 8.24). It has an astonishing ridge more than 10 kilometers high that spans nearly half its circumference, curiously aligned along the equator. No one knows its origin, but it is likely the result of tectonic activity. Moreover, much of Iapetus appears coated in dark dust that apparently comes from Phoebe (see Figure 8.12), a small moon on which impacts can easily eject dust that then spirals inward toward Iapetus.

Enceladus provided an even bigger surprise: This moon is barely 500 kilometers across—small enough to fit inside the borders of Colorado—and yet it shows clear evidence of *ongoing* geological activity (Figure 8.25). Its surface has very few impact craters—and some regions have none at all—telling us that recent geological activity has erased older craters. The strange grooves near its south pole are measurably warmer than the surrounding terrain, and photographs show this region venting huge clouds of water vapor and ice crystals, some containing salt and rock dust. These fountains must have some subsurface source, and careful measurements of the way Enceladus wobbles on its axis as it orbits Saturn have led scientists to suspect that Enceladus has a global, subsurface ocean of liquid water or of a colder water/ammonia mixture. The ocean is estimated to lie 30 to 40 kilometers beneath the moon's surface and may be up to 30 kilometers in depth. This, in turn, makes us wonder about possible life on Enceladus. Internal heat on Enceladus comes from tidal heating through an orbital resonance (with Dione), though scientists were surprised to learn that the heating is enough to make Enceladus active today.

Enceladus is the smallest moon in the solar system known to be geologically active today.

think about it The *Cassini* mission was scheduled to end shortly after this book was published in 2017, with scientists taking some risks with the spacecraft during its final year in hopes of gathering spectacular new results. What did the spacecraft discover during its final year? What happened to it at the end, and why?

Moons of Uranus and Neptune We know far less about the moons of Uranus and Neptune, because they have been photographed close-up only once each, during the *Voyager 2* flybys of the 1980s. Nevertheless, we again see evidence of surprising geological activity.

Uranus has five medium-size moons (and no large moons), and at least three of them show evidence of past volcanism or tectonics. Miranda, the smallest of the five, is the most surprising (Figure 8.26). Despite its small size, it shows tremendous tectonic features and relatively few craters. Apparently, it underwent geological activity well after the heavy bombardment ended [Section 6.3], erasing its early craters.

The surprises continue with Neptune's moon Triton (Figure 8.27). Triton is a strange moon to begin with: It is a large moon, but it orbits Neptune "backward" (opposite to Neptune's rotation) and at a high inclination to Neptune's equator. These are telltale signs of a moon that was captured rather than formed in the disk of gas around its planet. No one knows how a moon as large as Triton could have been captured, but models suggest one possible mechanism: Triton may have once been a member of a binary Kuiper belt object that passed so close to Neptune that Triton lost energy and was captured while its companion gained energy and was flung away at high speed.

Triton's geology is just as surprising as its origin. It is smaller than our own Moon, yet its surface shows evidence of relatively recent geo-

Triton orbits Neptune "backward" and shows evidence of relatively recent geological activity.

logical activity. Some regions show signs of past volcanism, while others show wrinkly ridges (nicknamed "cantaloupe terrain") that appear tectonic in nature. Triton even has a very thin atmosphere that has left some wind streaks on its surface. It's likely that Triton was originally captured into an elliptical orbit, which may have led to enough tidal heating to explain its geological activity.

◆ **Why are jovian moons more geologically active than small rocky planets?**

Based on what we learned when studying the geology of the terrestrial worlds, the active geology of the jovian moons seems out of character with their sizes. Numerous jovian moons remained geologically active

Tidal heating plus the easy melting and deformation of ices means that even small icy moons can sustain geological activity.

far longer than Mercury or our Moon, yet they are no bigger and in many cases much smaller in size. However, there are two crucial differences between the jovian moons and the terrestrial worlds: composition and tidal heating.

Because they formed far from the Sun, most of the jovian moons contain ices that can melt or deform at far lower temperatures than rock. As a result, they can experience geological activity even when their interiors have cooled to temperatures far below those of rocky worlds. Indeed, except on Io, most of the volcanism that has occurred in the outer solar system is probably "ice volcanism" that produces a

▲ **FIGURE 8.26**

The surface of Uranus's moon Miranda shows astonishing tectonic activity despite its small size. The cliff walls seen in the inset are higher than those of the Grand Canyon on Earth.

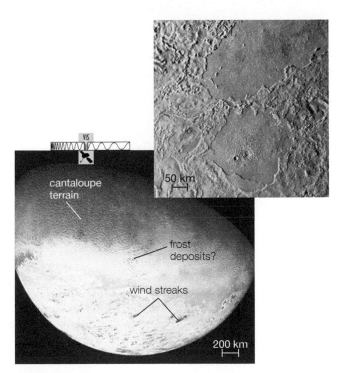

▲ **FIGURE 8.27**

Neptune's moon Triton shows evidence of a surprising level of past geological activity. Main image: Triton's southern hemisphere as seen by *Voyager 2*. Inset: The close-up shows lava-filled impact basins similar to the lunar maria, but the lava was water or slush rather than molten rock.

Terrestrial Planet Geology

- Internal heat, primarily from radioactive decay, can cause volcanic and tectonic activity.
- Only large planets retain enough internal heat to stay geologically active today.
- Example: Mars (photo above) probably retains some internal heat. If it had been smaller, like Mercury, it would be geologically "dead" today. If it had been larger, like Earth, it would probably have much more active and ongoing tectonics and volcanism.

Jovian Moon Geology

- Tidal heating can cause tremendous geological activity on moons with elliptical orbits around massive planets.
- Even without tidal heating, icy materials can melt and deform at lower temperatures than rock, increasing the likelihood of geological activity.
- Together, these effects explain why icy moons are much more likely to have ongoing geological activity than rocky terrestrial worlds of the same size.
- Example: Ganymede (photo above) shows evidence of recent geological activity, even though it is similar in size to the geologically dead terrestrial planet Mercury.

▲ **FIGURE 8.28**

Jovian moons can be much more geologically active than terrestrial worlds of similar size because of their icy compositions and tidal heating, which is not an important factor on the terrestrial worlds.

lava composed mainly of water, perhaps mixed with methane and ammonia.

The major lesson, then, is that "ice geology" is possible at far lower temperatures than "rock geology." This fact, combined in many cases with tidal heating, explains how the jovian moons have had such interesting geological histories despite their small sizes. Figure 8.28 summarizes the differences between the geology of jovian moons and that of the terrestrial worlds. We will see the role of ice geology again when we discuss Pluto in Chapter 9.

8.3 Jovian Planet Rings

The jovian planet systems have three major components: the planets themselves, the moons, and their rings. We have already studied the planets and their moons, so we now turn our attention to their amazing rings.

◆ What are Saturn's rings like?

You can see Saturn's rings through a backyard telescope, but learning their true nature requires higher resolution (Figure 8.29). From Earth, the rings appear to be continuous, concentric sheets of material separated by a large gap (called the *Cassini division*). Spacecraft images reveal

50,000 km

a This Earth-based telescopic view of Saturn makes the rings look like large, concentric sheets. The dark gap within the rings is called the *Cassini division*.

500 km

b This image of Saturn's rings from the *Cassini* spacecraft reveals many individual rings separated by narrow gaps.

10 m

c Artist's conception of particles in a ring system. Particles clump together because of gravity, but small random velocities cause collisions that break them up.

▲ **FIGURE 8.29**
Zooming in on Saturn's rings.

these "sheets" to be made of many individual rings, each separated from the next by a narrow gap. But even these appearances are somewhat deceiving. If we could wander into Saturn's rings, we'd find that they are made of countless icy particles ranging in size from dust grains to large boulders, sometimes clumped together by their mutual gravity. All are far too small to be photographed even from spacecraft passing nearby.

Ring Particle Characteristics Spectroscopy reveals that Saturn's ring particles are mostly made of relatively reflective water ice. The rings look bright where they contain enough particles to intercept sunlight and scatter it back toward us. We see gaps in places where there are few particles to reflect sunlight.

Each individual ring particle orbits Saturn independently in accord with Kepler's laws, so the rings are much like myriad tiny moons. The individual ring particles are so close together that they collide fre-

> Saturn's rings are made of vast numbers of icy particles ranging in size from dust grains to boulders, each circling Saturn according to Kepler's laws.

quently. In the densest parts of the rings, each particle collides with another every few hours. However, the collisions are fairly gentle: Despite the high orbital speeds of the ring particles, nearby ring particles orbit at nearly the same speed and in the same direction, and therefore touch only gently when they collide.

> **think about it** Which ring particles travel faster: those closer to Saturn or those farther away? Explain why. (*Hint:* Review Kepler's third law.)

The frequent collisions explain why Saturn's rings are one of the thinnest known astronomical structures. They span more than 270,000 kilometers in diameter but are only a few tens of *meters* thick. To understand how collisions keep the rings thin, imagine what would happen to a ring particle on an orbit slightly inclined to the central ring plane. The particle would collide with other particles every time its orbit intersected the ring plane, and its orbital tilt would be reduced with every collision. Before long, these collisions would force the particle to conform to the orbital pattern of the other particles, and any particle that moved away from the narrow ring plane would soon be brought back within it.

A gap moon (white dot) creates ripples as its gravity nudges particles that orbit faster than the moon (inside the gap) or slower (outside).

100 km

The 8-km-wide moon Daphnis clears a gap in the rings.

2000 km

▲ **FIGURE 8.30**
Small moons within the rings have important effects on ring structure (*Cassini* photos). The inset image was taken near Saturn's equinox, so the moon and ripples cast long shadows to the left.

9. Describe the atmosphere and surface features of Titan.
10. Why do we think Triton is a captured moon? How might its capture be relevant to its geological activity?
11. Briefly explain why icy moons can have active geology at much smaller sizes than rocky worlds.
12. What are planetary rings made of, and how do they differ among the four jovian planets? Briefly describe the effects of gap moons and orbital resonance on ring systems.
13. Explain why ring particles must be replenished over time, and where we think ring particles come from.

Test Your Understanding

Surprising Discoveries?

Suppose someone claimed to make the discoveries described below. (These are not real discoveries.) Decide whether each discovery should be considered reasonable or surprising. Explain clearly; not all of these have definitive answers, so your explanation is more important than your chosen answer.

14. Saturn's core is pockmarked with impact craters and dotted with volcanoes erupting lava.
15. Neptune's deep blue color is not due to methane, as previously thought, but instead is due to its surface being covered with an ocean of liquid water.
16. A jovian planet in another star system has a moon as big as Mars.
17. A planet orbiting another star is made primarily of hydrogen and helium and has approximately the same mass as Jupiter but the same size as Neptune.
18. A previously unknown moon orbits Jupiter outside the orbits of other known moons. It is the smallest of Jupiter's moons but has several large, active volcanoes.
19. A previously unknown moon orbits Neptune in the planet's equatorial plane and in the same direction that Neptune rotates, but it is made almost entirely of metals such as iron and nickel.
20. An icy, medium-size moon orbits a jovian planet in a star system that is only a few hundred million years old. The moon shows evidence of active tectonics.
21. A jovian planet is discovered in a star system that is much older than our solar system. The planet has no moons at all, but it has a system of rings as spectacular as the rings of Saturn.
22. Future observations discover rainfall of liquid water on Titan.
23. During a future mission to Uranus, scientists discover it is orbited by another 20 previously unknown moons.

Quick Quiz

Choose the best answer to each of the following. Explain your reasoning with one or more complete sentences.

24. Which lists the jovian planets in order of increasing distance from the Sun? (a) Jupiter, Saturn, Uranus, Pluto (b) Saturn, Jupiter, Uranus, Neptune (c) Jupiter, Saturn, Uranus, Neptune
25. Why does Neptune appear blue and Jupiter red? (a) Neptune is hotter, which means bluer thermal emission. (b) Methane in Neptune's atmosphere absorbs red light. (c) Neptune's air molecules scatter blue light, much as Earth's atmosphere does.
26. Why is Jupiter denser than Saturn? (a) It has a larger proportion of rock and metal. (b) It has a larger proportion of hydrogen. (c) Its higher mass and gravity compress its interior.
27. Some jovian planets give off more energy than they receive because of (a) fusion in their cores. (b) tidal heating. (c) ongoing contraction or differentiation.

28. The main ingredients of most moons of the jovian planets are (a) rock and metal. (b) frozen hydrogen compounds. (c) hydrogen and helium.
29. Why is Io more volcanically active than our moon? (a) Io is much larger. (b) Io has a higher concentration of radioactive elements. (c) Io has a different internal heat source.
30. What is unusual about Triton? (a) It orbits its planet backward. (b) It does not keep the same face toward its planet. (c) It is the only moon with its own rings.
31. Which moon shows evidence of rainfall and erosion by some liquid substance? (a) Europa (b) Titan (c) Ganymede
32. Saturn's many moons affect its rings through (a) tidal forces. (b) orbital resonances. (c) magnetic field interactions.
33. Saturn's rings (a) have looked basically the same since they formed along with Saturn. (b) were created long ago when tidal forces tore apart a large moon. (c) are continually supplied with new particles by impacts with small moons.

Process of Science

34. *Europan Ocean.* Scientists strongly suspect that Europa has a subsurface ocean, even though we cannot see through the surface ice. Briefly explain why scientists think this ocean exists. Is the "belief" in a Europan ocean scientific? Explain.
35. *Breaking the Rules.* As discussed in Chapter 7, the geological "rules" for the terrestrial worlds tell us that a world as small as Io should not have any geological activity. However, the *Voyager* images of Io's volcanoes proved that the old "rules" had been wrong. Based on your understanding of the nature of science [Section 3.4], should this be seen as a failure in the process of science? Defend your opinion.
36. *Unanswered Question.* Choose one unanswered question about a jovian planet or moon. Write a few paragraphs discussing the question and the specific types of evidence needed to answer it.

Group Work Exercise

37. *Comparing Jovian Moons.* **Roles:** *Scribe* (collects data and takes notes on the group's activities), *Proposer* (proposes hypotheses and explanations of the data), *Skeptic* (points out weaknesses in the hypotheses and explanations), *Moderator* (leads group discussion and makes sure everyone contributes). **Activity:** Compare the moons of Jupiter, drawing on the data in Appendix E.
    a. Collect data on Jupiter's four largest moons from Table E.3 in Appendix E and determine which moon has the greatest density.
    b. Use Table E.3 to determine what other solar system moon most resembles the moon from part (a) in mass, radius, and density.
    c. Propose a hypothesis about the composition of the moon from part (a), based on its resemblance to the moon from part (b), and examine potential concerns about the viability of the hypothesis.
    d. Use Table E.3 to determine whether there is a trend in density with orbital distance among the major moons of Jupiter; briefly describe any trends.
    e. Suggest a hypothesis that accounts for any trend found in part (d), and discuss potential concerns with the hypothesis.
    f. Develop and describe an experiment that could test the hypotheses in parts (c) and (e).

more like an unusually large comet. In the 1990s, astronomers began to discover other Pluto-like objects in this region, with the only major difference being that these other objects were smaller than Pluto. Apparently, Pluto was not so unusual in this part of the solar system.

As time passed, larger and larger objects were found in the Kuiper belt, culminating with the 2005 discovery of Eris (Figure 9.3), which is about the same size as Pluto but about 27% larger in mass. Eris is named for a Greek goddess who caused strife and arguments among humans, a commentary on the arguments its discovery caused about the definition of "planet." After all, if Pluto was a planet, then surely the more massive Eris must be one as well. This also led scientists to question the status of the numerous objects only slightly smaller than Pluto. Would they too become "planets"?

In 2006, the International Astronomical Union created the *dwarf planet* category to accommodate Pluto, Eris, and other "small bodies" that are large enough to be round (see Special Topic, page 7). Two other members of the Kuiper belt—Makemake and Haumea*—have also been designated dwarf planets, as has the asteroid Ceres. However, because the definition depends on roundness and we may not always know the precise shape of a distant object, dozens of other objects may yet join the list. Figure 9.4 compares the sizes of several dwarf planets and potential dwarf planets to that of Earth.

For most practical purposes, we now have straightforward definitions: Asteroids are rocky leftover planetesimals that orbit the Sun, comets are icy leftover planetesimals, and dwarf planets can be either asteroids or comets that are large enough to be round. However, even these seemingly simple boundaries can be fuzzy. One difficult case concerns the Kuiper belt, where all the objects from the smallest boulders to the largest dwarf planets probably share the same basic composition of ice and rock. In other words, they are all essentially comets of different sizes. That is why we often refer to all of them as *comets* of the Kuiper belt. However, some astronomers object to calling objects "comets" if they never venture into the inner solar system and show tails. As a result, you may also hear these objects referred to as *Kuiper belt objects* (*KBOs*) or *trans-Neptunian objects* (*TNOs*).

> In terms of composition, Pluto, Eris, and other large objects of the Kuiper belt are essentially large comets.

think about it Suppose that we someday discover an object in the Kuiper belt (or in the similar zone of another star system) that is Pluto-like in composition but as large in size as Earth. Under current definitions, the fact that it orbits in the same region as many similar objects would qualify it as a dwarf planet. Does that seem reasonable for an object the size of Earth? How would *you* classify it? Defend your opinion.

Meteors and Meteorites

In everyday language, we often use the terms *meteors* and *meteorites* interchangeably. Technically, however, a **meteor** (which means "a thing in the air") is only a flash of light caused by a particle of dust or rock entering our atmosphere at high speed, not the particle itself. Meteors are sometimes called *shooting stars* or *falling stars*, because some people once thought they really were stars falling from the sky.

The vast majority of the particles that make meteors are no larger than peas and burn up completely before reaching the ground. Only in rare cases is a meteor caused by a chunk of rock large enough to survive

---

*Haumea is actually oblong, but it counts as a dwarf planet because it would be round if not for its high rotation rate.

▲ **FIGURE 9.3**

Eris and its moon, photographed by the Hubble Space Telescope.

▲ **FIGURE 9.4**

The largest known objects of the Kuiper belt (as of 2016) and asteroid belt, along with their known moons, shown to scale with Earth for comparison. All except Pluto, Ceres, and Vesta are paintings based on guesses about their appearances. Pluto, Eris, Makemake, Haumea, and Ceres are officially considered dwarf planets, but some of the others may yet join the list.

▲ FIGURE 9.5
This large meteorite, called the Ahnighito Meteorite, is located at the American Museum of Natural History in New York. Its dark, pitted surface is a result of its fiery passage through Earth's atmosphere.

the plunge through our atmosphere and leave a **meteorite** (which means "associated with meteors") on the ground. Meteorites are usually covered with a dark, pitted crust resulting from their fiery passage through the atmosphere (Figure 9.5).

The origin of meteorites was long a mystery, but we now know that the vast majority of meteorites come from the asteroid belt, which means they are essentially either very small asteroids or pieces of asteroids. However, in a few cases, scientists have identified meteorites with compositions that appear to match either the Moon or Mars, and careful analysis makes us very confident that these meteorites were indeed chipped off these worlds. This makes sense: Moderately large impacts can blast surface material from terrestrial worlds into interplanetary space, where the rocks can orbit the Sun until they come crashing down on another world. Calculations show that it is not surprising that we should have found a few meteorites from the Moon and Mars in this way. These *lunar meteorites* and *Martian meteorites* therefore represent direct samples from these worlds, which makes them very valuable for scientific study.

9.2 Asteroids

We are now ready to turn our attention to studying asteroids. Scientifically, these small bodies are very important, because many of them remain much as they were when they first formed, some 4½ billion years ago. They therefore have clues to the story of our solar system's birth encoded in their compositions, locations, and numbers.

◆ What are asteroids like?

Asteroids come in a wide variety of sizes and shapes. The largest—dwarf planet Ceres—contains nearly as much mass as all other asteroids put together and is just under 1000 kilometers in diameter, or a little less than one-third the diameter of our Moon. Its low density and location in the outer part of the asteroid belt suggest that water ice makes up a significant fraction of its composition. The *Dawn* spacecraft entered orbit of Ceres in March 2015, giving us our first close-up look at this remarkable world (Figure 9.6). As expected, Ceres is covered by craters left by many past impacts. But it also held some surprises, including bright spots on its surface, which might be made of salt or other mineral deposits left behind as water vaporized and disappeared.

Prior to reaching Ceres, the *Dawn* spacecraft spent about 14 months (during 2011 and 2012) orbiting Vesta, the second-largest asteroid by mass. *Dawn* images revealed a battered world that is nearly 25% wider than it is tall (Figure 9.7). This irregular shape is probably a result of an impact that gouged out a huge crater near the south pole, which means that Vesta was probably once much more spherical in shape. Vesta may also have been volcanically active early in its history.

Besides Ceres and Vesta, about a dozen other asteroids are large enough that we would call them medium-size moons if they orbited a planet, but most asteroids are far smaller. Scientists estimate that there are more than a million asteroids that measure at least 1 kilometer across, and many more millions that are smaller in size. Despite their large numbers, asteroids don't add up to much in total mass. If we could put all the asteroids together (including Ceres and Vesta) and allow gravity to compress them into a

The total mass of all asteroids is much less than the mass of any terrestrial planet.

Mysterious bright spots on this crater floor are probably salt or other mineral deposits.

20 km

x5

x5

A mountain 4 km tall rises above otherwise bland surroundings, offering no clue to its origin (x5 vertical exaggeration).

20 km

▲ **FIGURE 9.6**

The dwarf planet Ceres, imaged by the *Dawn* spacecraft. The global view shows abundant craters and unexplained cracks and faults, while the insets focus on some of the most intriguing mysteries.

sphere, they'd make an object less than 2000 kilometers in diameter—just over half the diameter of our Moon.

Spacecraft visits have begun to reveal the character of small asteroids as well as large ones. Small asteroids come in diverse shapes (Figure 9.8), because their gravity is too weak to reshape them into spheres. Many may also be fragments of larger asteroids that were shattered in collisions. Some spacecraft have even been designed to return asteroid samples to Earth. The first was Japan's *Hayabusa* mission, which in 2010 returned a small dust sample from the asteroid Itokawa (see Figure 9.8d). The follow-up *Hayabusa 2*, launched in 2014, is on its way to collecting an asteroid sample in 2018 that is scheduled to be returned to Earth in 2020. NASA's ambitious *Osiris-REX* mission, launched in 2016, aims to return a sample in 2023 from an asteroid called 101955 Bennu, thought to be a carbon-rich asteroid that may be similar to the types of objects that brought many of the ingredients for oceans, atmosphere, and life to Earth.

◆ What do meteorites tell us about asteroids and the early solar system?

We can learn even more about asteroids by studying samples of them, and while spacecraft are only beginning to collect samples directly, we

Vesta

Vesta is much wider (across the equator) than it is tall . . .

. . . in part because a huge impact gouged out a crater near its south pole.

VIS

Equatorial view

South pole view

◀ **FIGURE 9.7**

Global images of Vesta taken by the *Dawn* spacecraft. The dashed circle is the outline of the huge polar crater.

Dodge Those Asteroids!

Science fiction movies often show brave spacecraft pilots navigating through crowded fields of asteroids, dodging this way and that as they heroically pass through with only a few bumps and bruises. It's great drama, but not very realistic. The asteroid belt looks crowded in Figure 9.10, but in reality it is an enormous region of space. Despite their large numbers, asteroids are so far apart on average that it would take incredibly bad luck to crash into one by accident. Indeed, spacecraft must be carefully guided to fly close enough to an asteroid to take a decent photograph. Future space travelers will have plenty of dangers to worry about, but dodging asteroids is not likely to be one of them.

9.3 Comets

We now turn our attention to comets. Although we now know that Pluto and other large objects of the Kuiper belt are essentially large comets, for most of human history the only known comets were the relatively small ones that sometimes enter the inner solar system and grow long tails. In this section, we'll explore modern understanding of small comets and how we learned that they come from the Kuiper belt and Oort cloud.

◆ Why do comets grow tails?

Far from the Sun, small comets must look much like small asteroids, with assorted shapes made possible by the fact that gravity is too weak to compress them into spheres. But they differ from asteroids in composition, as we expect for objects that formed in the cold outer solar system: Comets are basically chunks of ice mixed with rocky dust and some more complex chemicals, and hence they are often described as "dirty snowballs."

The Flashy Lives of Comets   The "dirty snowball" idea explains how comets grow tails when they are heated by the Sun. To see what happens, let's follow the comet path shown in Figure 9.12.

Far from the Sun, the comet is completely frozen—in essence, the "dirty snowball" in solid form. For a comet plunging inward, we call this frozen center the **nucleus** of the comet. As a comet accelerates toward the Sun, its surface temperature increases, and ices begin to vaporize into gas that easily escapes the comet's weak gravity. Some of the escaping gas drags away dust particles from the nucleus, and the gas and dust create a huge, dusty atmosphere called a **coma.** The coma grows as the comet continues into the inner solar system, and some of the gas

> When a comet nears the Sun, its ices can vaporize into gas and carry off dust, creating a coma and long tails.

▼ **FIGURE 9.12**
A comet grows a coma and tail around its nucleus only if it happens to come close to the Sun. Most comets never do this, instead remaining perpetually frozen in the far outer solar system.

Far from the Sun, the nucleus is frozen.

Nucleus warms and ice begins to vaporize into gas.

Gas coma begins to form around nucleus when comet is about 5 AU from Sun.

Tails form by about 1 AU from Sun; tails point away from Sun.

Dust tail is pushed by sunlight.

Earth's orbit

solar radiation

solar wind

Solar heating diminishes; coma and tail disappear between 3 and 5 AU from Sun.

Larger particles are unaffected by sunlight or solar wind.

Plasma tail is swept back by solar wind.

a This diagram (not to scale) shows the changes that occur when a comet's orbit takes it on a passage into the inner solar system.

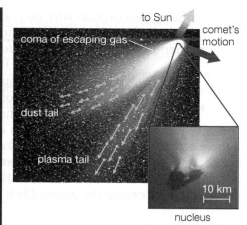

to Sun

comet's motion

coma of escaping gas

dust tail

plasma tail

nucleus

10 km

b Anatomy of a comet. The larger image is a ground-based photo of Comet Hale-Bopp. The inset shows the nucleus of Halley's Comet photographed by the *Giotto* spacecraft.

and dust is pushed away from the Sun, forming the comet's tails. Comet tails can be hundreds of millions of kilometers in length.

Comets have two visible tails. The **plasma tail** consists of gas that is ionized by ultraviolet light from the Sun and pushed outward by the solar wind. That is why the plasma tail extends almost directly away from the Sun at all times. The **dust tail** consists of dust-size particles that are unaffected by the solar wind and instead are pushed outward by the much weaker pressure of sunlight itself (*radiation pressure*). The dust tail therefore points generally away from the Sun, but has a slight curve back in the direction the comet came from.

After the comet loops around the Sun and begins to head back outward, vaporization declines, the coma dissipates, and the tails disappear. Nothing happens until the comet again comes sunward—in a century, a millennium, a million years, or perhaps never. Comets that do return eventually use up their ices, some crumbling into pieces and others becoming inactive nuclei.

Spacecraft missions have taught us more about comets. Our first clear view of a comet nucleus came from the European Space Agency's *Giotto* spacecraft, which flew past Halley's Comet during its 1986 visit to the inner solar system (see Figure 9.12b). In 2004, NASA's *Stardust* spacecraft captured dust particles from Comet Wild 2 (pronounced "vilt two"), returning them to Earth for scientific study. In 2005, NASA's *Deep Impact* mission sent a 370-kilogram projectile crashing into Comet Tempel 1 at 37,000 kilometers per hour. The impact created a plume of dust from the surface—so much dust that the comet must have been dust-covered to a depth of tens of meters—and hot gas composed of material vaporized from deep within the comet. Spectroscopy of this gas showed that the comet contains many complex organic molecules.

More recently, the European Space Agency's *Rosetta* mission began orbiting Comet 67P/Churyumov-Gerasimenko (Comet C-G for short) when it was still almost fully frozen in 2014, then stayed with the comet for more than a year as it approached and passed perihelion (Figure 9.13). *Rosetta* also sent a small lander, named *Philae*, to the surface of the comet, though it did not anchor itself as planned and therefore returned less data than had been hoped. Nevertheless, *Rosetta* and *Philae* already provided a wealth of information on the nature and behavior of comets. One of the most

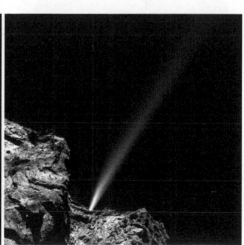

a September 2014, before substantial comet activity had begun.

b November 2014.

c Close-up of a jet shortly before perihelion in August 2015.

▲ **FIGURE 9.13**
Comet "C-G" (67P/Churyumov-Gerasimenko) as imaged by the *Rosetta* spacecraft.

interesting results shows that the water ice that drives cometary activity near the Sun is hidden under a substantial crust of dusty material that is composed of rock and carbon-bearing molecules. Virtually no ice is exposed at the surface. This explains the striking features in Figure 9.13c, in which we see jets of water vapor emanating from pits, or "sinkholes," where the crust has collapsed, exposing the ice at depth.

Comet Tails and Meteor Showers   Comets also eject sand- to pebble-size particles that are too big to be affected by either the solar wind or sunlight. These particles essentially form a third, invisible tail that follows the comet around its orbit. They are also the particles responsible for most meteors and meteor showers.

The sand- to pebble-size particles are much too small to be seen themselves, but they enter the atmosphere at such high speeds that they make the surrounding air glow with heat. It is this glow that we see as the brief but brilliant flash of a *meteor*, lasting only until the particle is vaporized by the heat.

Comet dust is sprinkled throughout the inner solar system, but the "third tails" of ejected particles are concentrated along the orbits of comets. As a result, while you can typically see a few meteors on any clear night,

A comet ejects small particles that cause meteor showers when Earth crosses the comet's orbit.

many more are visible on those nights when our planet is crossing a comet's orbit. You may see dozens of meteors per hour during one of these **meteor showers,** which recur at about the same time each year because the orbiting Earth passes through a particular comet's orbit at the same time each year. The meteors of a meteor shower generally appear to radiate from a particular direction in the sky, for essentially the same reason that snow or heavy rain seems to come from a particular direction in front of a moving car (Figure 9.14). Because more meteors hit Earth from

▼ **FIGURE 9.14**
The geometry of meteor showers.

Snowflakes and meteors appear to radiate from a single direction based on our motion relative to them.

a Meteors appear to radiate from a particular point in the sky for the same reason that we see snow or heavy rain come from a single point in front of a moving car.

b This digital composite photo, taken in Australia during the 2001 Leonid meteor shower, shows meteors as streaks of light radiating from the same point in the sky. The large rock is Uluru, also known as Ayers Rock. Note that, by eye, you would not see so many meteors all at once; each meteor would flash across your sky for a few seconds, and even in the best meteor showers you'd likely see one only every few minutes.

the front than from behind (just as more snow hits the front windshield of a moving car), meteor showers are best observed in the predawn sky, when part of the sky faces in the direction of Earth's motion. Table 9.1 lists major annual meteor showers and their parent comet, if known.

see it for yourself Try to observe the next meteor shower (see Table 9.1); be prepared with a star chart, a marker pen, and a dim (preferably red) flashlight. Each time you see a meteor, record its path on your star chart. Record at least a dozen meteors, and try to determine the *radiant* of the shower—that is, the constellation from which the meteors appear to radiate. Does the meteor shower live up to its name?

◆ Where do comets come from?

We've stated that comets we see in the inner solar system come from two vast reservoirs of comets in the distant outer solar system. But we've never actually seen any small comets at such great distances from the Sun, so you may wonder how we know they are out there. The answer is relatively simple: The comets that we see in the inner solar system must come from *somewhere*, and we can figure out where that somewhere must be by tracing their orbits back. We can then estimate numbers by figuring out how many must reside at great distances to explain the average number that enter the inner solar system each year.

Most comets that visit the inner solar system do not orbit the Sun in the same direction as the planets, and their elliptical orbits have random orientations. Tracing their orbits back shows that they come from far beyond the planets—sometimes nearly a quarter of the distance to the nearest star. These comets must come plunging sunward from the vast, spherical region of space that we call the *Oort cloud*. Be sure to note that the Oort cloud is *not* a cloud of gas, but rather a collection of many individual comets. Based on the number of Oort cloud comets that visit the inner solar system, the Oort cloud must contain about a trillion (10^{12}) comets.

A smaller number of the comets that visit the inner solar system travel around the Sun in the same direction and in nearly the same plane as the planets, and their elliptical orbits carry them no more than about twice as far from the Sun as Neptune. These comets must come from the donut-shaped *Kuiper belt* that lies beyond the orbit of Neptune. Figure 9.15 contrasts the general features of the Kuiper belt and the Oort cloud.

How did comets end up in these far-flung regions of the solar system? The only answer that makes scientific sense comes from thinking about what happened to the leftover icy planetesimals that roamed the region in which the jovian planets formed.

The leftover planetesimals that cruised the spaces between Jupiter, Saturn, Uranus, and Neptune were doomed to suffer either a collision or a close gravitational encounter with one of the young jovian planets. Recall that when a small object passes near a large planet, the planet is hardly affected but the small object may be flung off at high speed [Section 4.4]. The planetesimals that escaped being swallowed therefore tended to be flung off in all directions. Some may have been cast away at such high speeds that they completely escaped the solar system. The rest ended up on orbits with very large average distances from the Sun, becoming the comets of the Oort cloud. The random directions in which these comets were flung explain why the Oort cloud is roughly spherical in shape. Oort cloud comets are so far from the Sun that they can be nudged by the gravity of nearby stars (and even by the mass of the

TABLE 9.1	Major Annual Meteor Showers	
Shower Name	**Approximate Date**	**Associated Comet**
Quadrantids	January 3	?
Lyrids	April 22	Thatcher
Eta Aquarids	May 5	Halley
Delta Aquarids	July 28	?
Perseids	August 12	Swift-Tuttle
Orionids	October 22	Halley
Taurids	November 3	Encke
Leonids	November 17	Tempel-Tuttle
Geminids	December 14	Phaeton
Ursids	December 23	Tuttle

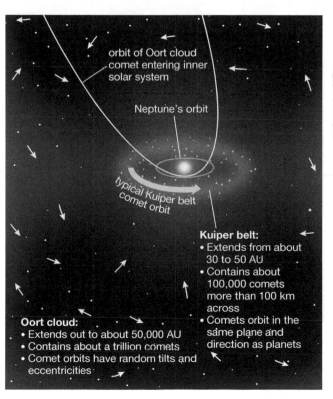

▲ **FIGURE 9.15**
The comets we occasionally see in the inner solar system come from two major reservoirs in the outer solar system: the Kuiper belt and the Oort cloud.

The graph above (Figure 9.27) shows how often impacts occur for objects of different sizes. The photo above shows Comet Tempel 1 moments before the *Deep Impact* spacecraft crashed into it.

1. Estimate Comet Tempel 1's diameter, using the scale bar in the photo above.

2. According to the graph above, how frequently do objects the size of Comet Tempel 1 strike Earth?
   a. once in Earth's history
   b. about once every hundred million years
   c. about once every million years
   d. about once every thousand years

3. Consider an object twice the size of Comet Tempel 1. What kind of damage would this object cause if it hit our planet?
   a. mass extinction
   b. widespread devastation and climate change
   c. atmospheric explosion or a small crater

4. Meteor Crater in Arizona is about 1.2 kilometers across. According to the graph, about how big was the object that made this crater? (*Note*: Be sure to read the axis labels carefully.)
   a. 1 meter   b. 10 meters
   c. 100 meters   d. 1 kilometer

5. How often do objects big enough to create craters like Meteor Crater impact Earth?
   a. once in Earth's history
   b. about once every ten thousand years
   c. about once every few million years
   d. about once every day, but most burn up in the atmosphere or land in the ocean

---

exercises and problems

MasteringAstronomy®   For instructor-assigned homework and other learning materials, go to MasteringAstronomy®.

Review Questions

Short-Answer Questions Based on the Reading

1. Briefly define *asteroid, comet, dwarf planet, meteor,* and *meteorite.* How did the discovery of Eris force astronomers to reconsider the definition of *planet*?

2. How large are asteroids? How does the total mass of all asteroids compare to the mass of a terrestrial world?

3. Distinguish between *primitive meteorites* and *processed meteorites* in terms of both composition and origin.

4. What do meteorites and spacecraft observations tell us about the geology of asteroids?

5. Where is the *asteroid belt* located, and why? Explain how orbital resonances with Jupiter affect the asteroid belt.

6. What produces the *coma* and *tails* of a comet? What is the *nucleus*? Why do the tails point away from the Sun?

7. How are *meteor showers* linked to comets, and why do they recur at about the same time each year?

8. Describe the *Kuiper belt* and *Oort cloud* in terms of their locations and the orbits of comets within them. How did comets come to exist in these two regions?

9. Briefly describe Pluto and Charon. Why won't Pluto collide with Neptune? How do we think Charon formed?

10. Briefly describe the evidence suggesting that an impact caused the *mass extinction* that killed off the dinosaurs. How might the impact have led to the mass extinction?

11. How often should we expect impacts of various sizes on Earth? How serious a threat do we face from these impacts?

12. Briefly summarize the role of the jovian planets in shaping the orbits of small bodies in the solar system and in influencing life on Earth.

Test Your Understanding

⚙ Surprising Discoveries?

Suppose someone claimed to make the discoveries described below. (These are not real discoveries.) Decide whether each discovery should be considered reasonable or surprising. More than one right answer may be possible, so explain your answer clearly.

13. A small asteroid that orbits within the asteroid belt has an active volcano.

14. Scientists discover a meteorite that, based on radiometric dating, is 7.9 billion years old.

15. An object that resembles a comet in size and composition is discovered orbiting in the inner solar system.

16. Studies of a large object in the Kuiper belt reveal that it is made almost entirely of rocky (as opposed to icy) material.

17. Astronomers discover a previously unknown comet that will be brightly visible in our night sky about 2 years from now.

18. A mission to Eris finds that it has lakes of liquid water on its surface.

19. Geologists discover a crater from a 5-kilometer object that impacted Earth more than 100 million years ago.

20. Archaeologists learn that the fall of ancient Rome was caused in large part by an asteroid impact in Asia.

21. In another solar system, astronomers discover an object the size of Earth orbiting its star at the distance of the Kuiper belt.

22. Astronomers discover an asteroid with an orbit suggesting that it will impact Earth in the year 2064.

Quick Quiz

Choose the best answer to each of the following. Explain your reasoning with one or more complete sentences.

23. The asteroid belt lies between the orbits of (a) Earth and Mars. (b) Mars and Jupiter. (c) Jupiter and Saturn.

24. Jupiter nudges the asteroids through the influence of (a) tidal forces. (b) orbital resonances. (c) magnetic fields.

25. Can an asteroid be pure metal? (a) No; all asteroids contain rock. (b) Yes; it must have formed where only metal could condense in the solar nebula. (c) Yes; it must be from the core of a shattered asteroid.

26. Did a large terrestrial planet ever form in the region of the asteroid belt? (a) No, because there was never enough mass there. (b) No, because Jupiter prevented one from accreting. (c) Yes, but it was shattered by a giant impact.

27. What does Pluto most resemble? (a) a terrestrial planet (b) a jovian planet (c) a comet

28. How big an object causes a typical "shooting star"? (a) a grain of sand or a small pebble (b) a boulder (c) an object the size of a car

29. Which have the most elliptical and tilted orbits? (a) asteroids (b) Kuiper belt comets (c) Oort cloud comets

30. Which are thought to have formed farthest from the Sun? (a) asteroids (b) Kuiper belt comets (c) Oort cloud comets

31. About how often does a 1-kilometer object strike Earth? (a) every year (b) every million years (c) every billion years

32. What would happen if a 1-kilometer object struck Earth? (a) It would break up in the atmosphere without causing widespread damage. (b) It would cause widespread devastation and climate change. (c) It would cause a mass extinction.

⚙ Process of Science

33. *The Pluto Debate.* Research the decision to demote Pluto to dwarf planet. In your opinion, is this a good example of the scientific process? Does it exhibit the hallmarks of science described in Chapter 3? Compare your conclusions to opinions you find about the debate, and describe how you think astronomers should handle this or similar debates in the future.

34. *Life or Death Astronomy.* In most cases, the study of the solar system has little direct effect on our lives. But the discovery of an asteroid or comet on a collision course with Earth is another matter. How should the standards for verifiable observations described in Chapter 3 apply in this case? Is the potential danger so great that any astronomer with any evidence of an impending impact should spread the word as soon as possible? Or is the potential for panic so great that even higher standards of verification ought to be applied? What kind of review process, if any, would you set in place? Who should be informed of an impact threat, and when?

Group Work Exercise

35. *Assessing Impact Danger.* **Roles:** *Scribe* (collects data and takes notes on the group's activities), *Proposer* (proposes hypotheses and explanations of the data), *Skeptic* (points out weaknesses in the hypotheses and explanations), *Moderator* (leads group discussion and makes sure everyone contributes). **Activity:** Assess the risks we face on Earth from meteorite and comet impacts as follows.

    a. Consider the question of the odds that human civilization will be destroyed by an impact during your lifetime. Determine the kinds of information you would need, develop a method for making the estimate, and write down your method.

    b. Analyze Figure 9.27 and determine whether it contains any of the necessary information.

    c. Apply your group's method to estimate the probability that civilization will be destroyed by an impact during your lifetime, which you can assume to be 100 years for the purpose of this exercise.

    d. Estimate the probability that an impact will cause "widespread devastation" somewhere on Earth during your lifetime.

    e. Finding near-Earth asteroids early greatly increases our chances of deflecting them. Given the probabilities from parts c and d and considering the damage these events would cause, decide as a group how much money per year should be spent on finding near-Earth asteroids and explain your reasoning.

Investigate Further

Short-Answer/Essay Questions

36. *The Role of Jupiter.* Suppose that Jupiter had never existed. Describe at least three ways in which our solar system would be different, and clearly explain why.

37. *Life Story of an Iron Atom.* Imagine that you are an iron atom in a processed meteorite made mostly of iron. Tell the story of how you got to Earth, beginning from the time you were part of the gas in the solar nebula 4.6 billion years ago. Include as much detail as possible. Your story should be scientifically accurate but also creative and interesting.

38. *Asteroids vs. Comets.* Contrast the compositions and locations of comets and asteroids, and explain in your own words why they have turned out differently.

39. *Comet Tails.* Describe in your own words why comets have tails. Why do most comets have two distinct visible tails, and why do the tails go in different directions? Why is the third, invisible tail of small pebbles of interest to us on Earth?

40. *Oort Cloud vs. Kuiper Belt.* Explain in your own words how and why there are two different reservoirs of comets. Be sure to discuss where the two groups of comets formed and what kinds of orbits they travel on.

41. *Project: Dirty Snowballs.* If there is snow where you live or study, make a dirty snowball. (The ice chunks that form behind tires work well.) How much dirt does it take to darken snow? Find out by allowing your dirty snowball to melt in a container and measuring the approximate proportions of water and dirt afterward.

Quantitative Problems

Be sure to show all calculations clearly and state your final answers in complete sentences.

42. *Adding Up Asteroids.* It's estimated that there are a million asteroids 1 kilometer across or larger. If a million asteroids 1 kilometer across were all combined into one object, how big would it be? How many 1-kilometer asteroids would it take to make an object as large as Earth? (*Hint:* You can assume they're spherical. The expression for the volume of a sphere is $\frac{4}{3}\pi r^3$, where r is the radius.)

43. *Impact Energies.* A relatively small impact crater 20 kilometers in diameter could be made by a comet 2 kilometers in diameter traveling at 30 kilometers per second (30,000 m/s).
    a. Assume that the comet has a total mass of 4.2×10^{12} kilograms. What is its total kinetic energy? (*Hint:* The kinetic energy is equal to $\frac{1}{2}mv^2$, where m is the comet's mass and v is its speed. If you use mass in kilograms and velocity in m/s, the answer for kinetic energy will have units of joules.)
    b. Convert your answer from part a to an equivalent in megatons of TNT, the unit used for nuclear bombs. Comment on the degree of devastation such a comet could cause if it struck a populated region on Earth. (*Hint:* One megaton of TNT releases 4.2×10^{15} joules of energy.)

44. *The "Near Miss" of Toutatis.* The 5-kilometer asteroid Toutatis passed a mere 1.5 million kilometers from Earth in 2004. Suppose Toutatis were destined to pass *somewhere* within 1.5 million kilometers of Earth. Calculate the probability that this "somewhere" would have meant that it slammed into Earth. Based on your result, do you think it is fair to call the 2004 passage a "near miss"? Explain. (*Hint:* You can calculate the probability by considering an imaginary dartboard of radius 1.5 million kilometers in which the bull's-eye has Earth's radius, 6378 kilometers.)

45. *Room to Roam.* It's estimated that there are a trillion comets in the Oort cloud, which extends out to about 50,000 AU. What is the total volume of the Oort cloud, in cubic AU? How much space does each comet have in cubic AU, on average? Take the cube root of the average volume per comet to find the comets' typical spacing in AU. (*Hints:* For the purpose of this calculation, you can assume the Oort cloud fills the whole sphere out to 50,000 AU. The volume of a sphere is given by $\frac{4}{3}\pi r^3$, where r is the radius.)

46. *Comet Dust Accumulation.* A few hundred tons of comet dust are added to Earth daily from the millions of meteors that enter our atmosphere. Estimate the time it would take for Earth to get 0.1% heavier at this rate. Is this mass accumulation significant for Earth as a planet? Explain.

🌑 Discussion Questions

47. *Rise of the Mammals.* Suppose the impact 65 million years ago had not occurred. How do you think our planet would be different? For example, do you think that mammals still would eventually have come to dominate Earth? Would we be here? Defend your opinions.

48. *How Should Kids Count Planets?* The demotion of Pluto from planet to dwarf planet affected many teachers because they had to change from talking about nine planets to eight, and even a decade after the demotion many teachers still haven't fully accepted it. Should they? How would you recommend that school teachers deal with the new definitions? Be sure to consider both alternative definitions and the fact that it remains possible that the International Astronomical Union may change the definitions again in the future.

Web Projects

49. *Asteroid and Comet Missions.* Learn about a current or planned space mission to study asteroids or comets. What are its scientific goals? Write a one- to two-page summary of your findings.

50. *Impact Hazards.* Many groups are searching for near-Earth asteroids that might impact our planet. They use something called the Torino Scale to evaluate the possible danger posed by an asteroid based on how well we know its orbit. What is this scale? What object has reached the highest level on this scale? What were the estimated chances of impact, and when?

51. *Beneficial Asteroids.* Learn about one of several efforts under way to mine asteroids for human benefit. How far along are the efforts? Discuss the issues that will determine if they succeed.

10 Other Planetary Systems
The New Science of Distant Worlds

20 AU
0.5″

This infrared image from the Large Binocular Telescope shows direct detection of four planets (marked b, c, d, e) orbiting the star HR 8799. Light from the star itself (center) was mostly blocked out during the exposure, as indicated by the solid red circle.

The Copernican revolution, which taught us that Earth is a planet orbiting the Sun, opened up the possibility that planets might also orbit other stars. Still, until the 1990s, no such planets were known. But then another scientific revolution began, and the list of known extrasolar planets now is in the thousands and growing rapidly.

The advancing science of extrasolar planets has dramatic implications for our understanding of our place in the universe. The fact that planets are common in the universe makes it seem more likely that we might someday find life elsewhere, perhaps even intelligent life. Moreover, having many more worlds to compare to our own vastly enhances our ability to learn how planets work, which may help us better understand our home planet, Earth. It also allows us to test the nebular theory of solar system formation in new settings. In this chapter, we'll focus our attention on the exciting new science of other planetary systems.

10.1 Detecting Planets Around Other Stars

We've known for centuries that other stars are distant suns, making it natural to suspect that they would have their own planetary systems. The nebular theory of solar system formation, well established decades ago, made such systems seem even more likely, because it predicts that planetary systems should form as a natural outcome of the processes that accompany the birth of any star. However, it took many decades for technology to reach the point at which this prediction could be put to the test through a search for planets around other stars, or **extrasolar planets** for short. The result has been an astounding success for the theory.

◆ How do we detect planets around other stars?

Detecting extrasolar planets poses a huge technological challenge for two basic reasons. First, as we discussed in Chapter 1, planets are extremely tiny compared to the vast distances between stars. Second, stars are typically *a billion times* brighter than the light reflected by any orbiting planets, so starlight tends to overwhelm any planetary light in photographs. This problem is somewhat lessened—but not eliminated—if we observe in infrared light, because planets emit their own infrared light and stars are usually dimmer in the infrared.

The first step in understanding how scientists are overcoming these challenges is to recognize that there are two general ways of learning about a distant object: *directly*, which means by obtaining images or spectra of the object, and *indirectly*, which means by inferring the object's existence or properties without actually seeing it. While scientists have achieved some success in direct detection (such as the image that opens this chapter), we will need significant advances in technology before we will be able to obtain higher-resolution images or spectra. As a result, nearly all current understanding of extrasolar planets comes from indirect study. There are two major indirect approaches to finding and studying extrasolar planets:

1. Observing the motion of a star to detect the subtle gravitational tugs of orbiting planets

2. Observing changes to a star's brightness that occur when one of its planets passes in front of the star as viewed from Earth

Almost all extrasolar planets detected to date have been found indirectly rather than through direct observation.

The earliest discoveries of extrasolar planets came primarily through the first approach, but the current champion of extrasolar planet discoveries— NASA's *Kepler* mission—used the second. We can learn even more when we can combine both indirect approaches, because each can provide different information about a distant planet.

Gravitational Tugs Although we usually think of a star as remaining still while planets orbit around it, that is only approximately correct. In reality, all the objects in a star system, including the star itself, orbit the system's "balance point," or *center of mass*. To understand how this fact allows us to discover extrasolar planets, imagine the viewpoint of extraterrestrial astronomers observing our solar system from afar.

Let's start by considering only the influence of Jupiter (Figure 10.1). Jupiter is the most massive planet, but the Sun still outweighs it by about a thousand times. As a result, the center of mass between the Sun and Jupiter lies about one-thousandth of the way from the center of the Sun to the center of Jupiter, putting it just outside the Sun's visible surface. In other words, what we usually think of as Jupiter's 12-year orbit around the Sun is really a 12-year orbit around their center of mass. Because the Sun and Jupiter are always on opposite sides of the center of mass (otherwise it wouldn't be a "center"), the Sun must orbit this point with the same 12-year period. The Sun's orbit traces out only a small ellipse with each 12-year period, because the Sun's average orbital distance is barely larger than its own radius. Nevertheless, with sufficiently precise measurements, extraterrestrial astronomers could detect this orbital movement of the Sun and thereby deduce the existence of Jupiter, even without having observed Jupiter itself. They could even determine Jupiter's mass from the orbital characteristics of the Sun as it goes around the center of mass. A more massive planet at the same distance would pull the center of mass farther from the Sun's center, giving the Sun a larger orbit. Because the Sun's period around the center would still be 12 years, the larger orbit would mean a faster orbital speed around the center of mass.

see it for yourself To see how a small planet can make a big star wobble, find a pencil and tape a heavy object (such as a set of keys) and a lighter object (perhaps a few coins) to opposite ends. Tie a string (or piece of floss) at the balance point—the center of mass—so that the pencil is horizontal. Then tap the lighter object into "orbit" around the heavier object. What does the heavier object do, and why? How does your setup correspond to a planet orbiting a star? Experiment further with objects of different weights or shorter pencils; try to explain the differences you see.

Planets exert gravitational tugs on their star, causing the star to orbit around the system's center of mass.

The other planets also exert gravitational tugs on the Sun, each adding a small additional effect to the effects of Jupiter (Figure 10.2). In principle, with

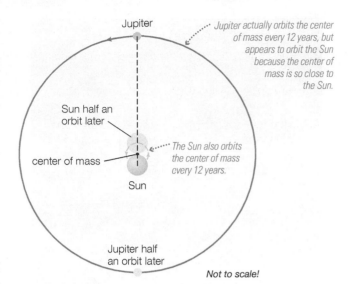

▲ FIGURE 10.1

This diagram shows how both the Sun and Jupiter orbit around their mutual center of mass, which lies very close to the Sun. The diagram is not to scale; the sizes of the Sun and its orbit are exaggerated about 100 times compared to the size shown for Jupiter's orbit, and Jupiter's size is exaggerated even more.

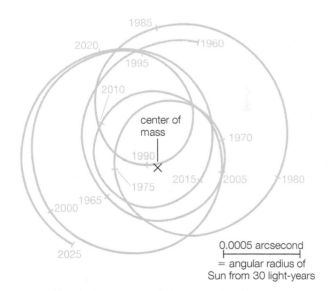

▲ FIGURE 10.2

This diagram shows the orbital path of the Sun around the center of mass of our solar system as it would appear from a distance of 30 light-years away, for the period 1960–2025. Notice that the entire range of motion during this period is only about 0.0015 arcsecond, which is almost 100 times smaller than the angular resolution of the Hubble Space Telescope. Nevertheless, if alien astronomers could measure this motion, they could learn of the existence of planets in our solar system.

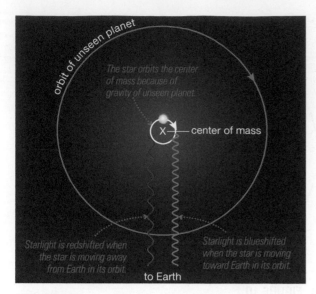

▲ FIGURE 10.3

The Doppler method for discovering extrasolar planets: The star's Doppler shift alternates toward the blue and toward the red, allowing us to detect its slight motion—caused by an orbiting planet—around the center of mass.

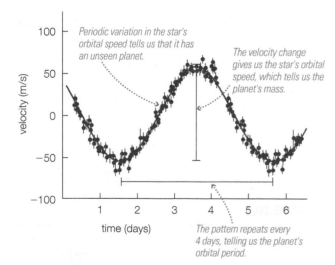

▲ FIGURE 10.4

A periodic Doppler shift in the spectrum of the star 51 Pegasi reveals the presence of a large planet with an orbital period of about 4 days. Dots are actual data points; bars through dots represent measurement uncertainty.

sufficiently precise measurements of the Sun's orbital motion made over many decades, an extraterrestrial astronomer could deduce the existence of all the planets of our solar system. If we turn this idea around, it means we can search for planets in other star systems by carefully watching for the tiny orbital motion of a star around the center of mass of its star system.

The Astrometric Method Astronomers use two distinct observation methods to search for the gravitational tugs of planets on stars. The first, called the **astrometric method** (*astrometry* means "measurement of the stars"), uses very precise measurements of stellar positions in the sky to look for the slight motion caused by orbiting planets. If a star "wobbles" gradually around its average position (the center of mass), we must be observing the influence of unseen planets.

The primary difficulty with the astrometric method is that we are looking for changes to position that are very small even for nearby stars, and these changes become smaller for more distant stars. In addition, the stellar motions are largest for massive planets orbiting far from their star, but the long orbital periods of such planets mean that it can take decades to notice the motion. As a result, the astrometric method has been of only limited use to date. However, the European Space Agency's *GAIA* mission, launched in 2013, should soon change this. *GAIA* has a goal of obtaining astrometric observations of a billion stars in our galaxy with an accuracy of 10 microarcseconds, which should enable it to detect thousands of extrasolar planets.

> The *astrometric method* searches for small "wobbles" in a star's position.

The Doppler Method The other method of searching for gravitational tugs due to orbiting planets is the **Doppler method**, which searches for a star's orbital movement around the center of mass by looking for changing Doppler shifts in its spectrum [Section 5.2]. Recall that the Doppler effect causes a blueshift when a star is moving toward us and a redshift when it is moving away from us, so alternating blueshifts and redshifts (relative to a star's average Doppler shift) indicate orbital motion around a center of mass (Figure 10.3).

As an example, Figure 10.4 shows data from the first discovery of an extrasolar planet around a Sun-like star: the 1995 discovery of a planet orbiting the star called 51 Pegasi. The 4-day period of the star's motion must be the orbital period of its planet. We therefore know that the planet lies so close to the star that its "year" lasts only 4 Earth days, which means its surface temperature is probably over 1000 K. The Doppler data also allow us to determine the planet's approximate mass, because a more massive planet has a greater gravitational effect on the star (for a given orbital distance) and therefore causes the star to move at higher speed around the system's center of mass. In the case of 51 Pegasi, the data show that the planet has about half the mass of Jupiter. Scientists therefore refer to this planet as a **hot Jupiter**, because it has a Jupiter-like mass but a much higher surface temperature.

> The *Doppler method* searches for alternating blueshifts and redshifts in a star's spectrum.

The Doppler method has proven very successful. As of 2016, it has been used to detect about 700 planets, including more than 100 in multiplanet systems. Keep in mind that because the Doppler method searches for gravitational tugs from orbiting planets, it is much better for finding massive planets like Jupiter than small planets like Earth. It's also best suited to identifying planets that orbit relatively close to their

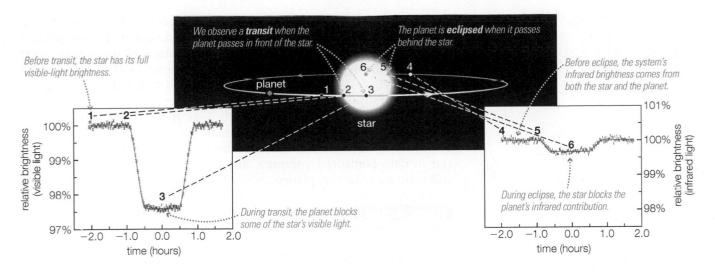

Before transit, the star has its full visible-light brightness.

We observe a **transit** when the planet passes in front of the star.

The planet is **eclipsed** when it passes behind the star.

Before eclipse, the system's infrared brightness comes from both the star and the planet.

planet

star

During transit, the planet blocks some of the star's visible light.

During eclipse, the star blocks the planet's infrared contribution.

star, because being closer means a stronger gravitational tug and hence a greater velocity for the star as it orbits the system's center of mass. Shorter orbits also allow easier confirmation of a planet's existence, because it is easier to record multiple repeats of the Doppler curve.

Transits The second general approach to detecting planets indirectly relies on searching for slight changes in a star's brightness caused by orbiting planets. If we were to examine a large sample of stars with planets, a small number of these systems—probably about 1%—would by chance be aligned in such a way that one or more of the star's planets would pass directly between us and the star once each orbit. The result is a **transit**, in which the planet appears to move across the face of the star, causing a small, temporary dip in the system's brightness (Figure 10.5). The larger the planet, the more dimming it will cause. Some transiting planets also undergo a measurable **eclipse** as the planet goes behind the star. Eclipse observations are more easily accomplished in the infrared, because planets contribute a greater proportion of a system's infrared brightness than its visible-light brightness.

The **transit method** searches for transits and eclipses by carefully monitoring a star system's brightness over an extended period of time. Because most stars exhibit intrinsic variations in brightness, we can be confident that we have detected a planet only if we observe the dips in brightness to repeat with a regular period, indicating that the same planet is passing in front of the star at the same time in each orbit.

If a planet happens to orbit edge-on as seen from Earth, its star will dim slightly as the planet passes in front of its star.

The period of the repeated transits is the orbital period of the planet. Scientists generally require at least three repeated transits before concluding that a planet is probably responsible, meaning at least about 3 years of monitoring to detect a planet in an Earth-like orbit around a Sun-like star.

think about it Suppose you were an alien astronomer searching for planets going around our Sun. Where would your star system have to be located in order for you to observe transits across the Sun? Which planets in our solar system would be the easiest to discover through transits? Explain.

Transits have been observed with many telescopes (including some as small as backyard telescopes), but the vast majority of transit detections to date came from NASA's *Kepler* mission, which searched for planetary transits from 2009 to 2013. *Kepler* monitored about 150,000 stars

▲ **FIGURE 10.5**

This diagram represents transits and eclipses of the planet orbiting the star HD 189733. The graph shows that each transit lasts about 2 hours, during which the star's visible-light brightness dips by about 2.5%. The eclipses are observable in the infrared, because the star blocks the infrared contribution of the planet. The transits and eclipses each occur once during every 2.2-day orbit of the planet.

for transits, measuring their brightnesses about every 30 minutes. Based on data that had been analyzed by mid-2016, scientists had already identified about 2000 stars being orbited by a total of more than 4000 planet "candidates," including dozens that are as small as Earth. The term "candidates" is used because even though *Kepler* data show three (or more) transits, the existence of these planets has not yet been confirmed by follow-up observations (such as detection by the Doppler method); as a result, there's still a small possibility that some "candidates" are artifacts of something besides an orbiting planet that causes a star to dim. Statistically, though, at least about 90% of the candidates will turn out to be real planets.

think about it As this book went to press, two new transit missions— NASA's *TESS* and the European Space Agency's *CHEOPS*—were slated for launch in late 2017. Find the goals and current status of these missions. How will they build on *Kepler*'s discoveries?

Other Strategies Cosmic Context Figure 10.6 (pages 272–273) summarizes the major planet detection methods, both indirect and direct. However, several other methods have also had some success. For example, more than a dozen planets have been detected by what is sometimes called *microlensing*, which is a type of gravitational lensing [Section 18.2] in which the light of a star is temporarily magnified as another star passes in front of it and bends its light. Careful study of the microlensing event can reveal whether the foreground star has planets. The major drawback to this method is that the special alignment necessary for microlensing is a one-time event, which generally means that there is no opportunity for confirmation or follow-up observations. A different strategy takes advantage of the fact that many stars are surrounded by disks of dust. A planet within such a disk can exert small gravitational tugs on dust particles to produce gaps, waves, or ripples that may be detectable. As we learn more about extrasolar planets, new search methods are sure to arise.

10.2 The Nature of Planets Around Other Stars

The mere existence of planets around other stars has changed our perception of our place in the universe, because it shows that our planetary system is not unique. Scientifically, however, we want to know much more than just that these planets exist. In this section, we'll explore what we have learned to date about planets around other stars.

◆ What properties of extrasolar planets can we measure?

Despite the challenge of detecting extrasolar planets, we can learn a surprising amount about them. Depending on the method or methods, we can determine such planetary characteristics as orbital period and distance, orbital eccentricity, mass, size, density, and even a little bit about a planet's atmospheric composition and temperature.

Orbital Period and Distance All three of the major indirect detection methods tell us a planet's orbital period. The astrometric method allows us to observe the star's orbital motion around the system's center of mass, which means we know the star's orbital period; the planet's orbital period must be the same. For the Doppler method, a detected planet's orbital period is simply the time between peaks in the star's velocity curve (see Figure 10.4), and for the transit method, the orbital period is the time between repeated transits.

Once we know the orbital period, we can determine average orbital distance (semimajor axis) with Newton's version of Kepler's third law [Section 4.4]. Recall that for a small object like a planet orbiting a much more massive object like a star, this law expresses a relationship between the star's mass, the planet's orbital period, and the planet's average distance. We generally know the masses of the stars with extrasolar planets (through methods we'll discuss in Chapter 12). Therefore, using the star's mass and the planet's orbital period, we can calculate the planet's average orbital distance.

The major detection methods all tell us orbital period, from which we can calculate orbital distance.

Orbital Eccentricity All planetary orbits are ellipses, but recall that ellipses vary in eccentricity, which is a measure of how "stretched out" they are (see Figure 3.13). The planets in our solar system all have nearly circular orbits (low eccentricity), which means that their actual distances from the Sun are always relatively close to their average distances. Planets with higher eccentricity swing in close to their star on one side of their orbit and go much farther from their star on the other side.

We can determine eccentricity from both the astrometric method and the Doppler method, though most measurements to date come from Doppler data. A planet with a perfectly circular orbit travels at a constant speed around its star, so its velocity curve is perfectly symmetric. Any asymmetry in the velocity curve tells us that the planet is moving with varying speed along the orbit and therefore must have a more eccentric elliptical orbit.

Planetary Mass Both the astrometric method and the Doppler method measure motions caused by the gravitational tug of a planet, so both can in principle allow us to estimate planetary masses. These methods tell us about planetary mass because, for a given orbital distance, a more massive planet will cause its star to move at higher velocity around the center of mass.

There is an important caveat for the Doppler method. Recall that Doppler shifts reveal only the part of a star's motion directed toward or away from us (see Figure 5.15). As a result, the Doppler shift tells us a star's full orbital velocity only when we view its orbit precisely edge-on. In all other cases, the velocity inferred from Doppler shifts will be less than the full orbital velocity, which means that the mass we calculate will be the planet's *minimum* possible mass (or a "lower limit" mass). Statistically, however, we expect that the actual planetary mass should be no more than double the minimum mass in at least about 85% of all cases, so masses from the Doppler method provide relatively good estimates for most planets.

Planetary Size Transit observations are presently the only means by which we can measure a planet's size or radius. The basic idea is easy to understand: The more of a star's light that a planet blocks during a transit, the larger the planet must be.

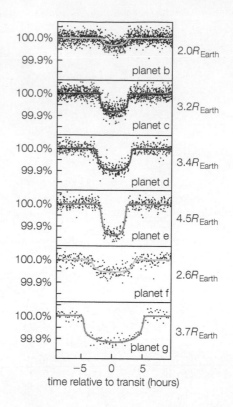

FIGURE 10.7

Transits from the six planets of the Kepler 11 system, known as Kepler 11b through Kepler 11g. (Kepler 11a is the star.) The black line shows the brightness of the star Kepler 11 over a 110-day period. Colored dots indicate transits by six different planets; in some cases, more than one planet transits at the same time. The panels at right show the dips due to each planet separately, and indicate the planet's size in Earth radii.

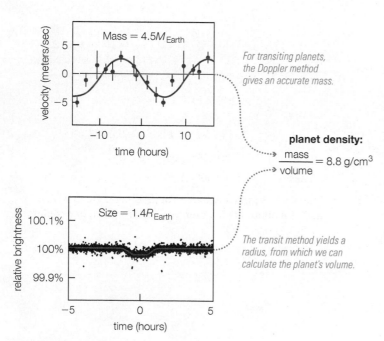

FIGURE 10.8

This diagram summarizes how we can combine data from the Doppler and transit methods to calculate a planet's average density. Data are for the planet Kepler 10b. (The final density calculation requires converting the mass to grams and the volume to units of cubic centimeters.)

The Kepler 11 planetary system offers a great example. Figure 10.7 shows the brightness of the star Kepler 11 over a 110-day period. Each downward dip represents a transit in which a planet blocks a small fraction of the starlight. Careful study shows that there are six different planets (represented by the colored dots) that transit the star. The panels show a transit of each planet in more detail, along with the planet's size calculated from the depth of the dip. When we combine these sizes with the orbital periods and distances, we find that this system's planets have sizes ranging from 2 to 5 times Earth's size and all orbit between 0.1 and 0.5 AU from their star. Transported to our solar system, the six planets would lie inside Venus's orbit.

The astrometric and Doppler methods tell us about planetary mass, while the transit method tells us planetary size.

think about it New data are coming in so quickly that the records for lowest-mass planet and smallest-size planet change rapidly. Do a Web search to find the extrasolar planet that currently holds the record for lowest confirmed *mass* and for smallest measured *size*.

Planetary Density No single method measures a planet's average density (mass divided by volume), but we can calculate it if we know a planet's size from the transit method and its mass from the Doppler method. Note that we can get a precise density value in this case, because transiting planets must have edge-on orbits, so the Doppler method gives an exact (rather than minimum) mass in these cases. Figure 10.8 shows the process applied to a planet known as Kepler 10b.

Atmospheric Composition and Temperature Although detailed understanding of the atmospheres and temperatures of extrasolar planets will have to await technology capable of direct observations

TABLE 10.1 Major Ways of Measuring Properties of Extrasolar Planets

	Planetary Property	Method(s) Used	Explanation
Orbital Properties	period	Doppler, astrometric, or transit	We directly measure orbital period.
	distance	Doppler, astrometric, or transit	We calculate orbital distance from orbital period using Newton's version of Kepler's third law.
	eccentricity	Doppler or astrometric	Velocity curves and astrometric star positions reveal eccentricity.
Physical Properties	mass	Doppler or astrometric	We calculate mass based on the amount of stellar motion caused by a planet's gravitational tug.
	size (radius)	transit	We calculate size based on the amount of dip in a star's brightness during a transit.
	density	transit plus Doppler	We calculate density by dividing the mass by the volume (using the size from the transit method).
	atmospheric composition, temperature	transit or direct detection	Transits and eclipses provide data on atmospheric composition and temperature.

and spectra, careful analysis of data from transits and eclipses can provide some information.

Infrared observations of eclipses provide the key data for temperature. Recall that planets generally emit infrared light, and the amount of infrared emission (per unit area) depends on a planet's temperature. As a planet goes behind its star, the system's infrared brightness will drop because we are no longer seeing the planet's infrared emission. The extent of the drop tells us how much infrared the planet emits, and we can combine this amount of infrared emission with the planet's radius (measured by the transits) to calculate an approximate temperature.

Transits and eclipses can also provide limited information about atmospheric composition. For a planet with an atmosphere, astronomers compare spectra of the system taken with the planet in front of (for transits) or behind (for eclipses) its star to spectra taken at other times. Careful analysis of differences between these spectra can reveal spectral lines caused by the planet's atmosphere. Because we generally know what gases are responsible for particular spectral lines, we can infer the existence of these gases in the planet's atmosphere.

Table 10.1 summarizes how we measure planetary properties.

◆ How do extrasolar planets compare with planets in our solar system?

The number of known extrasolar planets for which we have measured key properties is now large enough that we are beginning to gain insight into how these planets compare to the planets of our own solar system. Let's explore the general features of extrasolar planets as we know them today.

Orbital Properties A few extrasolar planets have been found with sizes and orbits similar to those of Earth (Figure 10.9). However, many others exhibit one or both of two orbital properties that seem surprising in light of what we know about our own solar system. First, many of them orbit quite close to their stars—in many cases much closer than Mercury orbits the Sun—even though they seem to be Jupiter-like in mass or size. Second, many have relatively large eccentricities, a clear contrast with the nearly circular orbits of planets in our solar system.

Part of the reason for these surprising properties is the nature of our detection methods. Recall that all the methods require much more time to discover planets with long orbital periods—those orbiting far from their stars—than planets with short orbital periods. Since we haven't been

cosmic calculations 10.1

Finding Sizes of Extrasolar Planets

We determine a planet's radius from the fraction of a star's light blocked during a transit. Viewed against the sky, both the star and the planet appear as tiny circular disks. These disks are far too small for our telescopes to resolve, but the fraction of the star's light that is blocked must be equal to the area of the planet's disk (r_{planet}^2) divided by the area of the star's disk (r_{star}^2):

$$\frac{\text{fraction of}}{\text{light blocked}} = \frac{\text{area of planet's disk}}{\text{area of star's disk}} = \frac{\pi r_{planet}^2}{\pi r_{star}^2} = \frac{r_{planet}^2}{r_{star}^2}$$

Solving for the planet's radius, we find

$$r_{planet} = r_{star} \times \sqrt{\text{fraction of light blocked}}$$

Example: Figure 10.5 shows a transit of the star HD 189733. The star's radius is about 800,000 kilometers ($1.15 R_{Sun}$), and the planet blocks 1.7% of the star's light during a transit. What is the planet's radius?

Solution: We simply plug the given data into the above formula:

$$r_{planet} = r_{star} \times \sqrt{\text{fraction of light blocked}}$$
$$= 800{,}000 \text{ km} \times \sqrt{0.017}$$
$$\approx 100{,}000 \text{ km}$$

The planet's radius is about 100,000 kilometers, which makes it about 40% larger in radius than Jupiter (radius 71,500 kilometers).

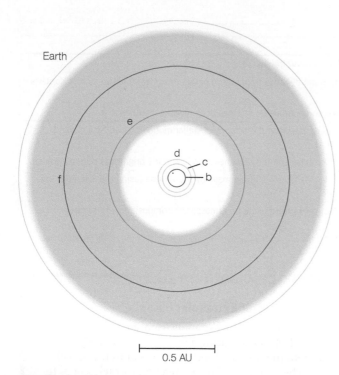

▲ FIGURE 10.9

A top-down view of planetary orbits in the Kepler 11 system, compared to Earth's orbit. The green region shows the *habitable zone* [Section 19.3] of this planetary system; the habitable zone is interior to that around our Sun because the Kepler 11 star is one-fifth as bright as the Sun. The two planets in the habitable zone (shaded green) are "super-Earths," having radii 40% and 60% greater than Earth's.

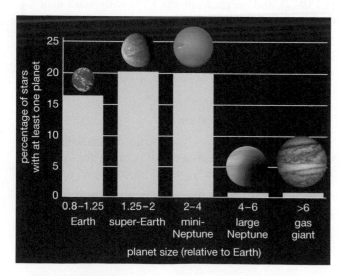

▲ FIGURE 10.10

This bar chart shows the estimated proportions of all stars that have planets of different size categories, based on *Kepler* results. Because *Kepler* data have been analyzed only for planets with relatively short orbital periods to date, these estimates are nearly certain to increase as additional data are studied.

observing extrasolar planets for very long, it's only natural that most of our discoveries would be of planets that are close-in with short orbital periods.

It's more challenging to understand why Jupiter-size planets are found close-in, since the nebular theory predicts that large planets should form far from their star. High eccentricities also pose a challenge, since the nebular theory provides a natural explanation for the nearly circular orbits in our solar system. Indeed, as we'll discuss in the next section, these observations forced scientists to reconsider the nebular theory, and while it has survived this scrutiny and even been strengthened, we have added features to it that we had not recognized when studying only the planets in our own solar system.

Many extrasolar planets orbit surprisingly close to their stars or with surprisingly high orbital eccentricity.

Another interesting surprise came from studying binary star systems. Scientists had not been sure whether planets could form in binary star systems, but data from the *Kepler* mission have shown that they can, at least in some cases. So some worlds have two (or more) "suns" in the sky, much like the fictional planet Tatooine depicted in *Star Wars*.

Sizes, Masses, and Densities The *Kepler* mission detected so many planets that scientists can use statistics to estimate the proportions of all stars that have planets of various sizes. Figure 10.10 shows results from these statistics. Two remarkable conclusions are already apparent. First, planets are common: By looking across all size categories, astronomers conclude that at least 70% of all stars harbor at least one planet. Second, small planets appear to outnumber large planets by a significant margin, suggesting that Earth-size planets are also very common. Keep in mind that the statistics remain incomplete: Because planets with larger orbits take longer to make the repeated transits necessary for confidence in a *Kepler* detection, and because small planets are more difficult to detect, the current statistics reflect only planets with relatively short orbital periods (in most cases, periods less than about 50 days for small planets and up to 250 days for large planets). As more data from the mission are analyzed, the estimated fractions of stars with planets can only increase.

The fact that the current statistics are dominated by planets that orbit relatively close to their stars means that most of the planets represented in Figure 10.10 are probably too hot to harbor life. However, Figure 10.11 shows *Kepler* data in a different way: as a graph of planet size versus orbital period. At first glance, the empty space at the lower right might seem to suggest that there are few Earth-size planets in Earth-size orbits. But the lack of data points in this region of the graph stems from the extreme difficulty in detecting the infrequent, shallow transits such planets make. Accounting statistically for these effects, scientists now estimate that about 20% of stars are likely to have a planet less than twice Earth's size in an orbit within the region around the star in which liquid water could potentially exist on the planet's surface (the *habitable zone* [Section 19.3]). These planets could potentially be homes to life.

In general, smaller planets seem to be more common than larger ones.

In order to determine the general nature of an extrasolar planet, such as whether it is terrestrial or jovian, we need to determine its mass as well as its size, so that we can calculate its average density. Although we currently have both size and mass data for only a limited set of planets, the results already reveal a surprise: The density range for extrasolar planets is significantly wider than that for the planets in our own solar system. At the extremes, we've identified planets with average densities as great as that of iron and as low as that of Styrofoam, and we've found planets with almost every average density in between.

The Nature of Extrasolar Planets

We now come to the key question about extrasolar planets: Do they fall into the same terrestrial and jovian categories as the planets in our solar system, or do we find additional types of planets?

We cannot yet know for certain, because we do not yet have direct ways of obtaining spectra with sufficient detail to determine the compositions of extrasolar planets. Nevertheless, because we have measured the abundances of different chemical elements among other stars, we know that all planetary systems must start out from gas clouds generally similar in composition to the solar nebula. That is, all star systems are born from gas clouds containing at least about 98% hydrogen and helium, sprinkled with much smaller amounts of hydrogen compounds, rock, and metal (see Table 6.3). Given this fact, knowing a planet's average density gives us great insight into its likely composition, even if we cannot observe it directly.

More specifically, we can use our understanding of the behavior of different materials to create *models* that will tell us the expected composition of a planet based on its mass and radius, from which we can also calculate its average density. The results are shown in Figure 10.12 for a sample of planets for which both mass (usually from the Doppler method) and radius (from transits) are known. Be sure you understand the following key features of the figure:

- The horizontal axis shows planetary mass, in units of Earth masses. (The top of the graph shows the equivalent values in Jupiter masses.) Notice that this axis uses a scale that rises by powers of 10 because the masses vary over such a wide range.

- The vertical axis shows planetary radius in units of Earth radii. (The right side of the graph shows the equivalent values in Jupiter radii.)

- Each dot represents one planet for which both mass and radius have been measured. Planets discussed in this chapter are called out by name. Planets of our solar system are marked in green.

- The paintings around the graph show artist conceptions of what representative worlds might look like.

- Average density is easy to calculate from mass and radius, but the different scales used on the two axes make it difficult to read average density directly from the graph. To help with that, the three curves extending from the lower left to the top show three representative average densities.

- The colored regions indicate models representing the expected compositions of planets with the indicated combinations of mass and radius.

As you study Figure 10.12, you'll notice that extrasolar planets show much more variety than the planets of our own solar system. For example, HAT-P-32b has more than twice Jupiter's radius despite having the same mass, giving it an average density of about 0.14 g/cm^3—similar to that of Styrofoam. This low average density is probably a result of the fact that this planet orbits only 0.035 AU from its star, putting it more than 10 times closer to its star than Mercury is to the Sun. The close-in orbit gives the planet a very high temperature, which should puff up the planet's atmosphere and may explain why it has such a large size relative to its mass. Near the other extreme, the planet COROT 14b is only slightly larger than Jupiter but several times as massive, giving it an average density near 8 g/cm^3, about the same as the density of iron. Although such a

Results for this region may be obtained as additional Kepler data are analyzed.

Earth analogs

▲ **FIGURE 10.11**

This figure shows the orbital periods and sizes of candidate planets identified from *Kepler* data. Although detecting the "Earth analogs" at the lower right is very difficult, the overall statistics suggest that about 20% of stars are likely to have such a planet.

we saw in Figure 10.12, many extrasolar planets do not fall neatly into either the terrestrial or the jovian category. An even more significant challenge is posed by the orbits of extrasolar planets. According to the nebular theory, jovian planets form as gravity pulls in gas around large, icy planetesimals that accrete in a spinning disk of material around a young star. The theory therefore predicts that jovian planets should form only in the cold outer regions of star systems (because it must be cold for ice to condense). The many known hot Jupiters that appear jovian in nature but have close-in orbits present a direct challenge to these ideas.

Explaining Planetary Orbits The nature of science demands that we question the validity of a theory whenever it is challenged by any observation or experiment [Section 3.4]. If the theory cannot explain the new observations, then we must revise or discard it. The surprising orbits of many known extrasolar planets have indeed caused scientists to reexamine the nebular theory of solar system formation.

Questioning began almost immediately once the first extrasolar planets were discovered. These planets were massive and had close-in orbits, making scientists wonder whether something might be fundamentally wrong with the nebular theory. For example, is it possible for jovian planets to form very close to a star? Astronomers addressed this question by studying many possible models of planet formation and reexamining the entire basis of the nebular theory. Several years of such reexamination did not turn up any good reasons to discard the basic theory, or any alternative means of forming jovian planets close to their stars. While we can't completely rule out the possibility that a major flaw has gone undetected, it now seems much more likely that the basic outline of the nebular theory is correct. Scientists therefore suspect that extrasolar jovian planets were indeed born with circular orbits far from their stars, and that those that now have close-in orbits underwent some sort of "planetary migration."

The idea of migration is not as strange as it may sound, and computer models of solar system formation suggest at least one likely mechanism: Migration may be caused by waves passing through a gaseous disk (Figure 10.13). The gravity of a planet moving through a disk can create waves that propagate through the disk, causing material to bunch up as the waves pass by. This bunched-up matter (in the wave peaks) then exerts a gravitational pull on the planet that tends to reduce its orbital energy, causing the planet to migrate inward toward its star.

This type of migration is not thought to have played a significant role in our own solar system, because the nebular gas was cleared out before it could have much effect. However, planets may form earlier in some other planetary systems, or the nebular gas may be cleared out later, allowing time for jovian planets to migrate substantially inward. In a few cases, the planets may form so early that they end up spiraling all the way into their stars. Indeed, astronomers have noted that some stars have an unusual assortment of elements in their outer layers, suggesting that they may have swallowed entire planets (including migrating jovian planets and possibly terrestrial planets shepherded inward along with the jovian planets). These ideas are not just hypothetical: One recently discovered planet appears to be on a million-year death spiral into its star.

Related mechanisms may explain the surprisingly high orbital eccentricities of many extrasolar planets. For example, planetary migration increases the chances that planets will influence each other gravitationally. In some cases, planets may pass close enough for a gravitational encounter [Section 4.4] in which one planet gains enough energy to escape from the star system entirely while the other is flung inward into a highly

The orbiting planet nudges gas and particles in the disk . . .

. . . causing material to bunch up. These dense regions in turn tug on the planet, causing it to migrate inward.

▲ **FIGURE 10.13**
This figure shows a simulation of waves created by a planet embedded in a disk of material surrounding its star.

elliptical orbit. In other cases, continuing gravitational tugs may lead to orbital resonances much like those that cause the orbits of Jupiter's moons Io, Europa, and Ganymede to be more elliptical than they would be otherwise (see Figure 8.15b).

Explaining Planetary Types Assuming we are correct about the role of planetary migration in explaining the surprising orbits of hot Jupiters, the basic tenets of the nebular theory seem to hold. That is, we expect rocky terrestrial worlds to form in the inner regions of solar systems and hydrogen-rich jovian planets to form in the outer regions, although migration may later cause some jovian planets to spiral inward (and likely alter the orbits of smaller planets as well). The remaining mystery, then, is why other systems seem to have planetary types that don't fall neatly into the terrestrial and jovian categories that we identify in our solar system.

Scientists still cannot fully explain the wide range of extrasolar planet properties, but we can envision possible explanations that seem to make sense and that would not fundamentally alter the nebular theory. For example, hydrogen-rich extrasolar planets vary in density by a factor of 100 (see Figure 10.12)—a range far greater than the density range we observe in our solar system—but it seems reasonable to think that much of this range is attributable to increases in temperature caused by some jovian planets being very close to their stars. As we've discussed, heating may puff up their atmospheres to large sizes and low densities, though models cannot yet account for the full density range. Higher densities can be explained by planets capturing even more hydrogen and helium gas than Jupiter, and compressing to smaller sizes due to higher gravity (see Figure 8.2b).

Similarly, the lack of "water world" planets in our solar system may not be as mysterious as it seems. Water worlds may be similar to Uranus and Neptune, though in some cases much smaller. These worlds may be much like the ice-rich planetesimals that seeded the formation of jovian planets in our solar system. In that case, perhaps whether water world planets exist depends on when a star clears its nebular gas, halting the epoch of planet formation. In our solar system, this did not occur until the ice-rich planetesimals pulled in vast quantities of hydrogen and helium gas from the solar nebula. Perhaps in other systems, an early solar wind blasted out the hydrogen and helium gas before it could be captured.

Super-Earths pose a different mystery: How did these planets gather so much rocky material? The answer is not yet known, though perhaps we should not be too surprised. After all, even though rocky material comprised less than 2% of the solar nebula, this still in principle was enough to build planets much larger than Earth. We may also need a better understanding of the conditions under which super-Earths or water worlds may capture hydrogen and helium gas, since such capture could lead to planets whose true nature is hiding under enormous envelopes of gas. With hundreds of new planets being discovered every year, other surprising planetary types are likely to be found in the future.

An Improved Nebular Theory The bottom line is that discoveries of extrasolar planets have shown us that the nebular theory was incomplete. It explained the formation of planets and the simple layout of a solar system such as ours. However, it needs new features—such as planetary migration and variations in the basic planetary types—to explain the differing layouts of other planetary systems. A much wider variety of system arrangements seems possible than we had guessed before the discovery of extrasolar planets.

◆ Are planetary systems like ours common?

The validation of the nebular theory leads us to perhaps the most profound question still to be addressed in our study of extrasolar planets: Given that we have not yet discovered other planetary systems that are quite like ours, does this mean that our solar system is of a rare type, or does it simply mean that we have not yet acquired enough data to see how common systems like ours really are?

This is a profound question because of its implications for the way we view our place in the universe. If planetary systems like ours are common, then it seems reasonable to imagine that Earth-like planets—and perhaps life and civilizations—might also be common. But if our solar system is a rarity or even unique, then Earth might be the lone inhabited planet in our galaxy or even the universe.

As we've discussed, current evidence from both transit detections (see Figure 10.7) and Doppler discoveries already strongly supports the idea that planetary systems are common. We've also discussed statistical evidence indicating that as many as 20% of stars may be orbited by an approximately Earth-size planet in the habitable zone. Even the nearest star besides the Sun, Proxima Centauri, has a planet not too much larger than Earth within its habitable zone. However, we do not yet know the actual nature of these worlds, and despite the large number of known planetary systems, it is still too soon to say whether any of these planetary systems are genuinely "like ours." The bottom line is that we do not yet know whether planetary systems like ours are common, but more definitive answers should be coming over the next decade or two.

think about it Not long before most of today's college students were born, the only known planets were those of our own solar system. Today, the evidence suggests that many or most stars have planets. For the galaxy as a whole, that's a change in estimated number of planets from less than 10 to more than 100 billion. Do you think this change should alter our perspective on our place in the universe? Defend your opinion.

the big picture ▸ Putting Chapter 10 into Perspective

In this chapter, we have explored one of the newest areas of astronomy—the study of planetary systems beyond our own. As you continue your studies, please keep in mind the following important ideas:

- In a period of barely two decades, we have gone from knowing of no other planets around other stars to knowing that many or most stars have one or more planets. As a result, there is no longer any question that planets are common in the universe.

- The discovery of other planetary systems represents a striking confirmation of a key prediction of the nebular theory of solar system formation. Nevertheless, the precise characteristics of other planets and planetary systems pose challenges to details of the theory that scientists are still investigating.

- While we have already identified thousands of extrasolar planets or candidate planets, nearly all of these have been found with indirect methods. These methods allow us to determine many properties of the planets, but we will need direct images or spectra to learn about them in much more detail.

- It is too soon to know if planetary systems with layouts like ours are rare or common, but technology already exists that could allow us to answer this question and to learn if Earth-like planets are also common. It is only a matter of time until we know the answer to these fundamental questions.

my cosmic perspective The discovery that habitable worlds may be common even among relatively nearby stars means that, for the first time, we have evidence that could support the reality of many science fiction dreams of our future. Does this fact change the way you think about whether and how we should begin to reach for the stars?

10.1 Detecting Planets Around Other Stars

◆ How do we detect planets around other stars?

We can look for a planet's gravitational effect on its star through the **astrometric method**, which looks for small shifts in stellar position, or the **Doppler method**, which looks for the Doppler shifts that reveal the back-and-forth motion of stars. For the small fraction of planetary systems with orbits aligned edge-on to Earth, we can search for **transits**, in which a planet blocks a little of its star's light as it passes in front of the star.

10.2 The Nature of Planets Around Other Stars

◆ What properties of extrasolar planets can we measure?

All detection methods allow us to determine a planet's orbital period and distance from its star. The astrometric and Doppler methods can provide masses (or minimum masses), while the transit method can provide sizes. In cases where transit and Doppler methods are used together, we can determine average density. In some cases, transits (and eclipses) can provide other data, including limited data about atmospheric composition and temperature.

◆ How do extrasolar planets compare with planets in our solar system?

The known extrasolar planets have a much wider range of properties than the planets in our solar system. Many orbit much closer to their stars and with more eccentric orbital paths; some extrasolar jovian planets, called *hot Jupiters*, are also found close to their stars. We have also observed properties indicating planetary types, such as water worlds, that do not fall neatly into the traditional terrestrial and jovian categories.

10.3 The Formation of Other Planetary Systems

◆ Do we need to modify our theory of solar system formation?

Our basic theory seems sound, but we have had to modify it to allow for planetary migration and a wider range of planetary types than we find in our solar system. Many mysteries remain, but they are unlikely to require major change to the nebular theory of solar system formation.

◆ Are planetary systems like ours common?

Current evidence indicates that planetary systems are very common, though we do not yet have enough data to know for sure whether systems with layouts like ours—and possibly Earth-like planets—are also common.

---

visual skills check   Check your understanding of some of the many types of visual information used in astronomy. For additional practice, try the Chapter 10 Visual Quiz at MasteringAstronomy®.

This graph shows the periodic variations in the Doppler shift of a star caused by a planet orbiting around it. Positive velocities mean the star is moving away from Earth, and negative velocities mean the star is moving toward Earth. (You can assume that the orbit is viewed edge-on from Earth.)

1. How long does it take the star and planet to complete one orbit around their center of mass?

2. What maximum velocity does the star attain?

3. Match the star's positions at points 1, 2, 3, and 4 in the plot with the descriptions below.
   a. headed straight toward Earth
   b. headed straight away from Earth
   c. closest to Earth
   d. farthest from Earth

4. Match the planet's positions at points 1, 2, 3, and 4 in the plot with the descriptions in question 3.

5. How would the plot change if the planet were more massive (but remained at the same orbital distance)?
   a. It would not change, because it describes the motion of the star, not the planet.
   b. The peaks and valleys would get significantly larger (greater positive and negative velocities) because of larger gravitational tugs.
   c. The peaks and valleys would get significantly closer together (shorter period) because of larger gravitational tugs.

MasteringAstronomy® For instructor-assigned homework and other learning materials, go to MasteringAstronomy®.

Review Questions

1. Why are *extrasolar planets* hard to detect directly?
2. What are the two current major approaches to detecting extrasolar planets indirectly?
3. How can gravitational tugs from orbiting planets affect the motion of a star? Explain how alien astronomers could deduce the existence of planets in our solar system by observing the Sun's motion.
4. Briefly describe the *astrometric method*. What is the *GAIA* mission?
5. Briefly describe the *Doppler method*. Summarize the evidence that the planet orbiting 51 Pegasi is a *hot Jupiter*.
6. How does the *transit method* work? What was the *Kepler* mission?
7. Briefly summarize the planetary properties we can measure with current detection methods.
8. Why does the Doppler method generally allow us to determine only *minimum* planetary masses? In what cases can we be confident that we know precise masses? Explain.
9. How does the transit method tell us planetary size, and in what cases can we also learn mass and density?
10. How do the orbits of known extrasolar planets differ from those of planets in our solar system? Why are these orbits surprising?
11. Summarize the current state of knowledge about extrasolar planet masses and sizes. Based on the evidence, is it likely that smaller planets or larger planets are more common?
12. Summarize the key features shown in Figure 10.12, and briefly describe the nature of planets that would fit each of the model regions shown on the graph.
13. What is planetary migration, and how may it account for the surprising orbits of many extrasolar planets?
14. How can scientists account for the fact that extrasolar planets seem to come in a wider range of types than the planets of our solar system?
15. Overall, does the nebular theory seem adequate for describing the origins of other planetary systems? Explain.
16. Based on current evidence, how common are planetary systems?

Test Your Understanding

🜁 Does It Make Sense?

Decide whether the statement makes sense (or is clearly true) or does not make sense (or is clearly false). Explain clearly; not all these have definitive answers, so your explanation is more important than your chosen answer.

17. An extraterrestrial astronomer surveying our solar system with the Doppler method could discover the existence of Jupiter with just a few days of observation.
18. The fact that we have not yet discovered an Earth-size extrasolar planet in an Earth-like orbit tells us that such planets must be very rare.
19. Within the next few years, astronomers expect to confirm all the planet detections made with the astrometric and Doppler methods by observing transits of these same planets.
20. The infrared brightness of a star system decreases when a planet goes into eclipse.
21. Some extrasolar planets are likely to be made mostly of water.
22. Some extrasolar planets are likely to be made mostly of gold.
23. Current evidence suggests that there could be 100 billion or more planets in the Milky Way Galaxy.

24. It's the year 2018: The *Kepler 2* mission has announced the discovery of numerous planets with Neptune-like orbits around their stars.
25. It's the year 2020: Astronomers have successfully photographed an Earth-size planet, showing that it has oceans and continents.
26. It's the year 2040: Scientists announce that our first spacecraft to reach an extrasolar planet is now orbiting a planet in a planetary system located near the center of the Milky Way Galaxy.

Quick Quiz

Choose the best answer to each of the following. Explain your reasoning with one or more complete sentences.

27. Which method could detect a planet in an orbit that is face-on to Earth? (a) Doppler method (b) transit method (c) astrometric method
28. Which detection method(s) measure gravitational tug of a planet on its star, allowing us to estimate planetary mass? (a) the transit method only (b) the Doppler method only (c) the astrometric and Doppler methods
29. Which one of the following can the transit method tell us about a planet? (a) its mass (b) its size (c) the eccentricity of its orbit
30. To determine a planet's average density, we can use (a) the transit method alone. (b) the astrometric and Doppler methods together. (c) the transit and Doppler methods together.
31. Based on the model types shown in Figure 10.12, a planet made almost entirely of hydrogen compounds would be considered a (a) terrestrial planet. (b) jovian planet. (c) "water world."
32. Look at the dot for Jupiter in Figure 10.12, then at the red dot directly to Jupiter's left. Compared to the density of Jupiter, the density of the planet represented by that dot is (a) higher. (b) lower. (c) the same.
33. The term "super-Earth" refers to a planet that is (a) the size of Earth but with more water. (b) larger than Earth but on a close-in orbit that makes it much hotter than Earth. (c) similar in composition to Earth but larger in size.
34. What's the best explanation for the location of hot Jupiters? (a) They formed closer to their stars than Jupiter did. (b) They formed farther out like Jupiter but then migrated inward. (c) The strong gravity of their stars pulled them in close.
35. Based on computer models, when is planetary migration most likely to occur in a planetary system? (a) early in its history, when there is still a gaseous disk around the star (b) shortly after a stellar wind clears the gaseous disk away (c) late in its history, when asteroids and comets occasionally collide with planets
36. Based on current data, planetary systems appear to be (a) extremely rare. (b) present around at least about one-third of all stars. (c) present around at least 99% of all stars.

🜁 Process of Science

37. *When Is a Theory Wrong?* As discussed in this chapter, in its original form the nebular theory of solar system formation does not explain the orbits of many known extrasolar planets, but it can explain them with modifications such as allowing for planetary migration. Does this mean the theory was "wrong" or only "incomplete" before the modifications were made? Explain. Be sure to look back at the discussion in Chapter 3 of the nature of science and scientific theories.

38. *Unanswered Questions.* As discussed in this chapter, we are only just beginning to learn about extrasolar planets. Briefly describe one important but unanswered question related to the study of planets around other stars. Then write 2–3 paragraphs in which you discuss how we might answer this question in the future. Be as specific as possible, focusing on the type of evidence necessary to answer the question and how the evidence could be gathered. What are the benefits of finding answers to this question?

Group Work Exercise

39. *Time to Move On.* **Roles:** *Scribe* (takes notes on the group's activities), *Proposer* (proposes explanations to the group), *Skeptic* (points out weaknesses in proposed explanations), *Moderator* (leads group discussion and makes sure everyone contributes). **Activity:** A common theme in science fiction is "leaving home" to find a new planet for humans to live on. Now that we know about thousands of planets, we can start imagining how to choose.
   a. Make a list of characteristics that you would look for in a planet that might make a good home.
   b. Examine the planets in Figure 10.12. Does this graph give enough information to determine which planets might make good homes, or poor ones? If not, what's missing?
   c. Suppose you also knew the orbital distance for each of the planets in Figure 10.12. Would that make it easier to find potential good homes? Why or why not?

Investigate Further

Short-Answer/Essay Questions

40. *Explaining the Doppler Method.* Explain how the Doppler method works in terms an elementary school child would understand. It may help to use an analogy to explain the difficulty of direct detection and the general phenomenon of the Doppler shift.
41. *Comparing Methods.* What are the strengths and limitations of the Doppler and transit methods? What kinds of planets are easiest to detect with each method? Are there certain planets that each method cannot detect, even if the planets are very large? Explain. What advantages are gained if a planet can be detected by both methods?
42. *No Hot Jupiters Here.* How do we think hot Jupiters formed? Why didn't one form in our solar system?
43. *Low-Density Planets.* Only one planet in our solar system has a density less than 1 g/cm^3, but many extrasolar planets do. Explain why in a few sentences. (*Hint:* Consider the densities of the jovian planets in our solar system, given in Figure 8.1.)
44. *Detect an Extrasolar Planet for Yourself.* Most colleges and many amateur astronomers have the equipment necessary to detect known extrasolar planets using the transit method. All that's required is a telescope 10 or more inches in diameter, a CCD camera system, and a computer system for data analysis. The basic method is to take exposures of a few minutes' duration over a period of several hours around the times of predicted transit, and to compare the brightness of the star being transited to that of other stars in the same CCD frame. For complete instructions, see the study area of MasteringAstronomy.

Quantitative Problems

Be sure to show all calculations clearly and state your final answers in complete sentences.

45. *Lost in the Glare.* How hard would it be for an alien astronomer to detect the light from planets in our solar system compared to the light from the Sun itself?
   a. Calculate the fraction of the total emitted sunlight that reaches Earth. (*Hint:* Find the area of a sphere around the Sun with a radius equal to Earth's average orbital distance area $= 4\pi a^2$, then calculate the fraction of that area taken up by the disk of Earth [area $= \pi r_{Earth}^2$].)
   b. Earth reflects 29% of the Sun's light. Based on this fact and your answer from part a, what fraction of total sunlight is *reflected* by Earth? (*Hint:* Your answer will simply be the overall fraction of all the Sun's light that is reflected by Earth.)
   c. Would detecting Jupiter be easier or harder than detecting Earth? Comment on whether you think Jupiter's larger size or greater distance has a stronger effect on its detectability. You may neglect any difference in reflectivity between Earth and Jupiter.

46. *Transit of TrES-1.* The planet TrES-1, orbiting a distant star, has been detected by both the transit and the Doppler technique, so we can calculate its density and get an idea of what kind of planet it is.
   a. Using the method of Cosmic Calculations 10.1, calculate the radius of the transiting planet. The planetary transits block 2% of the star's light. The star that TrES-1 orbits has a radius of about 85% of our Sun's radius.
   b. The mass of the planet is approximately 0.75 times the mass of Jupiter, and Jupiter's mass is about 1.9×10^{27} kilograms. Calculate the average density of the planet. Give your answer in grams per cubic centimeter. Compare this density to the average densities of Saturn (0.7 g/cm^3) and Earth (5.5 g/cm^3). Is the planet terrestrial or jovian in nature? (*Hint:* To find the volume of the planet, use the formula for the volume of a sphere: $V = \frac{4}{3}\pi r^3$. Be careful with unit conversions.)

47. *Planet Around 51 Pegasi.* The star 51 Pegasi has about the same mass as our Sun. A planet discovered orbiting it has an orbital period of 4.23 days. The mass of the planet is estimated to be 0.6 times the mass of Jupiter. Use Kepler's third law to find the planet's average distance (semimajor axis) from its star. (*Hint:* Because the mass of 51 Pegasi is about the same as the mass of our Sun, you can use Kepler's third law in its original form, $p^2 = a^3$ [Section 3.3]. Be sure to convert the period into years before using this equation.)

Discussion Questions

48. *So What?* What is the significance of the discovery of extrasolar planets, if any? Justify your answer in the context of this book's discussion of the history of astronomy.
49. *Is It Worth It?* Thanks to rapidly advancing technology, we could probably now build space observatories capable of obtaining images and spectra of Earth-size planets around other stars, with enough resolution to be able to determine whether they are Earth-like, and perhaps even to detect spectral signatures that would indicate the presence of life. However, such observatories would likely cost several billion dollars. Suppose you were a member of the U.S. Congress. How much would you be willing to spend on such observatories? Defend your opinion.

Web Projects

50. *New Planets.* Research the latest extrasolar planet discoveries. Create a "planet journal," complete with illustrations as needed, with a page for each of at least three recently discovered planets. On each page, note the method that was used to find the planet, list any information we have about the nature of the planet, and discuss how the planet does or does not fit in with our current understanding of planetary systems.
51. *Extrasolar Planet Mission.* Learn about a proposed future mission to study extrasolar planets, including its proposed design, capabilities, and goals. Write a short report on your findings.

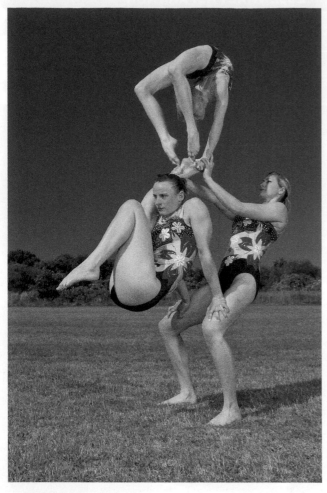

▲ FIGURE 11.1

An acrobat stack is in gravitational equilibrium: The lowest person supports the most weight and feels the greatest pressure, and the overlying weight and underlying pressure decrease for those higher up.

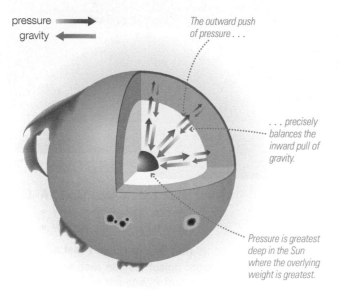

pressure ➡
gravity ⬅

The outward push of pressure . . .

. . . precisely balances the inward pull of gravity.

Pressure is greatest deep in the Sun where the overlying weight is greatest.

▲ FIGURE 11.2

Gravitational equilibrium in the Sun: At each point inside, the pressure pushing outward balances the weight of the overlying layers.

With both chemical processes and gravitational contraction ruled out as possible explanations for why the Sun shines, scientists were at a loss. There was no known way that an object the size of the Sun could generate so much energy for billions of years. A completely new type of explanation was needed, and it came with Einstein's publication of his special theory of relativity in 1905.

Einstein's theory included his famous equation $E = mc^2$, which tells us that mass itself contains an enormous amount of potential energy [Section 4.3]. Calculations showed that the Sun's mass contained more than enough energy to account for billions of years of sunshine, if the Sun could somehow convert some of its mass into thermal energy. It took a few decades for scientists to work out the details, but by the end of the 1930s we had learned that the Sun converts mass into energy through the process of *nuclear fusion* [Section 1.2].

The Sun shines by converting mass into energy through nuclear fusion.

How Fusion Started Nuclear fusion requires extremely high temperatures and densities (for reasons we will discuss in the next section). In the Sun, these conditions are found deep in the core. But how did the Sun become hot enough for fusion to begin in the first place?

The answer invokes the mechanism of gravitational contraction. Recall that our Sun was born about 4½ billion years ago from a collapsing cloud of interstellar gas [Section 6.2]. The contraction of the cloud released gravitational potential energy, raising the interior temperature and pressure. This process continued until the core finally became hot enough to sustain nuclear fusion, because only then did the Sun produce enough energy to give it the stability that it has today.

Gravitational contraction released the energy that made the Sun's core hot enough for fusion.

The Stable Sun The Sun continues to shine steadily today because it has achieved two kinds of balance that keep its size and energy output stable. The first kind of balance, called **gravitational equilibrium** (or *hydrostatic equilibrium*), is between the outward push of internal gas pressure and the inward pull of gravity. A stack of acrobats provides a simple example of gravitational equilibrium (Figure 11.1). The bottom person supports the weight of everybody above him, so his arms must push upward with enough pressure to support all this weight. At each higher level, the overlying weight is less, so it's a little easier for each additional person to hold up the rest of the stack.

Gravitational equilibrium works much the same in the Sun, except the outward push against gravity comes from internal gas pressure rather than an acrobat's arms. The Sun's internal pressure precisely balances gravity at every point within it, thereby keeping the Sun stable in size (Figure 11.2). Because the weight of overlying layers is greater as we look deeper into the Sun, the pressure must increase with depth. Deep in the Sun's core, the pressure makes the gas hot and dense enough to sustain nuclear fusion. The energy released by fusion, in turn, heats the gas and maintains the pressure that keeps the Sun in balance against the inward pull of gravity.

think about it Earth's atmosphere is also in gravitational equilibrium, with the weight of upper layers supported by the pressure in lower layers. Use this idea to explain why the air gets thinner at higher altitudes.

The second kind of balance is **energy balance** between the rate at which fusion releases energy in the Sun's core and the rate at which the

Two types of balance keep the Sun stable: Pressure balances gravity and fusion energy balances the energy radiated into space.

Sun's surface radiates this energy into space (Figure 11.3). Energy balance is important, because without it the balance between pressure and gravity would not remain steady. If fusion in the core did not replace the energy radiated from the surface, thereby keeping the total thermal energy content constant, then gravitational contraction would cause the Sun to shrink and force its core temperature to rise.

In summary, the answer to the question "Why does the Sun shine?" is that about 4½ billion years ago *gravitational contraction* made the Sun hot enough to sustain nuclear fusion in its core. Ever since, energy liberated by fusion has maintained *gravitational equilibrium* and *energy balance* within the Sun, keeping it shining steadily. The Sun was born with enough nuclear fuel to last about 10 billion years, which means it is now only about halfway through this 10-billion-year lifetime.

◆ What is the Sun's structure?

The Sun is essentially a giant ball of hot gas or, more technically, *plasma*—a gas in which atoms are ionized because of the high temperature. The differing temperatures and densities of the plasma at different depths give the Sun the layered structure shown in Figure 11.4. To help you make sense of the layering, let's imagine that you have a spaceship that can somehow withstand the immense heat and pressure as you take an imaginary journey from Earth to the center of the Sun.

Basic Properties of the Sun As you begin your journey from Earth, the Sun appears as a whitish ball of glowing gas. Just as astronomers have done in real life, you can use simple observations to determine basic properties of the Sun. Spectroscopy [Section 5.2] tells you that the Sun is made almost entirely of hydrogen and helium. From the Sun's angular size and distance, you can determine that its radius is just under 700,000 kilometers, or more than 100 times the radius of Earth. Even **sunspots,** which appear as dark splotches on the Sun's surface, can be larger in size than Earth.

You can measure the Sun's mass using Newton's version of Kepler's third law. It is about 2×10^{30} kilograms, which is some 300,000 times the mass of Earth and nearly 1000 times the mass of all the planets in our solar system put together. You can observe the Sun's rotation by tracking the motion of sunspots or by measuring Doppler shifts [Section 5.2] on opposite sides of the Sun. Unlike a spinning ball, the entire Sun does *not* rotate at the same rate: The solar equator completes one rotation in about 25 days, and the rotation period increases with latitude to about 30 days near the solar poles.

think about it As a brief review, describe how astronomers use Newton's version of Kepler's third law to determine the mass of the Sun. What two properties of Earth's orbit do we need to know?

The Sun releases an enormous amount of radiative energy into space. In science, we measure energy in units of *joules* [Section 4.3]. We define **power** as the *rate* at which energy is used or released. The standard unit of power is the **watt,** defined as 1 joule of energy per second; that is, 1 watt = 1 joule/s. For example, a 100-watt light bulb requires 100 joules of energy for every second it is left turned on. The

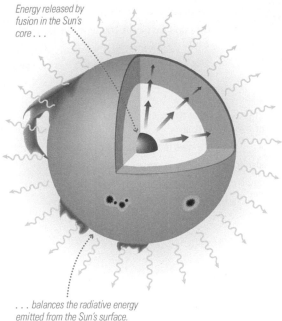

Energy released by fusion in the Sun's core . . .

. . . balances the radiative energy emitted from the Sun's surface.

▲ **FIGURE 11.3**
Energy balance in the Sun: Fusion supplies energy in the core at the same rate as the Sun radiates energy from its surface.

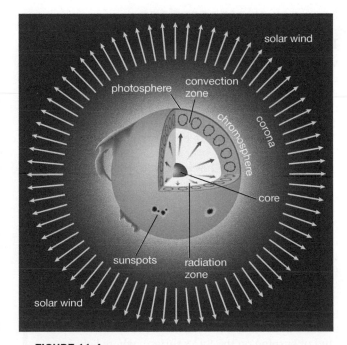

▲ **FIGURE 11.4**
The basic structure of the Sun.

TABLE 11.1 Basic Properties of the Sun

Radius (R_{Sun})	696,000 km (about 109 times the radius of Earth)
Mass (M_{Sun})	2×10^{30} kg (about 300,000 times the mass of Earth)
Luminosity (L_{Sun})	3.8×10^{26} watts
Composition (by percentage of mass)	70% hydrogen, 28% helium, 2% heavier elements
Rotation rate	25 days (equator) to 30 days (poles)
Surface temperature	5800 K (average); 4000 K (sunspots)
Core temperature	15 million K

Sun's total power output, or **luminosity,** is an incredible 3.8×10^{26} watts. Table 11.1 summarizes the basic properties of the Sun.

The Sun's Atmosphere Even at a great distance from the Sun, you and your spacecraft can feel slight effects from the **solar wind**—the stream of charged particles continually blown outward in all directions from the Sun. The solar wind helps shape the magnetospheres of planets (see Figure 7.6) and blows back the material that forms the plasma tails of comets [Section 9.3].

As you approach the Sun more closely, you begin to encounter the low-density gas that represents what we usually think of as the Sun's atmosphere. The outermost layer of this atmosphere, called the **corona,** extends several million kilometers above the visible surface of the Sun. The temperature of the corona is astonishingly high—about 1 million K—explaining why this region emits most of the Sun's X rays. However, the corona's density is so low that your spaceship feels relatively little heat, despite the million-degree temperature [Section 4.3].

Nearer the surface, the temperature suddenly drops to about 10,000 K in the **chromosphere,** the middle layer of the solar atmosphere and the region that radiates most of the Sun's ultraviolet light. Then you plunge through the lowest layer of the atmosphere, the **photosphere,** which is the visible surface of the Sun. Although the photosphere looks like a well-defined surface from Earth, it consists of gas far less dense than Earth's atmosphere. The temperature of the photosphere averages just under 6000 K, and its surface seethes and churns like a pot of boiling water. The photosphere is also where you'll find sunspots, regions of intense magnetic fields that would cause your compass needle to swing wildly about.

The Sun's upper atmosphere is much hotter than the visible surface, or photosphere, but its density is much lower.

common misconceptions

The Sun Is Not on Fire

We often say that the Sun is "burning," a term that conjures up images of a giant bonfire in the sky. However, the Sun does not burn in the same sense as a fire burns on Earth. Fires generate light through chemical changes that consume oxygen and produce a flame. The glow of the Sun has more in common with the glowing embers left over after the flames have burned out. Much like hot embers, the Sun's surface shines because it is hot enough to emit thermal radiation that includes visible light [Section 5.2].

Hot embers quickly stop glowing as they cool, but the Sun keeps shining because its surface is kept hot by the energy rising from its core. Because this energy is generated by nuclear fusion, we sometimes say that it is the result of "nuclear burning"—a term intended to suggest nuclear changes in much the same way that "chemical burning" suggests chemical changes. While it is reasonable to say that the Sun undergoes nuclear burning in its core, it is not accurate to speak of any kind of burning on the Sun's surface, where light is produced primarily by thermal radiation.

The Sun's Interior Up to this point in your journey, you may have seen Earth and the stars when you looked back. But blazing light engulfs you as you slip beneath the photosphere. You are inside the Sun, and incredible turbulence tosses your spacecraft about. If you can hold steady long enough to see what is going on around you, you'll notice spouts of hot gas rising upward, surrounded by cooler gas cascading down from above. You are in the **convection zone,** where energy generated in the solar core travels outward, transported by the rising of hot gas and falling of cool gas called *convection* [Section 7.1]. The photosphere above you is the top of the convection zone, and convection is the cause of the Sun's seething, churning surface.

About a third of the way down to the Sun's center, the turbulence of the convection zone gives way to the calmer plasma of the **radiation zone,** where energy moves outward primarily in the form of photons of light. The temperature rises to almost 10 million K, and your spacecraft is bathed in X rays trillions of times more intense than the visible light at the solar surface.

Inside the Sun, temperature rises with depth, reaching 15 million K in the core.

No real spacecraft could survive, but your imaginary one keeps plunging straight down to the solar **core.** There you finally find the source of the Sun's energy: nuclear fusion transforming hydrogen into helium. At the Sun's center, the temperature is about 15 million K, the density is more than 100 times that of water, and the pressure is 200 billion times that on Earth's surface.

The energy produced in the core today will take a few hundred thousand years to reach the surface.

With your journey complete, it's time to turn around and head back home. We'll continue this chapter by studying fusion in the solar core and then tracing the flow of the energy generated by fusion as it moves outward through the Sun.

11.2 Nuclear Fusion in the Sun

We've seen that the Sun shines because of energy generated by nuclear fusion, and that this fusion occurs under the extreme temperatures and densities found deep in the Sun's core. But exactly how does fusion occur and release energy? And how can we claim to know about something taking place out of sight in the Sun's interior?

Before we begin to answer these questions, it's important to realize that the nuclear reactions that generate energy in the Sun are very different from those used to generate energy in human-built nuclear reactors on Earth. Our nuclear power plants generate energy by splitting large nuclei—such as those of uranium or plutonium—into smaller ones. The process of splitting an atomic nucleus is called *nuclear fission*. In contrast, the Sun makes energy by combining, or fusing, two or more small nuclei into a larger one. That is why we call the process *nuclear fusion*. Figure 11.5 summarizes the difference between fission and fusion.

◆ How does nuclear fusion occur in the Sun?

Fusion occurs within the Sun because the 15 million K plasma in the solar core is like a "soup" of hot gas full of bare, positively charged atomic nuclei (and negatively charged electrons) whizzing about at extremely high speeds. At any time, some of these nuclei are on high-speed collision courses with each other. In most cases, electromagnetic forces deflect the nuclei, preventing collisions, because positive charges repel one another. However, if nuclei collide with sufficient energy, they can stick together (fuse) to form a heavier nucleus.

Sticking positively charged nuclei together is not easy. The **strong force,** which binds protons and neutrons together in atomic nuclei, is the only force in nature that can overcome the electromagnetic repulsion between two positively charged nuclei. In contrast to gravitational and electromagnetic forces, which drop off gradually as the distances between particles increase (by an inverse square law [Section 4.4]), the strong force is more like glue or Velcro: It overpowers the electromagnetic force over very small distances, but is insignificant when the distances between particles exceed the typical sizes of atomic nuclei. The key to nuclear fusion is pushing the positively charged nuclei close enough together for the strong force to outmuscle electromagnetic repulsion (Figure 11.6).

The high pressures and temperatures in the solar core are just right for fusion of hydrogen nuclei into helium nuclei. The high temperature

Positively charged nuclei fuse together if they pass close enough for the strong force to overpower electromagnetic repulsion.

is important because the nuclei must collide at very high speeds if they are to come close enough together to fuse. The higher the temperature, the more energetic the collisions, making fusion reactions more likely at higher temperatures. The high pressure of the overlying

▲ FIGURE 11.5
Nuclear fission splits a nucleus into smaller nuclei (not usually of equal size), while nuclear fusion combines smaller nuclei into a larger nucleus.

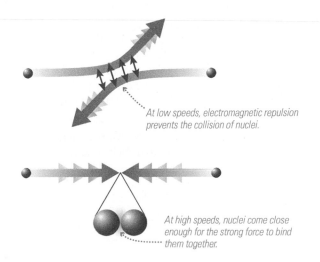

At low speeds, electromagnetic repulsion prevents the collision of nuclei.

At high speeds, nuclei come close enough for the strong force to bind them together.

▲ FIGURE 11.6
Positively charged nuclei can fuse only if a high-speed collision brings them close enough for the strong force to come into play.

Hydrogen Fusion by the Proton–Proton Chain

Step 1	Step 2	Step 3
Two protons fuse to make a deuterium nucleus (1 proton and 1 neutron). This step occurs twice in the overall reaction.	The deuterium nucleus and a proton fuse to make a nucleus of helium-3 (2 protons, 1 neutron). This step also occurs twice in the overall reaction.	Two helium-3 nuclei fuse to form helium-4 (2 protons, 2 neutrons), releasing two excess protons in the process.

Overall reaction

Key:
- n neutron
- p proton
- ° neutrino
- ● positron
- 〜 gamma ray

▲ **FIGURE 11.7**

In the Sun, four hydrogen nuclei (protons) fuse into one helium-4 nucleus by way of the proton–proton chain. Gamma rays and subatomic particles known as neutrinos and positrons carry off the energy released in the reaction.

cosmic calculations 11.1

The Ideal Gas Law

The pressure (P) of a gas depends on both its temperature (T) and its *number density* (n)—the number of particles contained in each cubic centimeter of gas. The *ideal gas law* expresses the relationship:

$$P = nkT$$

where $k = 1.38 \times 10^{-23}$ joule/K is *Boltzmann's constant*.

Example: The Sun's core density is about 10^{26} particles per cubic centimeter (which we write as 10^{26} cm^{-3}) and its temperature is about 15 million K (1.5×10^7 K). Compare the Sun's core pressure to that of Earth's atmosphere at sea level, where the density is about 2.4×10^{19} particles per cubic centimeter and the temperature is about 300 K.

Solution: Dividing the Sun's core pressure by Earth's atmospheric pressure, we find that their ratio is

$$\frac{P_{Sun(core)}}{P_{Earth(atmos)}} = \frac{n_{Sun}\, k\, T_{Sun}}{n_{Earth}\, k\, T_{Earth}}$$

$$= \frac{10^{26}\ cm^{-3} \times (1.5 \times 10^7\ K)}{(2.4 \times 10^{19}\ cm^{-3}) \times 300\ K}$$

$$= 2 \times 10^{11}$$

The Sun's core pressure is about 200 billion (2×10^{11}) times Earth's atmospheric pressure.

layers is necessary because, without it, the hot plasma of the solar core would simply explode into space, shutting off the nuclear reactions.

think about it The Sun generates energy by fusing hydrogen into helium, but as we'll see in later chapters, some stars fuse helium or even heavier elements. Do temperatures need to be higher or lower for the fusion of heavier elements? Why? (*Hint*: How does the positive charge of a nucleus affect its ability to fuse with another nucleus?)

The Proton–Proton Chain Let's investigate the Sun's fusion process in a little more detail. Recall that hydrogen nuclei are simply individual protons, while the most common form of helium consists of two protons and two neutrons(see Figure 5.6). The overall hydrogen fusion reaction therefore transforms four individual protons into a helium nucleus containing two protons and two neutrons:

4 ^{1}H   1 ^{4}He

This overall reaction actually proceeds through several steps involving just two nuclei at a time. The sequence of steps that occurs in the Sun is

Nuclear fusion in the Sun combines four hydrogen nuclei into one helium nucleus, releasing energy in the process.

called the **proton–proton chain,** because it begins with collisions between individual protons (hydrogen nuclei). Figure 11.7 illustrates the steps in the proton–proton chain. Notice that the overall reaction is just as described above, with four protons combining to make one helium nucleus. Energy is carried off by the gamma rays and subatomic particles (neutrinos and positrons) released in the process.

Fusion of hydrogen into helium generates energy because a helium nucleus has a mass slightly less (by about 0.7%) than the combined

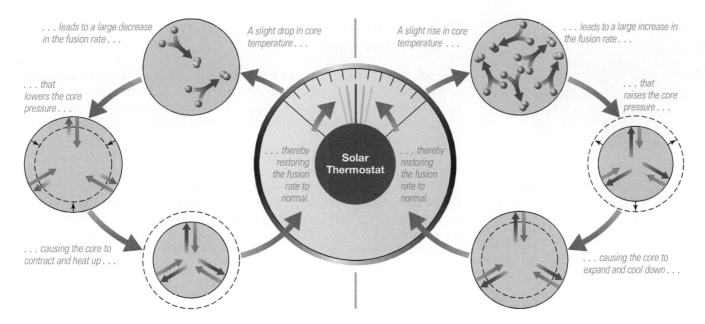

... leads to a large decrease in the fusion rate ...

A slight drop in core temperature ...

... that lowers the core pressure ...

... thereby restoring the fusion rate to normal.

... causing the core to contract and heat up ...

Center: Solar Thermostat

A slight rise in core temperature ...

... leads to a large increase in the fusion rate ...

... that raises the core pressure ...

... thereby restoring the fusion rate to normal.

... causing the core to expand and cool down ...

▲ FIGURE 11.8

The solar thermostat. Gravitational equilibrium regulates the Sun's core temperature. Everything is in balance if the amount of energy leaving the core equals the amount of energy produced by fusion. A rise in core temperature triggers a chain of events that causes the core to expand, lowering its temperature to the original value. A decrease in core temperature triggers an opposite chain of events, also restoring the original core temperature.

mass of four hydrogen nuclei. That is, when four hydrogen nuclei fuse into a helium nucleus, a little bit of mass disappears. This disappearing mass becomes energy in accord with Einstein's formula $E = mc^2$. Overall, fusion in the Sun converts about 600 million tons of hydrogen into 596 million tons of helium every second, which means that 4 million tons of matter is turned into energy each second. Although this sounds like a lot, it is a minuscule fraction of the Sun's total mass and does not affect the overall mass of the Sun in any measurable way.

The Solar Thermostat   Nuclear fusion is the source of all the energy the Sun releases into space. If the fusion rate varied, so would the Sun's energy output, and large variations in the Sun's luminosity would almost surely be lethal to life on Earth. Fortunately, the Sun fuses hydrogen at a steady rate, thanks to a natural feedback process that acts as a thermostat for the Sun's interior. To see how it works, let's examine what would happen if a small change were to occur in the core temperature (Figure 11.8).

Suppose the Sun's core temperature rose very slightly. The rate of nuclear fusion is very sensitive to temperature; a slight temperature increase would cause the fusion rate to soar as protons in the core collided more frequently and with more energy. Because energy moves slowly through the Sun's interior, this extra energy would be bottled up in the core, temporarily forcing the Sun out of energy balance and raising the core pressure. The push of this pressure would temporarily exceed the pull of gravity, causing the core to expand and cool. This cooling, in turn, would cause the fusion rate to drop back down until the core returned to its original size and temperature, restoring both gravitational equilibrium and energy balance.

Gravitational equilibrium and energy balance act together as a thermostat to keep the Sun's core temperature and fusion rate steady.

A slight drop in the Sun's core temperature would trigger an opposite chain of events. The reduced core temperature would lead to a decrease in the rate of nuclear fusion, causing a drop in pressure and contraction of the core. As the core shrank, its temperature would rise until the fusion rate returned to normal and restored the core to its original size and temperature.

▲ FIGURE 11.9

A photon in the solar interior bounces randomly among electrons, slowly working its way outward.

◆ How does the energy from fusion get out of the Sun?

The solar thermostat balances the Sun's fusion rate so that the amount of nuclear energy generated in the core equals the amount of energy radiated from the surface as sunlight. However, the journey of solar energy from the core to the photosphere takes hundreds of thousands of years.

Most of the energy released by fusion starts its journey out of the solar core in the form of photons. Although photons travel at the speed of light, the paths they take through the Sun's interior zigzag so much that it takes them a very long time to make any outward progress. Deep in the solar interior, the plasma is so dense that a photon can travel only a fraction of a millimeter in any direction before it interacts with an electron. Each time a photon collides with an electron, the photon gets deflected into a new random direction. The photon therefore bounces around the dense interior in a haphazard way (sometimes called a *random walk*) and only very gradually works its way outward from the Sun's center (Figure 11.9).

Energy released by fusion moves outward through the Sun's radiation zone (see Figure 11.4) primarily by way of these randomly bouncing photons. At the top of the radiation zone, where the temperature

Randomly bouncing photons carry energy through the deepest layers of the Sun, and convection carries energy through the upper layers to the surface.

drops to about 2 million K, the solar plasma absorbs photons more readily, rather than just bouncing them around. This absorption creates the conditions needed for convection, so above this level we find the Sun's convection zone. The rising of hot plasma and sinking of cool plasma form a cycle that transports energy outward from the base of the convection zone to the photosphere (Figure 11.10).

In the photosphere, the density of the gas is low enough that photons can escape to space. The energy produced hundreds of thousands of years earlier in the solar core then finally emerges from the Sun as thermal radiation [Section 5.2] coming from the almost 6000 K gas of the photosphere. Once in space, the photons travel away at the speed of light, bathing the planets in sunlight.

▼ FIGURE 11.10

The Sun's photosphere churns with rising hot gas and falling cool gas as a result of underlying convection.

Bright spots appear on Sun's surface where hot gas is rising . . .   *. . . then the gas sinks after it has cooled off.*

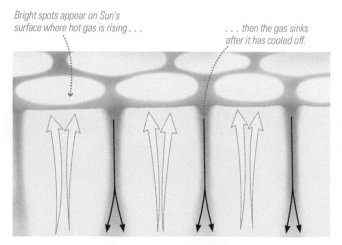

a This diagram shows convection beneath the Sun's surface: hot gas (yellow arrows) rises while cooler gas (black arrows) descends around it.

Hot gas is rising here . . .   *. . . and cooler gas is sinking here.*

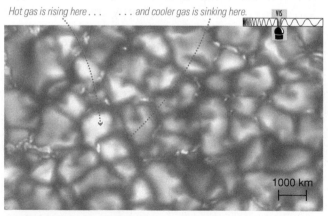

1000 km

b This photograph shows the mottled appearance of the Sun's photosphere. The bright spots correspond to the rising plumes of hot gas in the diagram in part a.

◆ How do we know what is happening inside the Sun?

We cannot see inside the Sun, so you may wonder how we can claim to know so much about what goes on underneath its surface. We can study the Sun's interior in three basic ways: through mathematical models, observations of solar vibrations, and observations of solar neutrinos.

Mathematical Models   The primary way we learn about the interior of the Sun (and other stars) is by creating *mathematical models* that use the laws of physics to predict internal conditions. A basic model starts with the Sun's observed composition and mass and then solves equations that describe gravitational equilibrium and energy balance. With the aid of a computer, we can use the model to calculate the Sun's temperature, pressure, and density at any depth. We can then predict the rate of nuclear fusion in the solar core by combining these calculations with knowledge about nuclear fusion gathered in laboratories here on Earth.

If a model is a good description of the Sun's interior, it should correctly predict the radius, surface temperature, luminosity, age, and other observable properties of the Sun. Current models predict these properties quite accurately, giving us confidence that we really do understand what is going on inside the Sun.

Solar Vibrations   A second way to learn about the inside of the Sun is to observe vibrations of the Sun's surface similar to the vibrations that earthquakes cause on Earth. Gas moving around in the solar interior generates vibrations that travel through the Sun like sound waves moving through air. We can observe these vibrations on the Sun's surface by looking for Doppler shifts [Section 5.2]. Light from portions of the surface that are rising toward us is slightly blueshifted, while light from portions that are falling away from us is slightly redshifted. The vibrations are relatively small but measurable (Figure 11.11).

We can deduce a great deal about the solar interior by carefully analyzing these vibrations. (By analogy to seismology on Earth, this type of study of the Sun is called *helioseismology—helios* means "sun.") Results to date confirm that our mathematical models of the solar interior are on the right track, while also providing data that help us to improve the models further.

The characteristics of solar vibrations support our mathematical models of the Sun's interior.

Solar Neutrinos   A third way to study the solar interior is to observe **neutrinos**, a type of subatomic particle produced by fusion in the core (see Figure 11.7). Don't panic, but about a *thousand trillion* of these solar neutrinos will zip through your body as you read this sentence—but they will do no damage at all. The reason is that neutrinos interact with other matter only through the *weak force* [Section 17.1] and gravity, not through the electromagnetic force. As a result, they can pass through almost anything. For example, an inch of lead will stop an X ray, but stopping an average neutrino would require a slab of lead more than a light-year thick!

In principle, neutrinos give us a direct way to study fusion in the Sun's core, because nearly all of them pass straight through the solar interior into space. Traveling at nearly the speed of light, they reach us just minutes after they were produced. In practice, their elusiveness makes neutrinos dauntingly difficult to detect. Nevertheless, neutrinos *do* occasionally interact with matter, and it is possible to capture a few solar neutrinos using a large enough detector (Figure 11.12). So that neutrino captures can be

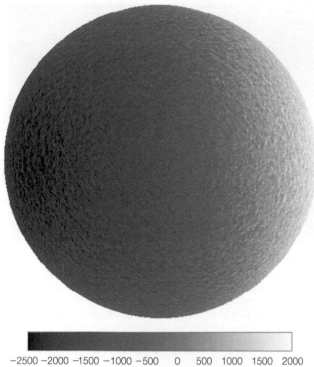

−2500 −2000 −1500 −1000 −500   0   500 1000 1500 2000
Velocity (m/s)

▲ **FIGURE 11.11**
This image shows vibrations on the Sun's surface that have been measured from Doppler shifts. Shades of orange show how quickly each spot on the Sun's surface is moving toward or away from us at a particular moment. Dark shades (negative velocities) represent motion toward us; light shades (positive velocities) represent motion away from us. The large-scale change in color from left to right reflects the Sun's rotation, and the small-scale ripples reflect the surface vibrations.

▲ **FIGURE 11.12**
This image shows neutrinos detected by the Super-Kamiokande neutrino observatory in Japan. Levels of color indicate the brightness of the neutrino signal, with red representing the strongest signal and blue representing the weakest. The grid shows the full sky, centered on the Sun, making it clear that the Sun is the source of these neutrinos. The neutrinos are produced by fusion and therefore represent direct proof that fusion really is responsible for the Sun's energy output.

▲ FIGURE 11.13

This photo shows the inside of the main vessel of the Borexino neutrino detector, located in a mine 1400 meters underground at Italy's Gran Sasso National Lab. During operations, the vessel is filled with 300 tons of a fluid that emits tiny flashes of light when a neutrino is captured; these flashes are recorded by the detectors visible on the inside of the sphere. Borexino has helped confirm that the number of neutrinos coming from the Sun agrees with the predictions of solar fusion models.

distinguished from reactions caused by other particles, neutrino detectors are usually placed deep underground or under the Antarctic ice. The overlying rock or ice blocks most other particles, but neutrinos pass right through.

The fact that we detect solar neutrinos provides direct proof that nuclear fusion is responsible for the Sun's energy. However, early attempts to detect solar neutrinos found only about one-third of the number expected based on the Sun's energy output. This disagreement between model predictions and observations came to be called the *solar neutrino problem*. It was solved in the early 2000s. The solution is this: Neutrinos come in three types, called *electron neutrinos, muon neutrinos,* and *tau neutrinos.* The early solar neutrino detectors could detect only electron neutrinos, which didn't seem like a problem at first, because fusion should produce only this type. However, we now know that neutrinos can change among the three types while passing through matter, so by the time solar neutrinos reach our detectors, only about one-third of them are still electron neutrinos. We can be confident in this solution, because more recent detectors that can detect all three neutrino types have confirmed that the total number of solar neutrinos matches predictions (Figure 11.13).

> Neutrinos provide a direct way to measure nuclear fusion in the Sun, and results indicate that fusion occurs as our models predict.

11.3 The Sun–Earth Connection

Energy liberated by nuclear fusion in the Sun's core eventually reaches the solar surface, where it helps create a wide variety of phenomena that we can observe from Earth. Sunspots are the most obvious of these phenomena. Because sunspots and other features of the Sun's surface change with time, they constitute what we call *solar weather,* or **solar activity**. The "storms" associated with solar weather are not just of academic interest. Sometimes they affect our day-to-day life on Earth. In this section, we'll explore solar activity and its far-reaching effects.

◆ What causes solar activity?

Most of the Sun's surface churns constantly with rising and falling gas, so it looks like the close-up photo shown in Figure 11.10b. However, larger features sometimes appear, including sunspots, huge explosions known as *solar flares,* and gigantic loops of hot gas extending high into the Sun's corona. All these features are created by magnetic fields, which form and change easily in the convecting plasma in the outer layers of the Sun.

Sunspots and Magnetic Fields Sunspots are the most striking features of the solar surface (Figure 11.14a). If you could look directly at a sunspot without damaging your eyes, it would be blindingly bright. Sunspots appear dark in photographs only because they are *less* bright than the surrounding photosphere. They are less bright because they are cooler: The temperature of the plasma in sunspots is about 4000 K, significantly cooler than the 5800 K plasma that surrounds them.

You may wonder how sunspots can be so much cooler than their surroundings. Gas usually flows easily, so you might expect the hotter gas around a sunspot to mix with the cooler gas within it, quickly warming the sunspot. The fact that sunspots stay relatively cool means that something must prevent hot plasma from entering them, and that something turns out to be magnetic fields.

b Very strong magnetic fields split the absorption lines in spectra of sunspot regions. The dark vertical bands are absorption lines in a spectrum of the Sun. Notice that these lines split where they cross the dark horizontal bands corresponding to sunspots.

a This close-up view of the Sun's surface shows two large sunspots and several smaller ones. Each of the big sunspots is roughly as large as Earth.

▲ **FIGURE 11.14**

Sunspots are regions of strong magnetic fields.

Detailed observations of the Sun's spectral lines reveal sunspots to be regions with strong magnetic fields. These magnetic fields can alter the energy levels in atoms and ions, causing some spectral lines to split into two or more closely spaced lines (Figure 11.14b). Wherever we see this effect (called the *Zeeman effect*), magnetic fields must be present. Scientists can therefore use this effect to map magnetic fields on the Sun.

To understand how sunspots stay cooler than their surroundings, we must investigate the nature of magnetic fields in a little more depth. Magnetic fields are invisible, but we can represent them by drawing **magnetic field lines** (Figure 11.15). These lines represent the directions in which compass needles would point if we placed them within the magnetic field. The lines are closer together where the field is stronger and farther apart where the field is weaker. Because these imaginary field lines are easier to visualize than the magnetic field itself, we usually discuss magnetic fields by talking about how the field lines would appear. Charged particles, such as the ions and electrons in the solar plasma, cannot easily move perpendicular to the field lines; instead, they follow spiraling paths along them.

Sunspots are regions kept cooler than the surrounding photosphere by strong magnetic fields.

Solar magnetic field lines act somewhat like elastic bands, twisted into contortions and knots by turbulent motions in the solar atmosphere. Sunspots occur where tightly wound magnetic fields poke nearly straight out from the solar interior (Figure 11.16a). These tight magnetic field lines suppress convection within the sunspot and prevent surrounding plasma from entering the sunspot. With hot plasma unable to enter the region, the sunspot plasma becomes cooler than that of the rest of the photosphere. Individual sunspots typically last up to a few weeks, dissolving when their magnetic fields weaken and allow hotter plasma to flow in.

Sunspots tend to occur in pairs, connected by a loop of magnetic field lines that can arc high above the Sun's surface (Figure 11.16b). Gas in the Sun's chromosphere and corona becomes trapped in these giant loops, called **solar prominences.** Some prominences rise to heights of more than 100,000 km above the Sun's surface. Individual prominences can last for days or even weeks.

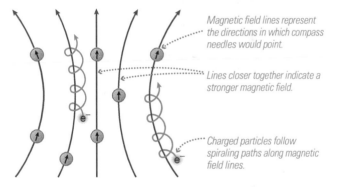

Magnetic field lines represent the directions in which compass needles would point.

Lines closer together indicate a stronger magnetic field.

Charged particles follow spiraling paths along magnetic field lines.

▲ **FIGURE 11.15**

We draw magnetic field lines (red) to represent invisible magnetic fields.

Magnetic fields trap gas.

$T \approx 5800$ K

sunspots $T \approx 4000$ K

$T \approx 5800$ K

convection cells

Magnetic fields of sunspots suppress convection and prevent surrounding plasma from sliding sideways into the sunspots.

a Pairs of sunspots are connected by tightly wound magnetic field lines.

▲ **FIGURE 11.16**

Strong magnetic fields keep sunspots cooler than the surrounding photosphere, while magnetic loops can arch from the sunspots to great heights above the Sun's surface.

b This X-ray photo (from NASA's *TRACE* mission) shows hot gas trapped within looped magnetic field lines.

Solar Storms The magnetic fields winding through sunspots and prominences sometimes undergo dramatic and sudden changes, producing short-lived but intense storms on the Sun. The most dramatic of these storms are **solar flares,** which emit bursts of ultraviolet and X-ray light along with charged particles moving at nearly the speed of light (Figure 11.17).

Flares generally occur in the vicinity of sunspots, which is why we think they are created by changes in magnetic fields. The leading model suggests that solar flares occur when magnetic field lines become so twisted and knotted that they can no longer bear the tension, causing them to snap suddenly and reorganize themselves into a less twisted configuration. The energy released in the process heats the nearby plasma to 100 million K over the next few minutes to hours, generating the intense radiation and high-speed particles that we see from solar flares.

Energy released when magnetic field lines snap can lead to dramatic solar storms, which sometimes eject bursts of energetic particles into space.

Heating of the Chromosphere and Corona As we've seen, many of the most dramatic weather patterns and storms on the Sun involve the very hot gas of the Sun's chromosphere and corona. But why is this gas so hot in the first place?

Recall that temperatures gradually decline as we move outward from the Sun's core to its photosphere. We might expect the decline to continue above the photosphere, but instead it reverses, making the chromosphere and corona much hotter than the Sun's surface. Some aspects of this heating remain a mystery today, but we have at least a general explanation: Strong magnetic fields carry energy upward from the churning solar surface to the chromosphere and corona. More specifically, the rising and falling of gas in the convection zone probably shakes tightly wound magnetic field lines beneath the solar surface, transmitting energy upward until it is ultimately deposited as heat. The same magnetic fields that keep sunspots cool therefore make the overlying plasma of the chromosphere and corona hot.

Observations support this model. The gas density in the chromosphere and corona is so low that we cannot see visible light from these

▲ **FIGURE 11.17**

This ultraviolet image (from *Solar Dynamics Observatory*) shows a solar flare erupting from the Sun's surface.

layers (except during a total eclipse when the bright photosphere is blocked from view; see Figure 2.26). However, the roughly 10,000 K plasma of the chromosphere emits strongly in the ultraviolet and the 1 million K plasma of the corona is the source of virtually all X rays from the Sun. X-ray images show that bright spots in the corona tend to be directly above sunspots in the photosphere (Figure 11.18), indicating that both are created by the same magnetic fields.

Magnetic fields deposit energy above the Sun's surface, heating the chromosphere and corona.

Notice that some regions of the corona barely show up in X-ray images; these regions, called **coronal holes,** are nearly devoid of hot coronal gas. More detailed analyses show that the magnetic field lines in coronal holes project out into space like broken rubber bands, allowing particles spiraling along them to escape the Sun altogether. These particles streaming outward from the corona are the source of the solar wind.

Flares and other solar storms sometimes eject large numbers of highly energetic charged particles from the Sun's corona. These particles travel outward from the Sun in huge bubbles that we call **coronal mass ejections** (Figure 11.19). These bubbles have strong magnetic fields and can reach Earth in a couple of days if they happen to be aimed in our direction.

Particles ejected from the Sun during periods of high activity can hamper radio communications, disrupt power delivery, and damage orbiting satellites.

Once a coronal mass ejection reaches Earth, it can create a *geomagnetic storm* in Earth's magnetosphere. On the positive side, these storms can lead to unusually strong auroras (see Figure 7.6) that can be visible throughout much of the United States. On the negative side, they can hamper radio communications, disrupt electrical power delivery, and damage the electronic components in orbiting satellites. They can also heat Earth's upper atmosphere, causing it to expand in a way that can increase drag on low-orbiting satellites, sometimes enough that they eventually plummet back to Earth.

◆ How does solar activity vary with time?

Solar weather is just as unpredictable as weather on Earth. Individual sunspots can appear or disappear at almost any time, and we have no way to know that a solar storm is coming until we observe it through our telescopes. However, long-term observations have revealed patterns in solar activity indicating that sunspots and solar storms are more common at some times than at others. They've also helped us understand the origin of the Sun's strong magnetic fields, which are responsible for all the solar activity we've discussed.

The Sunspot Cycle   The most notable pattern in solar activity is the **sunspot cycle**—a cycle in which the average number of sunspots on the Sun gradually rises and falls (Figure 11.20). At the time of *solar maximum,* when sunspots are most numerous, we may see dozens of sunspots on the Sun at one time. In contrast, we may see few, if any, sunspots at the time of *solar minimum.* The frequency of prominences, flares, and coronal mass ejections also follows the sunspot cycle, with these events being most common at solar maximum and least common at solar minimum.

▲ **FIGURE 11.18**

An X-ray image of the Sun reveals the 1 million K gas of the corona. Brighter regions (yellow) correspond to regions of stronger X-ray emission. The darker regions (such as near the north pole at the top of this photo) are *coronal holes* from which the solar wind escapes. (From the *Yohkoh* Space Observatory.)

▲ **FIGURE 11.19**

This X-ray image from the *Solar Dynamics Observatory* spacecraft shows a solar eruption that led to a coronal mass ejection on August 31, 2012.

a This graph shows how the number of sunspots on the Sun changes with time. The vertical axis shows the percentage of the Sun's surface covered by sunspots. The cycle has a period of approximately 11 years.

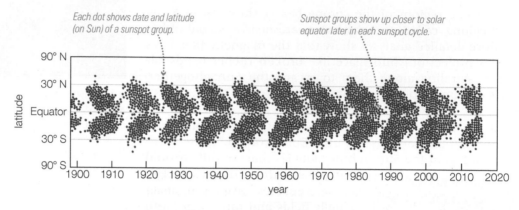

b This graph shows how the latitudes at which sunspot groups appear tend to shift during a single sunspot cycle.

▲ **FIGURE 11.20**

Sunspot cycle since about 1900.

Notice that the sunspot cycle varies from one period to the next (Figure 11.20a). The average length of time between maximums is 11 years, but we have observed it to be as short as 7 years and as long as 15 years. Observations going further back in time suggest that sunspot activity can sometimes cease almost entirely. For example, astronomers observed virtually no sunspots between the years 1645 and 1715, a period sometimes called the *Maunder minimum* (after E. W. Maunder, who identified it in historical sunspot records).

The average number of sunspots on the Sun rises and falls in an approximately 11-year cycle.

The locations of sunspots on the Sun also vary with the sunspot cycle (Figure 11.20b). As a cycle begins at solar minimum, sunspots form primarily at mid-latitudes (30° to 40°) on the Sun. The sunspots tend to form at lower latitudes as the cycle progresses, appearing very close to the solar equator as the next solar minimum approaches. Then the sunspots of the next cycle begin to form near mid-latitudes again.

A less obvious feature of the sunspot cycle is that something peculiar happens to the Sun's magnetic field at each solar maximum: The Sun's entire magnetic field starts to flip, turning magnetic north into magnetic south and vice versa. We know this because the magnetic field lines connecting pairs of sunspots (see Figure 11.16a) on the same side of the solar equator all tend to point in the same direction throughout an 11-year cycle. For example, all compass needles might point from the easternmost sunspot to the westernmost sunspot in each sunspot pair north of the solar equator. However, by the time the cycle ends at solar minimum, the magnetic field has reversed: In the subsequent solar cycle, the field lines connecting pairs of sunspots point in the opposite direction. The Sun's complete magnetic cycle (sometimes called the *solar cycle*) therefore averages 22 years, since it takes two 11-year sunspot cycles for the magnetic field to return to the way it started.

The Cause of the Sunspot Cycle   The precise reasons for the sunspot cycle are not fully understood, but the leading model ties it to a

Charged particles tend to push the field lines around with the Sun's rotation.

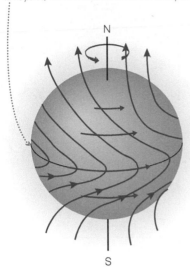

Because the Sun rotates faster near its equator than at its poles, the field lines bend ahead at the equator.

The field lines become more and more twisted with time, and sunspots form when the twisted lines loop above the Sun's surface.

▲ **FIGURE 11.21**

The Sun rotates more quickly at its equator than it does near its poles. Because gas circles the Sun faster at the equator, it drags the Sun's north–south magnetic field lines into a more twisted configuration. The magnetic field lines linking pairs of sunspots, depicted here as green and black blobs, trace out the directions of these stretched and distorted field lines.

combination of convection and the Sun's rotation. Convection is thought to dredge up weak magnetic fields generated in the solar interior, amplifying them as they rise. The Sun's rotation—faster at its equator than near its poles—then stretches and shapes these fields.

think about it Suppose you observe two sunspots: one near the Sun's equator and one directly north of it at 20° latitude. Where would you expect to see the two spots if you observed the Sun again a few days later? Would one still be directly north of the other? Explain.

Imagine what happens to magnetic field lines that start out running along the Sun's surface from south to north (Figure 11.21). At the equator, the lines circle the Sun every 25 days, but at higher latitudes, they lag behind. As a result, the lines gradually get wound more and more tightly around the Sun. This process, operating at all times over the entire Sun, produces the contorted field lines that generate sunspots and other solar activity.

The detailed behavior of these magnetic fields is quite complex, so scientists attempt to study it with sophisticated computer models. Using these models, scientists have successfully replicated many features of the sunspot cycle, including changes in the number and latitude of sunspots and the magnetic field reversals that occur about every 11 years. However, much remains mysterious, including why the period of the sunspot cycle varies and why solar activity is different from one cycle to the next.

The Sunspot Cycle and Earth's Climate Despite the changes that occur during the sunspot cycle, the Sun's total output of energy barely changes at all—the largest measured changes have been less than 0.1% of the Sun's average luminosity. However, the ultraviolet and X-ray output of the Sun, which comes from the magnetically heated gas of the chromosphere and corona, can vary much more significantly. Could any of these changes affect the weather or climate on Earth?

Some data suggest connections between solar activity and Earth's climate. For example, the Maunder minimum from 1645 to 1715, when solar activity seems to have virtually ceased, was a time of exceptionally low temperatures in Europe and North America known as the *Little Ice*

This graph compares the global average temperature and the amount of sunlight reaching Earth (the solar *irradiance*, measured in watts per square meter) since 1880. The light red and blue curves show annual changes while the dark curves show 11-year averages, which smooth out the effects of the 11-year solar cycle. Notice that, for recent decades, the amount of sunlight has remained approximately constant while Earth has warmed, ruling out the Sun as the cause of recent global warming.

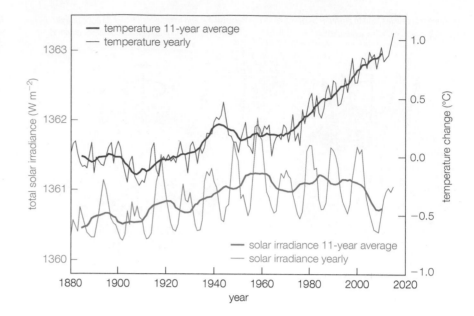

Age. However, no one knows whether the low solar activity caused these low temperatures or whether it was just a coincidence. Similarly, some researchers have claimed that certain weather phenomena, such as drought cycles or frequencies of storms, are correlated with the 11- or 22-year cycle of solar activity. A few scientists have even claimed that changes in the Sun may be responsible for Earth's recent global warming, but the Sun's energy output has actually remained nearly steady while the temperature has continued to rise (Figure 11.22), leaving little doubt that the warming is a result of human activity [Section 7.5]. Nevertheless, the study of solar activity's possible effects on climate remains an active field of research.

the big picture · Putting Chapter 11 into Perspective

In this chapter, we have examined our Sun, the nearest star. When you look back at this chapter, make sure you understand the following "big picture" ideas:

- The ancient mystery of why the Sun shines is now solved. The Sun shines with energy generated by fusion of hydrogen into helium in the Sun's core. After a journey through the solar interior lasting several hundred thousand years and an 8-minute journey through space, a small fraction of this energy reaches Earth and supplies sunlight and heat.

- The Sun shines steadily thanks to the balance between pressure and gravity (gravitational equilibrium) and the balance between energy production in the core and energy release at the surface (energy balance). These two

kinds of balance create a natural thermostat that regulates the Sun's fusion rate, keeping the Sun shining steadily and allowing life to flourish on Earth.

- The Sun's atmosphere displays its own version of weather and climate, governed by solar magnetic fields. Some solar weather, such as coronal mass ejections, clearly affects Earth's magnetosphere. Other claimed connections between solar activity and Earth's climate may or may not be real.

- The Sun is important not only as our source of light and heat, but also because it is the only star near enough for us to study in great detail. In the coming chapters, we will use what we've learned about the Sun to help us understand other stars.

my cosmic perspective The Sun affects us more directly than does any other astronomical object. It is the source of all our heat and light, and its "solar weather" can even affect our use of technology.

11.1 A Closer Look at the Sun

◆ **Why does the Sun shine?**

The Sun began to shine about 4½ billion years ago when **gravitational contraction** made its core hot enough to sustain nuclear fusion. It has shined steadily ever since because of two types of balance: (1) **gravitational equilibrium,** a balance between the outward push of pressure and the inward pull of gravity, and (2) **energy balance** between the energy released by fusion in the core and the energy radiated into space from the Sun's surface.

◆ **What is the Sun's structure?**

The Sun's interior layers, from the inside out, are the **core,** the **radiation zone,** and the **convection zone.** Atop the convection zone lies the **photosphere,** the surface layer from which photons can freely escape into space. Above the photosphere are the warmer **chromosphere** and the very hot **corona.**

11.2 Nuclear Fusion in the Sun

◆ **How does nuclear fusion occur in the Sun?**

The core's extreme temperature and density are just right for fusion of hydrogen into helium, which occurs via the **proton–**

proton chain. Because the fusion rate is so sensitive to temperature, gravitational equilibrium and energy balance act together as a thermostat to keep that rate steady.

◆ **How does the energy from fusion get out of the Sun?**

Energy moves through the deepest layers of the Sun—the core and the radiation zone—in the form of randomly bouncing photons. After energy emerges from the radiation zone, convection carries it the rest of the way to the photosphere, where it is radiated into space as sunlight. Energy produced in the core takes hundreds of thousands of years to reach the photosphere.

◆ **How do we know what is happening inside the Sun?**

We can construct theoretical models of the solar interior using known laws of physics and then check the models against observations of the Sun's size, surface temperature, and energy output. We also use studies of solar vibrations and solar **neutrinos.**

11.3 The Sun–Earth Connection

◆ **What causes solar activity?**

Sunspots and other changing features of the Sun constitute **solar activity,** which is caused by strong magnetic fields that contort and sometimes snap, creating phenomena that include **flares, prominences,** and **coronal mass ejections.** The magnetic fields also carry energy upward, depositing the heat that explains the high temperatures of the chromosphere and corona.

◆ **How does solar activity vary with time?**

The **sunspot cycle,** or the variation in the number of sunspots on the Sun's surface, has an average period of 11 years. The magnetic field flip-flops every 11 years or so, resulting in a 22-year magnetic cycle. The number of sunspots can vary dramatically from one cycle to the next, and sometimes sunspots seem to be absent altogether. The sunspot cycle and other solar activity are tied to the Sun's ever-changing magnetic field, which is created by the combination of convection and the Sun's rotation pattern (faster at the equator than at the poles).

Figure 11.20b, repeated above, shows the latitudes at which sunspots appeared on the surface of the Sun during the 20th century. Answer the following questions, using the information provided in the figure.

1. Which of the following years had the least sunspot activity?
   a. 1930
   b. 1949
   c. 1961
   d. 1987

2. What is the approximate range in latitude over which sunspots appear?

3. According to the figure, how do the positions of sunspots appear to change during one sunspot cycle? Do they get closer to or farther from the equator with time?

exercises and problems

MasteringAstronomy®   For instructor-assigned homework and other learning materials, go to MasteringAstronomy®.

Review Questions

1. Briefly describe how *gravitational contraction* generates energy. When was it important in the Sun's history? Explain.
2. What two forces are balanced in *gravitational equilibrium*? What does it mean for the Sun to be in *energy balance*?
3. State the Sun's luminosity, mass, radius, and average surface temperature, and put the numbers in perspective.
4. Briefly describe the distinguishing features of each of the layers of the Sun shown in Figure 11.4.
5. Distinguish between nuclear *fission* and *fusion*. Which one is used in nuclear power plants? Which one is used by the Sun?
6. Why does nuclear fusion require high temperatures and pressures?
7. What is the overall nuclear fusion reaction in the Sun? Briefly describe the proton–proton chain.
8. Describe how a natural "solar thermostat" keeps the core fusion rate steady in the Sun.
9. Describe how energy generated by fusion makes its way to the Sun's surface. How long does it take?
10. How do mathematical models help us learn about conditions inside the Sun, and what gives us confidence in the models?
11. What are *neutrinos*? What was the *solar neutrino problem*, and how was it solved?

12. What is *solar activity*? Describe key features including *sunspots*, *solar prominences*, *solar flares*, and *coronal mass ejections*.
13. How do magnetic fields keep sunspots cooler than the surrounding plasma? Explain.
14. Why are the chromosphere and corona best viewed with ultraviolet and X-ray telescopes, respectively? Briefly explain how we think the chromosphere and corona are heated.
15. What is the *sunspot cycle*? Describe the leading model for explaining it. Does the sunspot cycle influence Earth's climate?

Test Your Understanding

⟳ Does It Make Sense?

Decide whether the statement makes sense (or is clearly true) or does not make sense (or is clearly false). Explain clearly; not all of these have definitive answers, so your explanation is more important than your chosen answer.

16. Before Einstein, gravitational contraction appeared to be a perfectly plausible mechanism for solar energy generation.
17. The solar wind usually flows outward from the Sun, but sometimes it turns around and flows backward.
18. If fusion in the solar core ceased today, worldwide panic would break out tomorrow as the Sun began to grow dimmer.

19. Astronomers have recently photographed magnetic fields churning deep beneath the solar photosphere.
20. I wear a lead vest to protect myself from solar neutrinos.
21. There haven't been many sunspots this year, but there ought to be many more in about 5 years.
22. News of a solar flare caused concern among businesses involved in communication and electrical power generation.
23. By observing solar neutrinos, we can learn about nuclear fusion deep in the Sun's core.
24. If the Sun's magnetic field somehow disappeared, there would be no more sunspots on the Sun.
25. Scientists are currently building an infrared telescope designed to observe fusion reactions in the Sun's core.

Quick Quiz

Choose the best answer to each of the following. Explain your reasoning with one or more complete sentences.

26. Which of these groups of particles has the greatest mass? (a) a helium nucleus with two protons and two neutrons (b) four electrons (c) four individual protons
27. Which of these layers of the Sun is coolest? (a) core (b) radiation zone (c) photosphere
28. X-ray images of the Sun generally show the (a) photosphere. (b) chromosphere. (c) corona.
29. Scientists estimate the central temperature of the Sun using (a) probes that measure changes in Earth's atmosphere. (b) mathematical models of the Sun. (c) laboratories that create miniature versions of the Sun.
30. Sunspots appear darker than their surroundings because they (a) are cooler than their surroundings. (b) block some of the sunlight from the photosphere. (c) do not emit any light.
31. At the center of the Sun, fusion converts hydrogen into (a) plasma. (b) radiation and elements like carbon and nitrogen. (c) helium, energy, and neutrinos.
32. Solar energy leaves the core of the Sun in the form of (a) photons. (b) rising hot gas. (c) sound waves.
33. The fact that we observe neutrinos from the Sun provides direct evidence of (a) fusion in the Sun's core. (b) convection in the Sun's interior. (c) the existence of the solar wind.
34. What causes the cycle of solar activity? (a) changes in the Sun's fusion rate (b) changes in the organization of the Sun's magnetic field (c) changes in the speed of the solar wind
35. Which of these things poses the greatest hazard to communication satellites? (a) photons from the Sun (b) solar magnetic fields (c) particles from the Sun

◐ Process of Science

36. *Inside the Sun.* Scientists claim to know what is going on inside the Sun, even though we cannot directly observe the Sun's interior. What is the basis for these claims, and how are they aligned with the hallmarks of science outlined in Section 3.4?
37. *The Solar Neutrino Problem.* Early solar neutrino experiments detected only about a third of the number of neutrinos predicted by the theory of fusion in the Sun. Why didn't scientists simply abandon their model at this point? What features of the Sun did the model get right? What alternatives were there for explaining the mismatch between the predictions and the observations?

Group Work Exercise

38. *The Sun's Future.* **Roles:** *Scribe* (takes notes on the group's activities), *Proposer* (proposes explanations to the group), *Skeptic* (points out weaknesses in proposed explanations), *Moderator* (leads group discussion and makes sure everyone contributes). **Activity:** Consider what you have learned about how the Sun came to shine steadily with energy from fusion in its core, then discuss the following questions:
    a. What will happen to the core temperature of the Sun *after* its core runs out of hydrogen for fusion? Will the temperature go up or down?
    b. If you think the temperature will go up, will it rise forever? What could eventually stop the temperature from rising? If you think the temperature will go down, will it decrease forever? What could eventually stop it from falling?
    c. Propose and describe an Earth-based experiment or a set of stellar observations that could test your hypothesis from part (b).

Investigate Further

Short-Answer/Essay Questions

39. *The End of Fusion I.* Describe what would happen in the Sun if fusion reactions abruptly ceased.
40. *The End of Fusion II.* If fusion reactions in the Sun were to suddenly cease, would we be able to tell? If so, how?
41. *A Really Strong Force.* How would the interior temperature of the Sun be different if the strong force that binds nuclei together were 10 times as strong?
42. *Covered with Sunspots.* Describe what the Sun would look like from Earth if the entire photosphere were the same temperature as a sunspot.
43. *Inside the Sun.* Describe how scientists determine what the interior of the Sun is like. Could we send a probe into the Sun to measure what is happening there?
44. *Solar Energy Output.* Observations over the past century show that the Sun's visible-light output varies by less than 1%, but its X-ray output can vary by a factor of 10 or more. Explain why the changes in X-ray output can be so much more pronounced than the changes in visible-light output.
45. *An Angry Sun.* A *Time* magazine cover once suggested that an "angry Sun" was becoming more active as human activity changed Earth's climate. It's certainly possible for the Sun to become more active at the same time that humans are affecting Earth, but is it possible that the Sun could be responding to human activity? Can humans affect the Sun in any significant way? Explain.

Quantitative Problems

Be sure to show all calculations clearly and state your final answers in complete sentences.

46. *The Color of the Sun.* The Sun's average surface temperature is about 5800 K. Use Wien's law (see Cosmic Calculations 5.1) to calculate the wavelength of peak thermal emission from the Sun. What color does this wavelength correspond to in the visible-light spectrum? Why do you think the Sun appears white or yellow to our eyes?
47. *The Color of a Sunspot.* The typical temperature of a sunspot is about 4000 K. Use Wien's law (see Cosmic Calculations 5.1) to

formula comes from the fact that the surface area of a sphere is given by $4\pi \times \text{radius}^2$.)

In principle, we can always determine a star's apparent brightness by carefully measuring the amount of light per square meter we receive from the star. We can then use the inverse square law to calculate a star's luminosity if we can first measure its distance, or to calculate a star's distance if we know its luminosity.

think about it Suppose Star A is four times as luminous as Star B. How will their apparent brightnesses compare if they are both the same distance from Earth? How will their apparent brightnesses compare if Star A is twice as far from Earth as Star B? Explain.

Measuring Distance Through Stellar Parallax The most direct way to measure a star's distance is with *stellar parallax*, the small annual shifts in a star's apparent position caused by Earth's motion around the Sun [Section 2.4]. Astronomers measure stellar parallax by comparing observations of a nearby star made 6 months apart (Figure 12.3). The nearby star appears to shift against the background of more distant stars because we are observing it from two opposite points of Earth's orbit.

We can measure the distance to a nearby star by observing how its apparent location shifts as Earth orbits the Sun.

We can calculate a star's distance if we know the precise amount of the star's annual shift due to parallax. This means measuring the angle p in Figure 12.3, which we call the star's *parallax angle*. Notice that this angle would be smaller if the star were farther away, meaning that more distant stars have *smaller* parallax angles. Real stellar parallax angles are very small: Even the nearest stars have parallax angles of less than 1 arcsecond, well below the approximately 1 arcminute angular resolution of the naked eye.

By definition, the distance to an object with a parallax angle of 1 arcsecond is 1 parsec (pc), which is equivalent to 3.26 light-years. (The word *parsec* comes from combining the words *parallax* and *arcsecond*.) This leads to a simple formula for a star's distance: If we measure the parallax angle p in arcseconds, the star's distance d in parsecs is $d = 1/p$; we just multiply by 3.26 to convert from parsecs to light-years. For example, a star with a parallax angle $p = \frac{1}{10}$ arcsecond is 10 parsecs away, or $10 \times 3.26 = 32.6$ light-years. You may hear astronomers state distances in parsecs, kiloparsecs (1000 parsecs), or megaparsecs (1 million parsecs), but in this book we'll stick to distances in light-years.

think about it Suppose Star A has a parallax angle of 0.2 arcsecond and Star B has a parallax angle of 0.4 arcsecond. How does the distance of Star A from Earth compare to that of Star B?

Parallax was the first reliable technique astronomers developed for measuring distances to stars, and it remains the only technique that tells us stellar distances without any assumptions about the nature of stars. If we know a star's distance from its parallax angle, we can calculate its luminosity with the inverse square law for light. In fact, parallax measurements are the key to all other distance measurements in the universe, because astronomers use parallax measurements of the distances of nearby stars as the base of a chain of techniques that allows measurement of much greater distances [Section 16.2]. As of

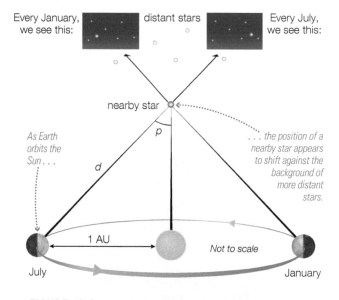

▲ FIGURE 12.3

Parallax makes the apparent position of a nearby star shift back and forth with respect to distant stars over the course of each year. The angle p, called the *parallax angle*, represents half the total parallax shift each year. If we measure p in arcseconds, the distance d to the star in parsecs is $1/p$. The angle in this figure is greatly exaggerated: All stars have parallax angles of less than 1 arcsecond.

2016, astronomers have made parallax measurements for more than 100,000 stars out to distances of more than 1500 light-years, and the European *GAIA* spacecraft is in the process of making parallax measurements for up to a billion stars, out to distances of tens of thousands of light-years.

The Luminosity Range of Stars   Now that we have discussed how we determine stellar luminosities, it's time to take a quick look at the results. We usually state stellar luminosities in comparison to the Sun's luminosity, L_{Sun}. For example, Proxima Centauri, the nearest of the three stars in the Alpha Centauri system and hence the nearest star besides our Sun, has only about 0.0006 times the luminosity of the Sun, or $0.0006L_{Sun}$. Betelgeuse, the bright left-shoulder star of Orion, has a luminosity of $120,000L_{Sun}$, meaning that it is 120,000 times as luminous as the Sun. Overall, studies of the luminosities of many stars have taught us two particularly important lessons:

- Stars come in a wide range of luminosities, with our Sun somewhere in the middle. The dimmest stars have luminosities $\frac{1}{10,000}$ times that of the Sun ($10^{-4}L_{Sun}$) while the brightest stars are about 1 million times as luminous as the Sun ($10^6 L_{Sun}$).
- Dim stars are far more common than bright stars. For example, even though our Sun is roughly in the middle of the overall range of stellar luminosities, it is brighter than the vast majority of stars in our galaxy.

The Magnitude System   Many astronomy resources (including star charts) describe the apparent brightnesses and luminosities of stars in an alternative way: They use the ancient *magnitude system* devised by the Greek astronomer Hipparchus (c. 190–120 B.C.). Although we won't make much use of this system in this book, it's useful to be familiar with it in case you encounter it elsewhere.

Hipparchus designated the brightest stars in the sky as "first magnitude," the next brightest "second magnitude," and so on. The faintest visible stars were magnitude 6. Today we call this type of designation an **apparent magnitude** because it describes how bright a star *appears* in the sky. Notice that the magnitude scale runs backward: A larger apparent magnitude means a dimmer apparent brightness. For example, a star of magnitude 4 is dimmer than a star of magnitude 1.

In modern times, the magnitude system has been extended and more precisely defined: Each difference of five magnitudes is defined to represent a factor of exactly 100 in brightness. For example, a magnitude 1 star is 100 times as bright as a magnitude 6 star, and a magnitude 3 star is 100 times as bright as a magnitude 8 star. As a result of this precise definition, stars can have fractional apparent magnitudes and a few bright stars have apparent magnitudes *less than* 1—which means *brighter* than magnitude 1. For example, the brightest star in the night sky, Sirius, has an apparent magnitude of –1.46.

The modern magnitude system also defines **absolute magnitude** as a way of describing stellar luminosity. A star's absolute magnitude is the apparent magnitude it would have *if* it were at a distance of 10 parsecs (32.6 light-years) from Earth. For example, the Sun's absolute magnitude is about 4.8, meaning that the Sun would have an apparent magnitude of 4.8 *if* it were 10 parsecs away from us—bright enough to be visible but not conspicuous on a dark night.

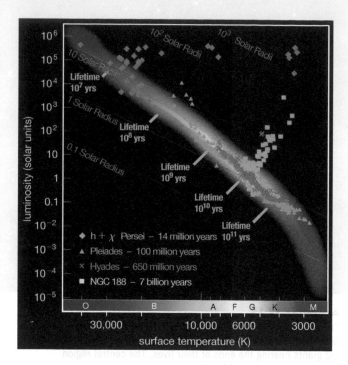

▲ **FIGURE 12.17**
This H-R diagram shows stars from the Pleiades and three other clusters. Their differing main-sequence turnoff points indicate very different ages.

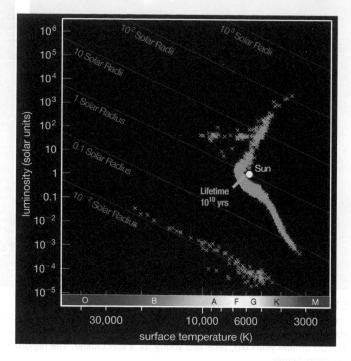

▲ **FIGURE 12.18**
This H-R diagram shows stars from the globular cluster M4. The main-sequence turnoff point is in the vicinity of stars like our Sun, indicating an age for this cluster of around 10 billion years. A more technical analysis of this cluster (which accounts for the lower abundance of heavy elements in these old stars) places its age at around 13 billion years.

cluster stars are older than 10 billion years. More precise studies of the turnoff points in globular clusters, coupled with theoretical calculations of stellar lifetimes, place the ages of these clusters at about 13 billion years, making them the oldest known objects in the galaxy and implying that they began to form within the first billion years of the universe's roughly 14-billion-year history.

the big picture   Putting Chapter 12 into Perspective

We have classified the diverse families of stars visible in the night sky. Much of what we know about stars, galaxies, and the universe itself is based on the fundamental properties of stars introduced in this chapter. Make sure you understand the following "big picture" ideas:

- All stars are made primarily of hydrogen and helium at the time they form. The differences between stars are primarily due to differences in mass and stage of life.

- Stars spend most of their lives as main-sequence stars that fuse hydrogen into helium in their cores. The most massive stars, which are also the hottest and most luminous, live only a few million years. The least massive

stars, which are coolest and dimmest, will survive until the universe is many times its present age.

- The key to recognizing the patterns among stars was the H-R diagram, which shows stellar surface temperatures on the horizontal axis and luminosities on the vertical axis. The H-R diagram is one of the most important tools of modern astronomy.

- Much of what we know about the universe comes from studies of star clusters. We can measure a star cluster's age by plotting its stars in an H-R diagram and determining the core hydrogen-fusion lifetime of the brightest and most massive stars still on the main sequence.

my cosmic perspective You may be used to seeing stars on clear, dark nights, but you probably never realized how diverse they are in size, color, and age. Next time you're looking up at the stars on a clear, dark night, try to find one of the brightest red supergiant stars, such as Betelgeuse or Antares, and notice its redder color.

12.1 Properties of Stars

◆ **How do we measure stellar luminosities?**

The **apparent brightness** of a star in our sky depends on both its **luminosity**—the total amount of light it emits into space—and its distance, as expressed by the **inverse square law for light.** We can therefore calculate luminosity from apparent brightness and distance; we can measure the latter through stellar parallax.

◆ **How do we measure stellar temperatures?**

We measure a star's surface temperature from its color or spectrum, and we classify stars according to the sequence of **spectral types** OBAFGKM, which runs from hottest to coolest. Cool, red stars of spectral type M are much more common than hot, blue stars of spectral type O.

◆ **How do we measure stellar masses?**

We can calculate the masses of stars in **binary star systems** using Newton's version of Kepler's third law if we can measure the orbital period and separation of the two stars.

12.2 Patterns Among Stars

◆ **What is a Hertzsprung-Russell diagram?**

An **H-R diagram** plots stars according to their surface temperatures (or spectral types) and luminosities. Most stars appear on the H-R diagram in the narrow strip known as the **main sequence. Giants** and **supergiants** are to the upper right of the main sequence and **white dwarfs** are to the lower left.

◆ **What is the significance of the main sequence?**

Stars on the main sequence are all fusing hydrogen into helium in their cores. A star's position along the main sequence depends on its mass: High-mass stars are at the upper left and masses of stars become progressively smaller as we move toward the lower right. Lifetimes vary in the opposite way, because higher-mass stars live shorter lives.

◆ **What are giants, supergiants, and white dwarfs?**

Giants and supergiants are stars that have exhausted their central core supplies of hydrogen for fusion and are undergoing other forms of fusion at a prodigious rate as they near the ends of their lives. White dwarfs are the exposed cores of stars that have already died, meaning they have no further means of generating energy through fusion.

12.3 Star Clusters

◆ **What are the two types of star clusters?**

Open clusters contain up to several thousand stars and are found in the disk of our galaxy. **Globular clusters** contain hundreds of thousands of stars, all closely packed together, and are found mainly in the halo of the galaxy.

◆ **How do we measure the age of a star cluster?**

Because all of a cluster's stars were born at about the same time, we can measure a cluster's age by finding the **main-sequence turnoff point** on an H-R diagram of its stars. The cluster's age is equal to the hydrogen core-fusion lifetime of the hottest, most luminous stars that remain on the main sequence. Open clusters are much younger than globular clusters, which can be as old as about 13 billion years.

visual skills check

Check your understanding of some of the many types of visual information used in astronomy. For additional practice, try the Chapter 12 Visual Quiz at MasteringAstronomy®.

The figure above, similar to Figure 12.13, uses zoom-ins to compare the sizes of giant and supergiant stars to the sizes of Earth and the Sun.

1. Suppose we wanted to represent all of these objects on the 1-to-10-billion scale from Chapter 1, on which the Sun is about the size of a grapefruit. Approximately how large in diameter would the star Aldebaran be on this scale?
   a. 40 centimeters (the size of a typical beach ball)
   b. 6 meters (roughly the size of a dorm room)
   c. 15 meters (roughly the size of a typical house)
   d. 70 meters (slightly smaller than a football field)

2. Approximately how large in diameter would the star Betelgeuse be on this same scale?
   a. 40 centimeters (the size of a typical beach ball)
   b. 6 meters (roughly the size of a dorm room)
   c. 130 meters (slightly larger than a football field)
   d. 3 kilometers (the size of a small town)

3. Approximately how large in diameter would the star Procyon B be on this same scale?
   a. 10 centimeters (the size of a large grapefruit)
   b. 1 centimeter (the size of a grape)
   c. 1 millimeter (the size of a grape seed)
   d. 0.1 millimeter (roughly the width of a human hair)

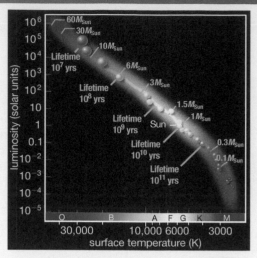

The H-R diagram above is identical to Figure 12.11. Answer the following questions based on the information given in the figure.

4. What are the approximate luminosity and lifetime of a star whose mass is 10 times that of the Sun?

5. What are the approximate luminosity and lifetime of a star whose mass is 3 times that of the Sun?

6. What are the approximate luminosity and lifetime of a star whose mass is twice that of the Sun?

exercises and problems

MasteringAstronomy® For instructor-assigned homework and other learning materials, go to MasteringAstronomy®.

Review Questions

1. Briefly explain how we can learn about the lives of stars even though their lives are far longer than human lives.

2. In what ways are all stars similar? In what ways can stars differ?

3. How is a star's *apparent brightness* related to its *luminosity*? Explain by describing the *inverse square law for light*.

4. How do we use *stellar parallax* to determine a star's distance, and how can we then determine its luminosity?

5. What do we mean by a star's *spectral type,* and how is it related to the star's surface temperature and color? Which types of stars are hottest and coolest in the spectral sequence OBAFGKM?

6. What are the three basic types of *binary star systems*? Why are *eclipsing binaries* so important for measuring masses of stars?

7. Draw a sketch of an Hertzsprung-Russell (H-R) diagram. Label the *main sequence, giants, supergiants,* and *white dwarfs.* Where on this diagram do we find stars that are cool and dim? Cool and luminous? Hot and dim? Hot and luminous?

8. What do we mean by a star's *luminosity class*? Briefly explain how we classify stars by spectral type and luminosity class.

9. What is the defining characteristic of a *main-sequence* star? Briefly explain why massive main-sequence stars are more luminous and have hotter surfaces than less massive main-sequence stars.

10. Which stars have longer lifetimes: massive stars or less massive stars? Explain why.

11. How do giants and supergiants differ from main-sequence stars? What are white dwarfs?

12. Why is a star's birth mass its most fundamental property?
13. Describe in general terms how *open clusters* and *globular clusters* differ in their numbers of stars, ages, and locations in a galaxy.
14. Explain why H-R diagrams look different for star clusters of different ages. How does the location of the *main-sequence turnoff point* tell us the age of the star cluster?

Test Your Understanding

◔ Does It Make Sense?

Decide whether the statement makes sense (or is clearly true) or does not make sense (or is clearly false). Explain clearly; not all of these have definitive answers, so your explanation is more important than your chosen answer.

15. Two stars that look very different must be made of different kinds of elements.
16. Two stars that have the same apparent brightness in the sky must also have the same luminosity.
17. Sirius looks brighter than Alpha Centauri, but we know that Alpha Centauri is closer because its apparent position in the sky shifts by a larger amount as Earth orbits the Sun.
18. Stars that look red-hot have hotter surfaces than stars that look blue.
19. Some of the stars on the main sequence of the H-R diagram are not converting hydrogen into helium.
20. The smallest, hottest stars are plotted in the lower left portion of the H-R diagram.
21. Stars that begin their lives with the most mass live longer than less massive stars because they have so much more hydrogen fuel.
22. Star clusters with lots of bright, blue stars of spectral types O and B are generally younger than clusters that don't have any such stars.
23. All giants, supergiants, and white dwarfs were once main-sequence stars.
24. Most of the stars in the sky are more massive than the Sun.

Quick Quiz

Choose the best answer to each of the following. Explain your reasoning with one or more complete sentences.

25. If the star Alpha Centauri were moved to a distance 10 times farther from Earth than it is now, its parallax angle would (a) get larger. (b) get smaller. (c) stay the same.
26. What do we need to measure in order to determine a star's luminosity? (a) apparent brightness and mass (b) apparent brightness and temperature (c) apparent brightness and distance
27. What two pieces of information would you need in order to measure the masses of stars in an eclipsing binary system? (a) the time between eclipses and the average distance between the stars (b) the period of the binary system and its distance from the Sun (c) the velocities of the stars and the Doppler shifts of their absorption lines
28. Which of these stars has the coolest surface temperature? (a) an A star (b) an F star (c) a K star
29. Which of these stars is the most massive? (a) a main-sequence A star (b) a main-sequence G star (c) a main-sequence M star
30. Which of these stars has the longest lifetime? (a) a main-sequence A star (b) a main-sequence G star (c) a main-sequence M star
31. Which of these stars has the largest radius? (a) a supergiant A star (b) a giant K star (c) a supergiant M star
32. Which of these stars has the greatest surface temperature? (a) a main-sequence B star (b) a supergiant A star (c) a giant K star

33. Which of these star clusters is youngest? (a) a cluster whose brightest main-sequence stars are white (b) a cluster whose brightest stars are red (c) a cluster containing stars of all colors
34. Which of these star clusters is oldest? (a) a cluster whose brightest main-sequence stars are white (b) a cluster whose brightest main-sequence stars are yellow (c) a cluster containing stars of all colors

◔ Process of Science

35. *Classification.* As discussed in the text, Annie Jump Cannon and her colleagues developed our modern system of stellar classification. Why do you think rapid advances in our understanding of stars followed so quickly on the heels of this effort? What other areas of science have had huge advances in understanding following an improved system of classification?
36. *Life Spans of Stars.* Scientists estimate the life span of a star by dividing the total amount of energy available for fusion by the rate at which the star radiates energy into space. Such calculations predict that the life spans of high-mass stars are shorter than those of low-mass stars. Describe one type of observation that can test this prediction and verify that it is correct.

Group Work Exercise

37. *Comparing Stellar Properties.* **Roles:** *Analyst 1* (analyzes data in Table F.1), *Scribe 1* (records results and conclusions about Table F.1), *Analyst 2* (analyzes data in Table F.2), *Scribe 2* (records results and conclusions about Table F.2). **Activity:** Work in pairs to answer the following questions, with Pair 1 using the data in Appendix Table F.1 and Pair 2 using the data in Appendix Table F.2.
    a. Count and record the number of stars of each spectral type (OBAFGKM) for both tables.
    b. Count and record the number of stars of each luminosity class (I, II, III, IV, V) for both tables.
    c. Compare the counts of spectral types in the two tables. Discuss any differences you find and develop a hypothesis that could explain them.
    d. Compare the counts of luminosity classes in the two tables. Discuss any differences you find and develop a hypothesis that could explain them.
    e. Write down the nearest star of each spectral type; if it cannot be determined, explain why.
    f. Determine whether there could be an O star within 200 light-years of the Sun based on the data in the tables, and explain your reasoning.

Investigate Further

Short-Answer/Essay Questions

38. *Stellar Data.* Consider the following data table for several bright stars. M_v is absolute magnitude, and m_v is apparent magnitude. Use these data to answer the following questions, and include a brief explanation with each answer. (*Hint:* Remember that the magnitude scale runs backward, so brighter stars have smaller or more negative magnitudes.)
    a. Which star appears brightest in our sky?
    b. Which star appears faintest in our sky?
    c. Which star has the greatest luminosity?
    d. Which star has the least luminosity?
    e. Which star has the highest surface temperature?
    f. Which star has the lowest surface temperature?

g. Which star is most similar to the Sun?

h. Which star is a red supergiant?

i. Which star has the largest radius?

j. Which stars have finished fusing hydrogen in their cores?

k. Among the main-sequence stars listed, which one is the most massive?

l. Among the main-sequence stars listed, which one has the longest lifetime?

Star	M_v	m_v	Spectral Type	Luminosity Class
Aldebaran	−0.2	+0.9	K5	III
Alpha Centauri A	+4.4	0.0	G2	V
Antares	−4.5	+0.9	M1	I
Canopus	−3.1	−0.7	F0	II
Fomalhaut	+2.0	+1.2	A3	V
Regulus	−0.6	+1.4	B7	V
Sirius	+1.4	−1.4	A1	V
Spica	−3.6	+0.9	B1	V

39. *Data Tables.* Study the spectral types listed in Appendix F for the 20 brightest stars and for the stars within 12 light-years of Earth. Why do you think the two lists are so different? Explain.

40. *Interpreting the H-R Diagram.* Using the information in Figure 12.10, describe how Proxima Centauri differs from Sirius.

41. *Parallax from Jupiter.* Suppose you could travel to Jupiter and observe changes in positions of nearby stars during one orbit of Jupiter around the Sun. Describe how those changes would differ from what we would measure from Earth. How would your ability to measure the distances to stars from the vantage point of Jupiter be different?

42. *An Expanding Star.* Describe what would happen to the surface temperature of a star if its radius doubled in size with no change in luminosity.

43. *Colors of Eclipsing Binaries.* Figure 12.8 shows an eclipsing binary system consisting of a small blue star and a larger red star. Explain why the decrease in apparent brightness of the combined system is greater when the blue star is eclipsed than when the red star is eclipsed.

44. *Visual and Spectroscopic Binaries.* Suppose you are observing two binary star systems at the same distance from Earth. Both are spectroscopic binaries consisting of similar types of stars, but only one of the binary systems is a visual binary. Which of these star systems would you expect to have the greater Doppler shifts in its spectra? Explain your reasoning.

45. *Life of a Star Cluster.* Imagine you could watch a star cluster from the time of its birth to an age of 13 billion years. Describe in one or two paragraphs what you would see happening during that time.

Quantitative Problems

Be sure to show all calculations clearly and state your final answers in complete sentences.

46. *The Inverse Square Law for Light.* Earth is about 150 million km from the Sun, and the apparent brightness of the Sun in our sky is about 1300 watts/m^2. Using these two facts and the inverse square law for light, determine the apparent brightness that we would measure for the Sun *if* we were located at the following positions.

a. Half Earth's distance from the Sun

b. Twice Earth's distance from the Sun

c. Five times Earth's distance from the Sun

47. *The Luminosity of Alpha Centauri A.* Alpha Centauri A lies at a distance of 4.4 light-years from Earth and has an apparent brightness in our night sky of 2.7×10^{-8} watt/m^2. Recall that 1 light-year $= 9.5 \times 10^{15}$ m.

a. Use the inverse square law for light to calculate the luminosity of Alpha Centauri A.

b. Suppose you have a light bulb that emits 100 watts of visible light. How far away would you have to put the light bulb for it to have the same apparent brightness as Alpha Centauri A in our sky? (*Hint:* Use 100 watts as L in the inverse square law for light, and use the apparent brightness given above for Alpha Centauri A. Then solve for the distance.)

48. *More Practice with the Inverse Square Law for Light.* Use the inverse square law for light to answer each of the following questions.

a. Suppose a star has the same luminosity as our Sun (3.8×10^{26} watts) but is located at a distance of 10 light-years from Earth. What is its apparent brightness?

b. Suppose a star has the same apparent brightness as Alpha Centauri A (2.7×10^{-8} watt/m^2) but is located at a distance of 200 light-years from Earth. What is its luminosity?

c. Suppose a star has a luminosity of 8×10^{26} watts and an apparent brightness of 3.5×10^{-12} watt/m^2. How far away is it from Earth? Give your answer in both kilometers and light-years.

d. Suppose a star has a luminosity of 5×10^{29} watts and an apparent brightness of 9×10^{-15} watt/m^2. How far away is it from Earth? Give your answer in both kilometers and light-years.

49. *Parallax and Distance.* Use the parallax formula to calculate the distance to each of the following stars. Give your answers in both parsecs and light-years.

a. Alpha Centauri: parallax angle of 0.7420 arcsecond

b. Procyon: parallax angle of 0.2860 arcsecond

50. *Radius of a Star.* Sirius A has a luminosity of $26L_{Sun}$ and a surface temperature of about 9400 K. What is its radius? (*Hint:* See Cosmic Calculations 12.2.)

Discussion Question

51. *Snapshot of the Heavens.* The beginning of the chapter likened the problem of studying the lives of stars to learning about human beings from a 1-minute glance at human life. What could you learn about human life by looking at a single snapshot of a large family, including babies, parents, and grandparents? How is the study of such a snapshot similar to what scientists do when they study the lives of stars? How is it different?

Web Projects

52. *Women in Astronomy.* Until fairly recently, men greatly outnumbered women in professional astronomy. Nevertheless, many women made crucial discoveries in astronomy throughout history—including the discovery of the spectral sequence for stars. Do some research about the life and discoveries of a female astronomer from any time period and write a two- to three-page scientific biography.

53. *Parallax Missions.* The European Space Agency's *Hipparcos* spacecraft made precise parallax measurements for more than 40,000 stars from 1989 to 1993, and the agency's *GAIA* mission is designed to measure parallax for many more stars. Learn about how these satellites can measure much smaller parallax angles than is possible from the ground and how those measurements affect our knowledge of the universe. Write a one- to two-page report on your findings.

13 Star Stuff

This composite photograph, made from X-ray, radio, and visible-light images, shows an exploding star that is ejecting newly made elements into interstellar space.

We inhale oxygen with every breath. Iron-bearing hemoglobin in our blood carries this oxygen through our bodies. Chains of carbon and nitrogen form the backbone of the proteins, fats, and carbohydrates in our cells. Calcium strengthens our bones, while sodium and potassium ions communicate signals through our nerves. What does all this biology have to do with astronomy? The profound answer is that life is based on elements created by stars.

In this chapter, we will discuss the origins of the elements in some detail by delving into the lives of stars. As you read, keep in mind that no matter how far removed the stars may seem from our everyday lives, they are connected to us in the most intimate way possible: Without the births, lives, and deaths of stars, none of us would be here. We are truly made from "star stuff."

13.1 Star Birth

The story of a star's life begins in the murky depths of interstellar space. Using main-sequence turnoff points [Section 12.3] to determine the ages of star clusters, we have found that the youngest clusters are always associated with dark clouds of gas and dust, indicating that these interstellar clouds are the birthplaces of stars. Theoretical models of star formation confirm this idea, telling us how the physical processes that occur in gas clouds ultimately give birth to stars. In this section, we'll explore the processes that give birth to stars, setting the stage for us to explore the rest of stellar life cycles in later sections of this chapter.

◆ How do stars form?

A star is born when gravity causes a cloud of interstellar gas to contract to the point at which the central object becomes hot enough to sustain nuclear fusion in its core. However, gravity does not always succeed in making an interstellar cloud contract, because the cloud's internal gas pressure can resist gravity.

Recall that our Sun remains stable in size because the inward pull of gravity is balanced by the outward push of gas pressure, a balance that we call *gravitational equilibrium* [Section 11.1]. The pressure is far weaker in the low-density gas of interstellar space, but so is the pull of gravity. In most places within our galaxy, gravity is not strong enough to overcome the internal pressure of interstellar gas, which is why star formation does not occur everywhere.

If you think about it, you'll realize that two things can help gravity win out over pressure and start the collapse of a cloud of gas: (1) higher density, because packing the gas particles closer together makes the gravitational forces between them stronger, and (2) lower temperature, because lowering a cloud's temperature reduces the gas pressure. We therefore expect star-forming clouds to be colder and denser than most other interstellar gas.

Stars are born in cold, dense clouds of gas whose pressure cannot resist gravitational contraction.

Observations confirm the idea that stars are born within the coldest and densest clouds, usually called **molecular clouds** because they are cold enough and dense enough to allow atoms to combine and form

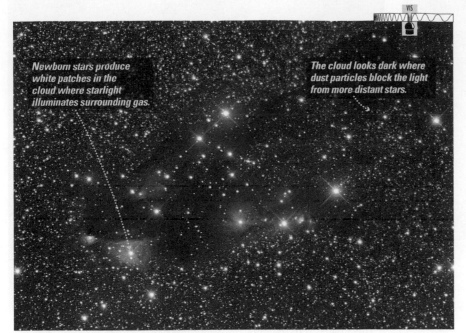

Newborn stars produce white patches in the cloud where starlight illuminates surrounding gas.

The cloud looks dark where dust particles block the light from more distant stars.

◄ FIGURE 13.1

A star-forming molecular cloud in the constellation Scorpius. The region pictured here is about 50 light-years across.

molecules (Figure 13.1). Typical molecular cloud temperatures are only 10–30 K. (Recall that 0 K is absolute zero; see Figure 4.10.) And while their densities are low enough that they would qualify as superb vacuums by earthly standards, molecular clouds are hundreds to thousands of times as dense as other regions of interstellar space. The molecular clouds that give birth to stars tend to be quite large, because more total mass also helps gravity overcome gas pressure. A typical star-forming cloud is thousands of times as massive as a typical star, and can give birth to many stars at the same time. That is why stars are usually born in clusters.

From Cloud to Protostar Once a large molecular cloud begins to collapse, gravity pulls the gas toward the cloud's densest regions, causing it to fragment into smaller pieces that each form one or more new stars (Figure 13.2). Each shrinking cloud fragment heats up as it contracts.

▼ FIGURE 13.2

Computer simulation of a fragmenting molecular cloud. Gravity attracts matter to the densest regions of a molecular cloud. If gravity can overcome pressure in these dense regions, they collapse to form even denser knots of gas. Each of these knots can form one or more new stars.

a The simulation begins with a turbulent gas cloud 1.2 light-years across, containing $50M_{Sun}$ of gas.

b Random motions in the cloud cause it to become lumpy, with some regions denser than others. If gravity can overcome pressure in these dense regions, they can collapse to form even denser lumps of matter.

c The large cloud therefore fragments into many smaller lumps of matter, and each lump can go on to form one or more new stars.

a This visible-light image from the Hubble Space Telescope shows part of the Eagle Nebula, a gas cloud in which stars are currently forming.

b This image from the Herschel Space Telescope shows infrared light from the Eagle Nebula, with the portion shown in part a outlined by the yellow square. Notice that the dark clouds in the visible-light image are glowing in the infrared image.

▲ **FIGURE 13.3**

Star-forming molecular clouds are cooler than stars and therefore emit infrared rather than visible light.

cosmic calculations 13.1

Conditions for Star Birth

As discussed in the text, gravity can win out over pressure to start the collapse of an interstellar cloud only when the gas temperature (T) is relatively low and the gas density (n) is relatively high. Exactly how cold and dense the cloud must be depends on the total amount of matter it contains: The more massive the cloud, the more easily gravity can win out. Astronomers have found a simple formula that tells us how massive a cloud must be for gravity to start its collapse:

$$M_{minimum} = 18M_{Sun}\sqrt{\frac{T^3}{n}}$$

where T is the gas temperature in Kelvin and n is the gas density in particles per cubic centimeter. $M_{minimum}$ is the minimum mass for making stars: Gravity can make a cloud collapse and give birth to stars only if the cloud's total mass is *greater* than $M_{minimum}$.

Example: A cloud has a temperature of 30 K and an average density of 300 particles per cubic centimeter. What mass must this cloud have in order to form stars?

Solution: We insert the values $T = 30$ K and $n = 300$ particles per cubic centimeter into the $M_{minimum}$ formula:

$$M_{minimum} = 18M_{Sun}\sqrt{\frac{30^3}{300}} = 18M_{Sun}\sqrt{90} \approx 171M_{Sun}$$

Gravity can cause this cloud to collapse and form stars only if the cloud's mass is greater than about $171M_{Sun}$.

The source of this heat is the gravitational potential energy [Section 4.3] released as gravity pulls each part of the cloud fragment closer to the center of the fragment. Early in the process of star formation, the contracting gas quickly radiates away much of this energy, preventing the temperature and pressure from building enough to resist gravity. The temperature of the cloud remains below 100 K, so it glows in long-wavelength infrared light (Figure 13.3).

As the cloud continues to contract, the growing density makes it increasingly difficult for radiation to escape, especially from the center. Once the central region of the cloud fragment becomes dense enough to trap infrared radiation so that it can no longer radiate away its heat, the central temperature and pressure begin to rise dramatically. The rising pressure pushes back against the crush of gravity, slowing the contraction. The dense center of the cloud fragment is now a **protostar—** the clump of gas that will become a new star. Gas from the surrounding cloud continues to rain down on the protostar, increasing its mass. Protostars are not yet true stars because their cores are not hot enough for nuclear fusion. Nevertheless, they can be quite luminous because of all the energy released by the infalling matter.

A molecular cloud fragment heats up as gravity makes it contract, producing a protostar at its center.

Disks and Jets Protostars rotate rapidly. Random motions of gas particles inevitably give a gas cloud some overall rotation, although it may be imperceptibly slow. Like an ice skater pulling in her arms, a shrinking cloud rotates increasingly fast in order to keep its total angular momentum the same [Section 4.3].

The rotation of the shrinking cloud fragment also produces a spinning disk of gas around the protostar (Figure 13.4). A disk forms because collisions between gas particles cause the cloud fragment to flatten along its rotation axis [Section 6.3], and the disk keeps spinning because angular momentum must be conserved. Planets may later form in the disk.

Observations show that many young protostars fire high-speed streams of gas, or **jets,** into interstellar space (Figure 13.5). We generally see two jets, shooting in opposite directions along the protostar's rotation axis. Sometimes the jets are lined with glowing blobs of gas, which are presumably clumps of matter swept up as the jets plow into the surrounding interstellar material.

Conservation of angular momentum ensures that protostars rotate rapidly and are surrounded by spinning disks of gas.

No one knows exactly how protostars generate these jets, but magnetic fields probably play an important role. A protostar's rapid rotation helps it generate a strong magnetic field, and this field may channel the jets along the rotation axis. In addition, the strong magnetic field helps the protostar generate a strong *protostellar wind*—an outward flow of particles similar to the *solar wind* [Section 11.1] but much stronger. Together, winds and jets probably help clear away the cocoon of gas that surrounds a forming star, revealing the protostar within. They also help the protostar shed some of its angular momentum by carrying material off into interstellar space, causing the protostar's rotation to slow down.

Single Star or Binary?

Angular momentum is also part of the reason so many stars belong to binary star systems. As a molecular cloud contracts, breaks up into fragments, and forms protostars, some of those protostars end up quite close to one another. Gravity can then pull two neighboring protostars closer together, but they don't crash into each other. Instead, they go into orbit around each other, because each pair of protostars has a certain amount of angular momentum. Pairs with large amounts of angular momentum have large orbits, and those with smaller amounts orbit closer together. If the two stars end up quite close to each other, they form what we call a **close binary** system. Stars in a close binary are typically separated by less than 0.1 AU and orbit each other every few days.

Neighboring protostars sometimes end up orbiting each other in binary star systems.

From Protostar to the Main Sequence

A protostar becomes a true star when its core temperature reaches 10 million K, hot enough for hydrogen fusion to operate efficiently. The core temperature continues to rise until fusion in the core generates enough energy to balance the energy lost from the surface in the form of radiation. Gravitational contraction then stops, because the star has achieved energy balance. It is now a main-sequence star [Section 12.2].

The length of time from the formation of a protostar to the birth of a main-sequence star depends on the star's mass. Massive stars do everything faster. The contraction of a high-mass protostar into a main-sequence star of spectral type O or B may take only a million years or less. A star like our Sun takes about 30 million years from the beginning of the protostellar stage to become a main-sequence star. A very-low-mass star of spectral type M may spend more than 100 million years as a protostar. The most massive stars in a young star cluster therefore may live and die before the smallest stars even begin to fuse hydrogen in their cores.

A protostar becomes a main-sequence star when it achieves energy balance between hydrogen fusion in its core and radiation from its surface.

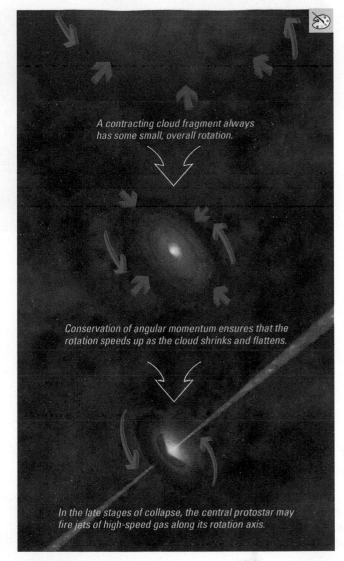

A contracting cloud fragment always has some small, overall rotation.

Conservation of angular momentum ensures that the rotation speeds up as the cloud shrinks and flattens.

In the late stages of collapse, the central protostar may fire jets of high-speed gas along its rotation axis.

▲ **FIGURE 13.4**
Artist's conception of star birth.

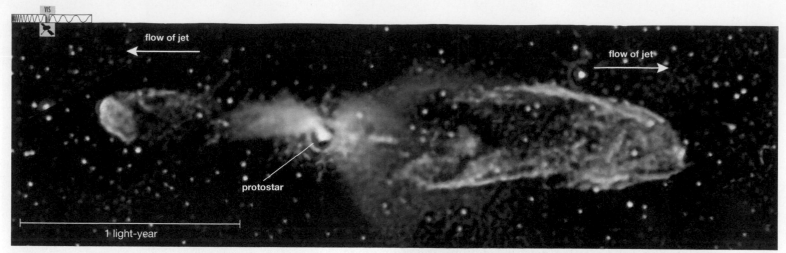

a This photograph shows two jets of material being shot in opposite directions by a protostar. The structures to the left and right of the protostar are formed as the jet material rams into surrounding interstellar gas.

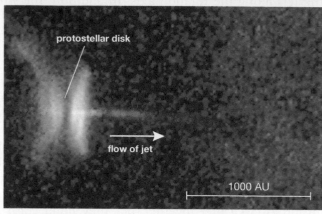

b This photograph shows a close-up view of a jet (red) and a disk of gas (green) around a protostar. We are seeing the disk nearly edge-on. The top and bottom surfaces of the disk are glowing, but we cannot see the darker middle layers of the disk.

▲ FIGURE 13.5

These photos show jets of gas shot from protostars into interstellar space.

▲ FIGURE 13.6

Demographics of newborn stars. This schematic diagram shows how many stars in each mass range are produced for every star greater than $10M_{Sun}$ in an episode of star formation. Very massive stars are relatively rare; lower-mass stars are much more common.

◆ How massive are newborn stars?

The masses of newborn stars seem to depend on the processes that govern clumping and fragmentation in star-forming clouds. We do not yet fully understand those processes, but we can observe the results.

Observations of young star clusters show that stars with low masses greatly outnumber stars with high masses. For every star with a mass above $10M_{Sun}$, there are typically 10 stars with masses between $2M_{Sun}$ and $10M_{Sun}$, 50 stars with masses between $0.5M_{Sun}$ and $2M_{Sun}$, and a few hundred stars with masses below $0.5M_{Sun}$ (Figure 13.6). Note that although the Sun lies toward the middle of the overall range of stellar masses, most stars in a new star cluster are less massive than the Sun. With the passage of time, the balance tilts even more in favor of the low-mass stars, because high-mass stars live short lives and die off early.

Limits on Stellar Masses There are limits on both the minimum and the maximum possible masses of stars. On the high-mass end, observations indicate that the maximum mass is around $150M_{Sun}$, though it might be higher. In any event, theoretical models suggest that stars with masses above about $100M_{Sun}$ should have such enormous energy output from their cores that they will ultimately drive their outer layers into space.

a Artist's conception of a brown dwarf, orbited by a planet (to its left) in a system with multiple stars. The reddish color approximates how a brown dwarf would appear to human eyes. The bands are shown because we expect brown dwarfs to look more like giant jovian planets than stars.

b An infrared image showing brown dwarfs (circled) in the constellation Orion. They are easier to spot in star-forming regions like this one than elsewhere in our galaxy, because young brown dwarfs still have much of the thermal energy left by the process of gravitational contraction. They therefore emit measurable amounts of infrared light.

▲ **FIGURE 13.7**

Brown dwarfs are "failed stars" that have masses lower than the $0.08M_{\text{Sun}}$ required to sustain core fusion.

On the low-mass end, calculations show that a protostar cannot become a true star unless its mass is at least $0.08M_{\text{Sun}}$, which is equivalent to about 80 times the mass of Jupiter. Below this mass, the protostar's gravity will be too weak to contract the core enough to reach the 10 million K threshold for efficient hydrogen fusion. In that case, the protostar will stabilize as a sort of "failed star" known as a **brown dwarf.** Brown dwarfs radiate primarily in the infrared and actually look deep red or magenta in color rather than brown (Figure 13.7). Because brown dwarfs do not sustain steady fusion in their cores, they cool with time as they radiate away their internal thermal energy. In essence, brown dwarfs occupy a fuzzy gap between what we call a planet and what we call a star.

> Stars more massive than about $100M_{\text{Sun}}$ blow off their outer layers, while protostars smaller than $0.08M_{\text{Sun}}$ become *brown dwarfs* that never get hot enough for efficient hydrogen fusion.

Pressure in Brown Dwarfs The source of the pressure that stops gravity from squeezing a brown dwarf's core to the point at which it could sustain fusion is quite different from the type of pressure we encounter in most other situations. Ordinary gas pressure is often called **thermal pressure** because it is closely linked to temperature: Raising the temperature increases the particle speeds and thereby raises the thermal pressure. However, calculations show that thermal pressure is insufficient to hold off gravity in a brown dwarf. Instead, the crush of gravity in a brown dwarf is halted by **degeneracy pressure,** a type of pressure that does not depend on temperature at all. It depends instead on the laws of *quantum mechanics* that also give rise to distinct energy levels in atoms [Section 5.2].

In much the same way that electrons in atoms are restricted to occupying only particular energy levels, quantum mechanics places restrictions

a When there are many more available places (chairs) than particles (people), a particle is unlikely to try to occupy the same place as another particle. The only pressure comes from the temperature-related motion of the particles.

b When the number of particles (people) approaches the number of available places (chairs), finding an available place requires that the particles move faster than they would otherwise. The extra motion creates degeneracy pressure.

▲ **FIGURE 13.8**

The auditorium analogy for degeneracy pressure. Chairs represent available places (quantum states) for electrons, and people who must keep moving from chair to chair represent electrons.

on how closely together electrons (and some other subatomic particles) can be packed in a gas. Under most circumstances, these restrictions have little effect on the motions or locations of the electrons, and hence little effect on the pressure. However, in a protostar with a mass below $0.08M_{Sun}$, the electrons become packed closely enough for these restrictions to matter. We can see how this fact leads to degeneracy pressure with a simple analogy.

Imagine an auditorium in which the laws of quantum mechanics dictate the spacing between chairs and people represent electrons (Figure 13.8). As though playing a game of musical chairs, the people are always moving from seat to seat, just as electrons must remain constantly in motion. Most objects are like auditoriums with many more available chairs than people, so the people (electrons) can easily find chairs as they move about. However, the cores of protostars with masses below $0.08M_{Sun}$ are like much smaller auditoriums with so few chairs that the people (electrons) fill nearly all of them. Because there are virtually no open seats, the people (electrons) can't all squeeze into a smaller section of the auditorium. This resistance to squeezing is the origin of degeneracy pressure. If the people were really like electrons, the laws of quantum mechanics would also require them to move faster and faster to find open seats as they were squeezed into a smaller section. However, their speeds would have nothing to do with temperature. Degeneracy pressure and the particle motion that goes with it arise *only* because of the restrictions on where the particles can go, which is why temperature does not affect them.

Brown dwarfs are supported against gravity by degeneracy pressure, which does not weaken with decreasing temperature.

The fact that degeneracy pressure does not rise and fall with temperature means that a brown dwarf's interior pressure remains stable even as it cools with time. As a result, gravity can never gain the upper hand and cause a brown dwarf to contract further, no matter how much the brown dwarf cools. In the constant battle of any "star" to resist the crush of gravity, brown dwarfs are winners, albeit dim ones. As we'll see in Chapter 14, degeneracy is also very important in the stellar corpses known as white dwarfs and neutron stars.

13.2 Life as a Low-Mass Star

A star's mass is its most important property. It determines not only a star's luminosity and surface temperature during its main-sequence (hydrogen core fusion) life [Section 12.2], but also its main-sequence lifetime and its ultimate fate. Stars of similar birth mass therefore lead similar lives and die in similar ways. However, the life stories of stars on the low end of the overall range of stellar masses are quite different from those of stars on the high end. As a result, we can simplify our discussion of stellar lives by dividing stars into three basic groups by mass:

- **Low-mass stars** are stars born with less than about 2 solar masses ($2M_{Sun}$) of material.

- **Intermediate-mass stars** have birth masses between about 2 and 8 solar masses.

- **High-mass stars** are those stars born with masses greater than about 8 solar masses.

We will focus primarily on the dramatic differences between the lives of low- and high-mass stars, beginning in this section with low-mass stars. The life stages of intermediate-mass stars are quite similar to the corresponding stages of high-mass stars until the very ends of their lives, so we include them in our discussion of high-mass stars.

You may wonder how we can be confident that we know the life stories of stars. Our confidence comes from a combination of theoretical modeling and observations. Astronomers use the known laws of physics to create mathematical models of stellar interiors, just as we use models to determine what is going on inside the Sun [Section 11.2]. These models predict both what is happening in a star at any stage of its life and how the star must change as its life continues. The models also predict what a star should look like from the outside at various stages of its life. By observing stars of different ages, we can test whether our models are successful in their predictions. The close correspondence between these models and observations gives us great confidence that we really do understand the lives of stars.

◆ What are the life stages of a low-mass star?

All low-mass stars go through life stages similar to those of the low-mass star that we know as our Sun. Let's therefore take our Sun as an example of a low-mass star, investigating how it will change over the course of its life.

Main-Sequence Stage In the grand hierarchy of stars, our Sun ranks as rather mediocre. We should be thankful for this mediocrity: If the Sun had been a high-mass star, it would have lasted only a few million years, dying before life could have arisen on Earth. Instead, the Sun has shone steadily for nearly 5 billion years as a main-sequence star, providing the light and heat that have allowed life to thrive on our planet. Its main-sequence life will continue for another 5 billion years or so.

As we discussed in Chapter 11, our Sun fuses hydrogen into helium in its core via the *proton–proton chain*. The Sun shines steadily because *gravitational equilibrium* (see Figure 11.2) and *energy balance* (see Figure 11.3) work together as a self-regulating *solar thermostat* that keeps the Sun's fusion rate and overall luminosity quite steady. Steady hydrogen fusion in the core is the basic characteristic of a star's main-sequence stage, which occupies about 90% of any star's total lifetime.

Stars spend about 90% of their lives shining steadily as main-sequence stars.

Other low-mass stars have similarly long lives, following the usual rule: Stars with mass greater than the Sun have main-sequence lifetimes shorter than the Sun's 10 billion years, and stars with mass lower than the Sun have longer lifetimes.

Red Giant Stage Hydrogen fusion supplies the thermal energy that keeps a main-sequence star in balance. But when the Sun's core hydrogen is finally depleted, nuclear fusion will cease. With no fusion to replace the energy the star radiates from its surface, the core will no longer be able to resist the inward pull of gravity, and it will begin to shrink. After 10 billion years of shining steadily, the Sun will enter an entirely new phase of life.

Somewhat surprisingly, the Sun's outer layers will expand outward during this new life stage, even though its core will be shrinking under the crush of gravity. Over a period of about a billion years—or about

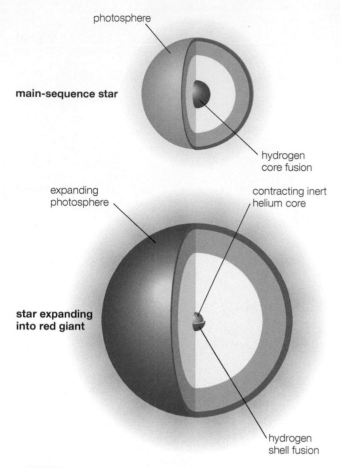

photosphere

main-sequence star

hydrogen
core fusion

expanding
photosphere

contracting inert
helium core

**star expanding
into red giant**

hydrogen
shell fusion

▲ **FIGURE 13.9**

After a star ends its main-sequence life, its inert helium core contracts while hydrogen shell fusion begins. The high rate of fusion in the hydrogen shell forces the star's upper layers to expand outward. (Not to scale.)

10% as long as its main-sequence lifetime—the Sun will grow in size and luminosity to become a **red giant.** At the peak of its red giant stage, the Sun will be more than 100 times as large in radius and more than 1000 times as luminous as it is today.

To understand why the Sun's outer layers will expand even while its core is shrinking, we need to think about the composition of the core at the end of the Sun's main-sequence life. After the core exhausts its hydrogen, it will be made almost entirely of helium, because helium is the product of hydrogen fusion. How-ever, the gas surrounding the core will still contain hydrogen that has never previously undergone fu-sion. Because gravity will shrink both the *inert* (non-fusing) helium core and the surrounding *shell* of hy-drogen, the hydrogen shell will soon become hot enough for **hydrogen shell fusion**—hydrogen fusion in a shell around the core (Figure 13.9). In fact, the shell will become so hot that hydrogen shell fusion will pro-ceed at a much higher rate than core hydrogen fusion does today. The higher fusion rate will generate enough energy to dramatically increase the Sun's luminosity and enough pressure to push the surrounding layers of gas outward. This expansion will also weaken the pull of gravity at the surface, allowing large amounts of mass to escape in a *stel-lar wind.* Observations of winds from red giants show that they carry away much more matter than the solar wind carries away from the Sun today.

After exhausting its core hydrogen, the Sun will expand to become a red giant, powered by rapid hydrogen fusion in a shell surrounding the core.

The situation will grow more extreme as long as the helium core re-mains inert. Today, the self-correcting feedback process of the solar ther-mostat regulates the Sun's fusion rate: A rise in the fusion rate causes the core to inflate and cool until the fusion rate drops back down (see Figure 11.8). In contrast, thermal energy generated in the hydrogen-fusing shell of a red giant cannot do anything to inflate the inert core that lies underneath. Instead, newly produced helium keeps adding to the mass of the helium core, amplifying its gravitational pull and shrink-ing it further. The hydrogen-fusing shell shrinks along with the core, growing hotter and denser. The fusion rate in the shell consequently rises, feeding even more helium to the core. The star is caught in a vi-cious circle with a broken thermostat.

The core and shell will continue to contract and heat up—with the Sun as a whole continuing to grow larger and more luminous—until the temperature in the inert helium core reaches about 100 million K. At that point, it will be hot enough for helium nuclei to begin to fuse together, and the Sun will enter the next stage of its life. Other low-mass stars expand into red giants in the same way, though the time required depends on the star's mass: Like all other phases of stellar lives, the process occurs faster for more massive stars and more slowly for less massive stars. In some very-low-mass stars, the inert helium core may never become hot enough to fuse helium. In that case, the core collapse will be halted by de-generacy pressure, leaving the star's corpse as a *helium white dwarf.*

The Sun's core will continue to shrink and hydrogen shell fusion will continue to intensify as the Sun grows into a red giant.

think about it Before you read on, briefly summarize why a star grows larger and brighter after it exhausts its core hydrogen. When does the growth of a red giant finally halt, and why? How would a star's red giant stage be different if the temperature required for helium fusion were around 200 million K, rather than 100 million K? Why?

Helium Fusion Recall that fusion occurs only when two nuclei come close enough together for the attractive *strong force* to overcome electromagnetic repulsion [Section 11.2]. Helium nuclei have two protons (and two neutrons) and hence a greater positive charge than a hydrogen nucleus with its single proton. The greater charge means that helium nuclei repel one another more strongly than hydrogen nuclei. **Helium fusion** therefore occurs only when nuclei slam into one another at much higher speeds than those needed for hydrogen fusion, which means that helium fusion requires much higher temperatures.

The helium fusion process (often called the *triple-alpha reaction* because helium nuclei are sometimes called *alpha particles*) converts three helium nuclei into one carbon nucleus:

$$3\ ^4\text{He} \qquad 1\ ^{12}\text{C}$$

Energy is released because the carbon-12 nucleus has a slightly lower mass than the three helium-4 nuclei, and the lost mass becomes energy in accord with $E = mc^2$.

The ignition of helium fusion in a low-mass star like the Sun has one subtlety. Theoretical models show that the thermal pressure in the inert helium core is too low to counteract gravity. Instead, the pressure fighting against gravity is *degeneracy pressure*—the same type of pressure that supports brown dwarfs. Because degeneracy pressure does *not* increase with temperature, the onset of helium fusion heats the core rapidly without causing it to expand in size, at least at first. Instead, the rising temperature causes the helium fusion rate to spike drastically in what is called a **helium flash.**

The helium flash releases an enormous amount of energy into the core. In a matter of seconds, the temperature rises so much that thermal pressure again becomes dominant and degeneracy pressure is no longer important. In fact, the thermal pressure becomes strong enough to push back against gravity. The core begins to expand and pushes the hydrogen-fusing shell outward, lowering its temperature and its fusion rate. The result is that, even though helium core fusion and hydrogen shell fusion are taking place simultaneously in the star (Figure 13.10), energy production falls from the peak it reached during the red giant stage, reducing the star's luminosity and allowing its outer layers to contract somewhat. As the outer layers contract, the star's surface temperature increases, so its color turns back toward yellow from red. After having spent about a billion years expanding into a luminous red giant, the Sun will decline in size and luminosity as it becomes a *helium core-fusion star.*

The sudden onset of helium fusion in the Sun's core will stop core shrinkage, and the Sun will become smaller and less luminous than it was as a red giant.

We can see examples of low-mass stars in all the life stages we have discussed so far in the H-R diagram of a globular cluster (Figure 13.11). Stars along the lower right, below the main-sequence turnoff point, are still in their hydrogen-fusing, main-sequence stage. Just above and to the right of the main-sequence turnoff point we see *subgiants*—stars that have just begun their expansion into red giants as their cores have shut down and hydrogen shell fusion has begun. The longer a star undergoes

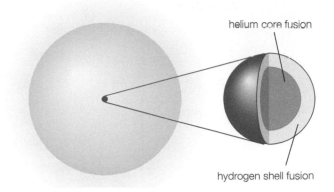

▲ **FIGURE 13.10**
Core structure of a helium core-fusion star. Helium fusion causes the helium core and hydrogen-fusing shell to expand and slightly cool, thereby reducing the overall energy generation rate in comparison to the rate during the red giant stage. The outer layers shrink, so a helium core-fusion star is smaller than a red giant of the same mass.

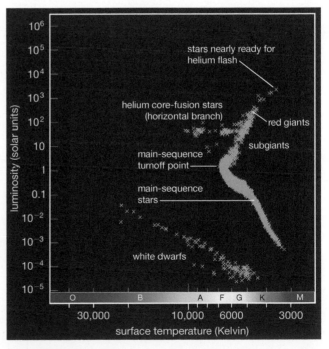

▲ **FIGURE 13.11**
An H-R diagram of a globular cluster showing low-mass stars in several different life stages.

hydrogen shell fusion, the larger and more luminous it becomes, which is why we see a continuous line of stars right up to the most luminous red giants. These are the red giants on the verge of a helium flash. The stars that have already undergone the helium flash and become helium core-fusion stars appear below and to the left of the red giants, because they are somewhat smaller, hotter, and less luminous than they were at the moment of helium flash. Because these helium core-fusion stars all have about the same luminosity but can differ in surface temperature, they trace out a horizontal line on the H-R diagram known as the *horizontal branch*.

◆ How does a low-mass star die?

It is only a matter of time until a helium core-fusion star converts all its core helium into carbon. In the Sun, the core helium will run out after about 100 million years—only about 1% as long as the Sun's 10-billion-year main-sequence lifetime. When the core helium is exhausted, fusion will again cease. The core, now made of the carbon produced by helium fusion, will begin to shrink once more under the crush of gravity.

Last Gasps The exhaustion of core helium will cause the Sun to expand once again, just as it did when it became a red giant. This time, the trigger for the expansion will be helium fusion in a shell around the inert carbon core. Meanwhile, hydrogen fusion will continue in a shell atop the helium layer. The Sun will have become a *double shell–fusion star*. Both shells will contract along with the inert core, driving their temperatures and fusion rates so high that the Sun will expand to an even greater size and luminosity than in its first red giant stage.

The furious fusion rates in the helium and hydrogen shells cannot last for more than a few million years. The Sun's only hope of extending its life at this stage lies with its carbon core, but this is a false hope for a low-mass star like the Sun. Carbon fusion is possible only at temperatures above about 600 million K, and degeneracy pressure will halt the collapse of the Sun's core before it ever gets that hot. With the carbon core unable to undergo fusion and provide a new source of energy, the Sun will finally have reached the end of its life.

> Core shrinkage will resume after helium core fusion ends, while both helium-fusing and hydrogen-fusing shells make the Sun bigger and more luminous than ever.

think about it Suppose the universe contained only low-mass stars. Would elements heavier than carbon exist? Why or why not?

The huge size of the dying Sun will give it only a very weak grip on its outer layers. As the Sun's luminosity and radius keep rising, its wind will grow stronger. Observations of other stars in this late stage of life show that their winds are an important source of the *interstellar dust grains* found in star-forming clouds. These dust grains form because the wind cools as it flows away from the star. At the point where the gas temperature has dropped to between about 1000 and 2000 K, some of the heavier elements in the wind begin to condense into microscopic clusters, forming small, solid particles of dust. This process of dust formation is much like the condensation that occurred in the solar nebula before the planets formed [Section 6.3]. The dust particles drift with the stellar wind into interstellar space, where they mix with other gas and dust in the galaxy.

Planetary Nebula The Sun's final end will be beautiful to those who witness it, as long as they stay far away. Through winds and other processes, the Sun will eject its outer layers into space, creating a huge shell

When it dies, the Sun will eject its outer layers into space as a planetary nebula, leaving its exposed core behind as a white dwarf.

of gas expanding away from the inert carbon core. The exposed core will still be very hot and will therefore emit intense ultraviolet radiation. This radiation will ionize the gas in the expanding shell, making it glow brightly as a **planetary nebula.** Figure 13.12 shows two of many known examples of planetary nebulae around other low-mass stars that have recently died in this way. Note that, despite their name, planetary nebulae have nothing to do with planets. The name comes from the fact that nearby planetary nebulae look much like planets through small telescopes, appearing as simple disks.

The glow of the Sun's planetary nebula will fade as the exposed core cools and the ejected gas disperses into space. The nebula will disappear within about 100,000 years, leaving the carbon core behind as a *white dwarf.* Recall from Chapter 12 that white dwarfs are small in radius and often quite hot. We can now understand why: They are small in radius because they are the exposed cores of dead stars, supported against the crush of gravity by degeneracy pressure. They are often hot because some of them were only recently the centers of stars, though over time they will cool and fade from view.

The Fate of Earth The death of the Sun will obviously have consequences for Earth, and some of these consequences will begin even before the Sun enters the final stages of its life. Although the Sun will shine steadily for the next 5 billion years of its hydrogen core-fusion life, theoretical models show that it will become slightly more luminous with time. This gradual rise in luminosity will be small compared to what will happen during the red giant stage, but it will probably be enough to cause a *runaway greenhouse effect* [Section 7.4] on Earth somewhere between about 1 and 4 billion years from now, making Earth's oceans boil away.

Temperatures on Earth will rise even more dramatically when the Sun finally exhausts its core supply of hydrogen, somewhere around the year A.D. 5,000,000,000, and conditions will become even worse as the Sun grows into a red giant over the next several hundred million years. Just before the helium flash, the Sun will be more than 1000 times as luminous as it is today, and this huge luminosity will heat Earth's surface to more than 1000 K. Clearly, any surviving humans will need to have found a new home.

The Sun will shrink and cool somewhat after the helium flash turns it into a helium core-fusion star, providing a temporary lull in Earth's incineration. However, this respite will last only 100 million years or so, and then Earth will suffer one final disaster. After exhausting its core helium, the Sun will expand again during its last million years. Its luminosity will soar to thousands of times what it is today, and its radius will grow to nearly the present radius of Earth's orbit—so large that solar prominences might lap at Earth's surface. Finally, the Sun will eject its outer layers as a planetary nebula that will drift away into interstellar space. If Earth is not destroyed, its charred surface will be

a Helix Nebula. The central white dot is the hot white dwarf.

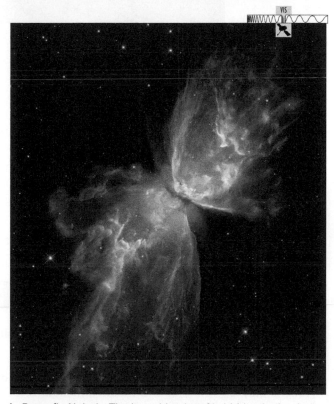

b Butterfly Nebula. The hot white dwarf is hidden in the dark ring of dust at the center.

▲ **FIGURE 13.12**
Hubble Space Telescope photos of planetary nebulae, which form when low-mass stars in their final death throes cast off their outer layers of gas, leaving behind the hot core that ejected the gas. The hot core ionizes and energizes the shells of gas that surround it. As the gas disperses into space, the hot core remains as a white dwarf.

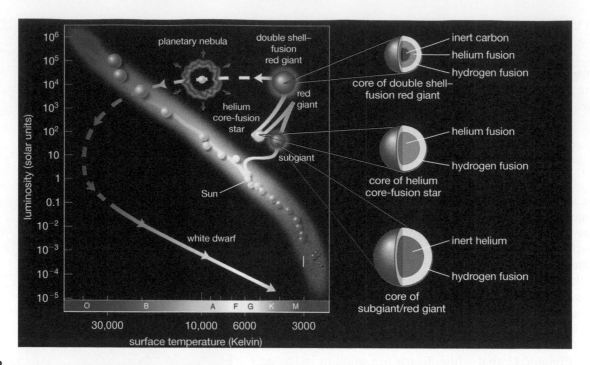

▲ FIGURE 13.13
The life track of our Sun from its main-sequence stage to the white dwarf stage. Core structure is shown at key stages.

cold and dark in the faint, fading light of the white dwarf that the Sun will have become.

The Sun's Life on an H-R Diagram We have discussed the Sun's life stages in general terms, but astronomers can determine with computer models how the Sun's surface temperature and luminosity will change during each stage of its life. We can plot the results on an H-R diagram, producing a **life track** (also called an *evolutionary track*) that shows the Sun's luminosity and surface temperature at each point in its life (Figure 13.13).

A star's life track on an H-R diagram shows how its properties change with time.

---

special topic   **How Long Is 5 Billion Years?**

The Sun's demise in about 5 billion years might at first seem worrisome, but 5 billion years is a very long time. It is longer than Earth has yet existed, and human time scales pale by comparison. A single human lifetime, if we take it to be about 100 years, is only 2×10^{-8}, or two hundred-millionths, of 5 billion years. Because 2×10^{-8} of a human lifetime is about 1 minute, we can say that a human lifetime compared to the life expectancy of the Sun is roughly the same as 60 heartbeats compared to a human lifetime.

What about human creations? The Egyptian pyramids have often been described as "eternal," but they are slowly eroding because of wind, rain, air pollution, and the impact of tourists. All traces of them will have vanished within a few hundred thousand years. While a few hundred thousand years may seem like a long time, the Sun's remaining lifetime is more than 1000 times longer.

On a more somber note, we can gain perspective on 5 billion years by considering evolutionary time scales. During the past century, our species has acquired sufficient technology and power to destroy human life totally, if we so choose. However, even if we make that unfortunate choice, some species (including many insects) are likely to survive.

Would another intelligent species ever emerge on Earth? We have no way to know, but we can look to the past for guidance. Many species of dinosaurs were biologically quite advanced, if not truly intelligent, when they were suddenly wiped out about 65 million years ago. Some small rodent-like mammals survived, and here we are 65 million years later. We therefore might guess that another intelligent species could evolve some 65 million years after a human extinction. If these beings also destroyed themselves, another species could evolve 65 million years after that, and so on.

Even at 65 million years per cycle, Earth would have *nearly 80* more chances for an intelligent species to evolve in 5 billion years (5 billion ÷ 65 million = 77). Perhaps one of those species will not destroy itself, and future generations might move on to other star systems by the time the Sun finally dies. Perhaps that species will be our own.

Remember that, although the life track cannot show it, the Sun spends most of its life as a main-sequence star fusing hydrogen in its core. The life track shows what happens once the Sun exhausts its core hydrogen supply and is no longer a main-sequence star. The life track goes generally upward as the Sun becomes a subgiant and then a red giant, because the Sun expands in size and luminosity while it undergoes hydrogen shell fusion. The track also goes slightly to the right during this stage, because the Sun's surface temperature falls a bit. The tip of the red giant stage represents the moment of helium flash, after which the Sun contracts in size, shown by the track going down and left, as the Sun becomes a helium core-fusion star. The life track again turns upward as the Sun enters its second red giant phase, this time with energy generated by fusion in shells of both helium and hydrogen. As the Sun ejects its planetary nebula, the dashed curve indicates that we are shifting from plotting the surface temperature of a red giant to plotting the surface temperature of the exposed stellar core left behind. The curve becomes solid again near the lower left, indicating that this core is a hot white dwarf. From that point, the curve continues downward and to the right as the white dwarf cools and fades.

13.3 Life as a High-Mass Star

Human life would be impossible without both low-mass stars and high-mass stars. The long lives of low-mass stars allow evolution to proceed for billions of years, but only high-mass stars produce the full array of elements on which life depends.

The early stages of a high-mass star's life are similar to the early stages of the Sun's life, except they proceed much more rapidly. But the late stages of life are quite different for high-mass stars. The cores of low-mass stars never become hot enough to fuse elements heavier than helium. Heavier nuclei contain more positively charged protons and therefore repel each other more strongly than lighter nuclei. As a result, these nuclei can fuse only at extremely high temperatures—temperatures that occur only in the cores of high-mass stars nearing the end of their lives, when the immense weight of their overlying layers bears down on a core that has already exhausted its hydrogen fuel.

The highest-mass stars proceed to fuse increasingly heavy elements until they have exhausted all possible fusion sources. When fusion finally stops for good, gravity causes the core to implode suddenly. As we will soon see, the implosion of the core causes the star to self-destruct in the titanic explosion we call a *supernova*. The fast-paced life and cataclysmic death of a high-mass star are surely among the great dramas of the universe.

◆ What are the life stages of a high-mass star?

Like all other stars, a high-mass star forms out of a cloud fragment that gravity forces to contract into a protostar. Just as in a low-mass star, hydrogen fusion begins when the gravitational potential energy released by the contracting protostar makes the core hot enough. However, hydrogen fusion proceeds through a different set of steps inside high-mass stars, which is part of the reason these stars live such brief but brilliant lives. As a specific example, let's investigate the life stages of a star born with 25 times the mass of the Sun ($25M_{Sun}$).

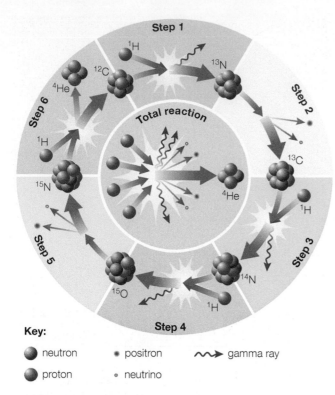

Key:

- neutron
- positron
- proton
- neutrino
- gamma ray

▲ FIGURE 13.14

This diagram illustrates the six steps of the CNO cycle by which massive stars fuse hydrogen into helium. Note that the overall result is the same as that of the proton–proton chain: Four hydrogen nuclei fuse to make one helium nucleus. The carbon, nitrogen, and oxygen nuclei help the overall cycle proceed, but these nuclei are neither consumed nor created.

Hydrogen Fusion in a High-Mass Star Recall that a low-mass star like our Sun fuses hydrogen into helium through the *proton–proton chain* (see Figure 11.7). In a high-mass star, gravitational compression makes the hydrogen core hotter than in lower-mass stars. The greater core temperature makes it possible for protons to slam into carbon, oxygen, or nitrogen nuclei as well as into other protons. As a result, hydrogen fusion in high-mass stars occurs through a chain of reactions called the **CNO cycle** (the letters *CNO* stand for carbon, nitrogen, and oxygen). Figure 13.14 shows the six steps of the CNO cycle.

Notice that the overall reaction of the CNO cycle is the same as that of the proton–proton chain: Four hydrogen nuclei fuse into one helium-4 nucleus. The amount of energy generated in each reaction cycle therefore is also the same—it is equal to the difference in mass between the four hydrogen nuclei and the one helium nucleus multiplied by c^2. However, hydrogen fusion proceeds much more rapidly through the CNO cycle than through the proton-proton chain in the cores of high-mass stars.

> A high-mass star lives a short life, rapidly fusing its core hydrogen into helium via the CNO cycle.

Becoming a Supergiant Our $25M_{Sun}$ star will begin to run low on hydrogen fuel after only a few million years. As its core hydrogen runs out, the star responds much like a low-mass star, but much faster. It develops a hydrogen-fusing shell, and its outer layers begin to expand outward, ultimately turning it into a *supergiant*. At the same time, the core contracts, and this gravitational contraction releases energy that raises the core temperature until it becomes hot enough to fuse helium into carbon. However, there is no helium flash in high-mass stars. Their core temperatures are so high that thermal pressure remains strong, preventing degeneracy pressure from becoming a factor. Helium core fusion therefore ignites gradually, just as hydrogen core fusion did at the beginning of the star's life.

Our high-mass star fuses helium into carbon so rapidly that it is left with an inert carbon core after just a few hundred thousand years. Once again, the absence of fusion leaves the core without an energy source to fight off the crush of gravity. The inert carbon core shrinks, the crush of gravity intensifies, and the core pressure, temperature, and density all rise. Meanwhile, a helium-fusing shell forms between the inert core and the hydrogen-fusing shell, and the star's outer layers swell further. Eventually, the core will become hot enough to fuse carbon into heavier elements, and the star will undergo another cycle of core fusion followed by shell fusion.

> Near the end of its life, a high-mass star expands to become a supergiant as fusion proceeds furiously in its core and surrounding shells.

The high-mass star's outward appearance responds relatively slowly to these interior changes. As each stage of core fusion ceases, fusion in the surrounding shells intensifies and further inflates the star's outer layers. Each time the core flares up, the outer layers contract somewhat, but the star's overall luminosity remains about the same. The result is that the star's life track zigzags across the top of the H-R diagram (Figure 13.15). In the most massive stars, the core changes so quickly that the outer layers have virtually no time to respond, and the star progresses steadily toward becoming a red supergiant.

One of these massive, red supergiant stars happens to be the star Betelgeuse, the upper left shoulder of Orion. Its radius is about 900 solar radii, about four times the Sun–Earth distance, and it is a relatively nearby 600 light-years away. We have no way of knowing what stage of nuclear fusion is taking place in Betelgeuse's core as we currently see it in the sky. It may have thousands of years of nuclear fusion still ahead, or it may be on the verge of death. If the latter is the case, then sometime soon we may witness one of the most dramatic events that ever occurs in the universe—a supernova explosion. To understand why a supernova happens, we need to look more closely at how high-mass stars make elements heavier than carbon.

◆ How do high-mass stars make the elements necessary for life?

A low-mass star can't make elements heavier than carbon because degeneracy pressure halts the contraction of its inert carbon core before it can get hot enough for fusion. The life of an intermediate-mass star ($2M_{Sun}$–$8M_{Sun}$) ends the same way. A high-mass star has no such problem, because the crush of gravity in a high-mass star keeps its carbon core so hot that degeneracy pressure never comes into play. After helium fusion stops, the gravitational contraction of the carbon core continues until it reaches the 600 million K required to fuse carbon into heavier elements.

Carbon fusion provides the core with a new source of energy that restores gravitational equilibrium, but only temporarily. In a $25M_{Sun}$ star, carbon fusion may last only a few hundred years. When the core carbon has been depleted, the core again begins to collapse, shrinking and heating once more until it can fuse a still heavier element. The star is engaged in the final phases of a desperate battle against the ever-strengthening crush of gravity. The star will ultimately lose the battle, but it will be a victory for life in the universe: In the process of its struggle against gravity, the star will produce the heavy elements of which Earth-like planets and living things are made.

Fusion of Heavier Nuclei The nuclear reactions in a high-mass star's final stages of life become quite complex, and many different reactions may take place simultaneously. The simplest sequence of fusion stages occurs through successive **helium-capture reactions**—reactions in which a helium nucleus fuses into some other nucleus (Figure 13.16a). Helium capture can fuse carbon into oxygen, oxygen into neon, neon into magnesium, and so on. At high enough temperatures, a star's core can fuse heavy nuclei to one another. For example, fusing carbon to oxygen creates silicon, fusing two oxygen nuclei creates sulfur, and fusing two silicon nuclei generates iron (Figure 13.16b). Some of these heavy-element reactions release free neutrons, which may fuse with heavy nuclei to make still rarer elements. The star is forging the variety of elements that, on Earth at least, became the stuff of life.

Each time the core depletes the elements it is fusing, it shrinks and heats until it becomes hot enough for other fusion reactions. Meanwhile, a new type of shell fusion ignites between the core and the overlying shells. Near the end, the star's central region resembles the inside of an onion, with layer upon layer of shells, each fusing different elements (Figure 13.17). During the star's final few days, iron begins to pile up in the silicon-fusing core.

> The core of a high-mass star eventually becomes hot enough for fusion to produce the elements of which we and Earth are made.

Iron: Bad News for the Stellar Core The core continues shrinking and heating while iron accumulates within it. If iron were like the elements in prior stages of nuclear fusion, this core contraction would stop when iron fusion ignited. However, iron is unique among the elements

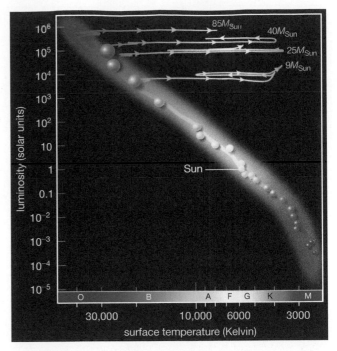

▲ **FIGURE 13.15**
Life tracks on the H-R diagram from main-sequence star to red supergiant for selected high-mass stars. Labels on the tracks give the star's mass at the beginning of its main-sequence life. (Based on models from A. Maeder and G. Meynet.)

a Helium-capture reactions.

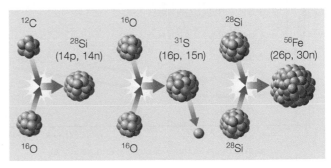

b Other reactions. (Note: Fusion of two silicon nuclei first produces nickel-56, which decays rapidly to cobalt-56 and then to iron-56.)

▲ **FIGURE 13.16**
A few of the many nuclear reactions that occur in the final stages of a high-mass star's life.

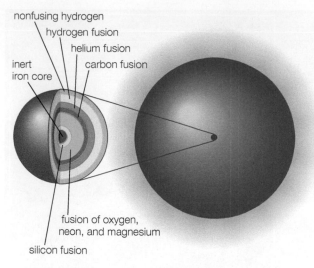

▲ FIGURE 13.17

The multiple layers of nuclear shell fusion in the core of a high-mass star during the final days of its life.

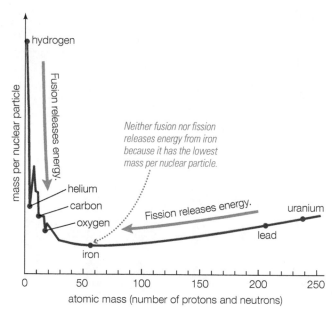

▲ FIGURE 13.18

Overall, the average mass per nuclear particle declines from hydrogen to iron and then increases. Selected nuclei are labeled to provide reference points. (This graph shows the most general trends only. A more detailed graph would show numerous up-and-down bumps superimposed on the general trends. The vertical scale is arbitrary, but shows the general idea.)

in a very important way: It is the one element from which it is *not* possible to generate any kind of nuclear energy.

To understand why iron is unique, remember that only two basic processes can release nuclear energy: *fusion* of light elements into heavier ones and *fission* of very heavy elements into not-so-heavy ones (see Figure 11.5). Recall that hydrogen fusion converts four protons (hydrogen nuclei) into a helium nucleus that consists of two protons and two neutrons. This fusion reaction generates energy (in accord with $E = mc^2$) because the *mass* of the helium nucleus is less than the combined mass of the four hydrogen nuclei that fused to create it, even though the total number of *nuclear particles* (protons and neutrons combined) does not change.

In other words, fusing hydrogen into helium generates energy because helium has a lower *mass per nuclear particle* than hydrogen. Similarly, fusing three helium-4 nuclei into one carbon-12 nucleus generates energy because carbon has a lower mass per nuclear particle than helium, which means that some mass disappears and becomes energy in this fusion reaction. The decrease in mass per nuclear particle from hydrogen to helium to carbon is part of a general trend shown in Figure 13.18.

The mass per nuclear particle tends to decrease as we go from light elements to iron, which means that fusion of light nuclei into heavier nuclei generates energy. This trend reverses beyond iron: The mass per nuclear particle tends to *increase* as we look to still heavier elements. As a result, elements heavier than iron can generate nuclear energy only through fission into lighter elements. For example, uranium has a greater mass per nuclear particle than lead, so uranium fission (which ultimately leaves lead as a by-product) must convert some mass into energy.

Iron has the lowest mass per nuclear particle of all nuclei and therefore cannot release energy by either fusion or fission. Once the matter in a stellar core turns to iron, it can generate no further energy. The core's only hope of resisting the crush of gravity lies with degeneracy pressure, but iron keeps piling up until even degeneracy pressure cannot support the core. What ensues is the ultimate nuclear waste catastrophe: The star explodes as a supernova, scattering all the newly made elements into interstellar space.

> A high-mass star's death is imminent when iron piles up in its core, because fusion of iron releases no energy.

think about it How would the universe be different if hydrogen, rather than iron, had the lowest mass per nuclear particle? Why?

Evidence for the Origin of Elements Before we look at how a supernova happens, let's consider the evidence that indicates we actually understand the origin of the elements. We cannot see inside stars, so we cannot directly observe elements being created. However, the signature of nuclear reactions in massive stars is written in the patterns of elemental abundances across the universe.

For example, if massive stars really produce heavy elements (that is, elements heavier than hydrogen and helium) and scatter these elements into space when they die, the total amount of these heavy elements in interstellar gas should gradually increase with time (because additional massive stars have died). We expect stars born recently to contain a greater proportion of heavy elements than stars born in the distant past, because the younger stars formed from interstellar gas that contained more heavy elements. Stellar spectra confirm this prediction: Elements besides hydrogen and helium can make up as little as 0.1% of the total mass of very old stars in globular clusters, while these elements can make up as much as 2–3% of the mass of young stars in open clusters.

We gain even more confidence in our model of elemental creation when we compare the abundances of various elements in the cosmos. Because helium-capture reactions add two protons (and two neutrons) at a time, we expect nuclei with even numbers of protons to outnumber those with odd numbers of protons that fall between them.

Measurements of element abundances in the cosmos confirm our models of how high-mass stars produce heavy elements.

Observations confirm that even-numbered nuclei such as carbon, oxygen, and neon have higher abundances than the elements in between them (Figure 13.19). Similarly, we expect elements heavier than iron to be extremely rare, because they are made primarily by rare fusion reactions (most of which occur shortly before or during a supernova). Again, observations verify this prediction.

▲ **FIGURE 13.19**

This graph shows the observed relative abundances of elements in the galaxy compared to the abundance of hydrogen (given as 1). For example, the abundance of nitrogen is about 10^{-4}, or 1/10,000, which means that there are about 10,000 times as many hydrogen atoms in the galaxy as nitrogen atoms.

◆ How does a high-mass star die?

Let's return now to our high-mass star, with iron piling up in its core. As we've discussed, it has no hope of generating any energy by fusing this iron. After shining brilliantly for a few million years, the star will not live to see another day.

The Supernova Explosion   The degeneracy pressure that briefly supports the inert iron core arises because the laws of quantum mechanics prohibit electrons from getting too close together. Once gravity pushes the electrons past the quantum mechanical limit, however, they can no longer exist freely. In an instant, the electrons disappear by combining with protons to form neutrons, releasing neutrinos in the process (Figure 13.20). The degeneracy pressure provided by the electrons instantly vanishes, and gravity has free rein.

In a fraction of a second, an iron core with a mass comparable to that of our Sun and a size larger than that of Earth collapses into a ball of neutrons just a few kilometers across. The collapse halts only because the neutrons have a degeneracy pressure of their own. The entire core then resembles a giant atomic nucleus. If you recall that ordinary atoms are made almost entirely of empty space [Section 5.1] and that almost all their mass is in their nuclei, you'll realize that a giant atomic nucleus must have an astoundingly high density.

The gravitational collapse of the core releases an enormous amount of energy—more than 100 times what the Sun will radiate over its entire 10-billion-year lifetime. Where does this energy go? It drives the star's outer layers into space in a titanic explosion called a **supernova.** The ball of neutrons left behind is called a **neutron star.** In some cases, the remaining mass may be so large that gravity also overcomes the degeneracy pressure associated with neutrons, and the core continues to collapse until it becomes a *black hole* [Section 14.3].

Theoretical models of supernovae successfully reproduce the observed energy outputs of real supernovae, but the precise mechanism of the explosion is not yet clear. Two general processes could contribute to the explosion. In the first process, degeneracy pressure halts the gravitational collapse by preventing neutrons from getting too close together and causes the core to rebound slightly and ram

When gravity overcomes degeneracy pressure in the iron core, the core collapses into a ball of neutrons and the star explodes in a supernova.

▲ **FIGURE 13.20**

During the final, catastrophic collapse of a high-mass stellar core, electrons and protons combine to form neutrons, accompanied by the release of neutrinos.

Algol shortly after its birth. The higher-mass star (left) evolved more quickly than its lower-mass companion (right).

Algol at onset of mass transfer. When the more massive star expanded into a red giant, it began losing some of its mass to its normal, hydrogen core-fusion companion.

Algol today. As a result of the mass transfer, the red giant has shrunk to a subgiant, and the normal star on the right is now the more massive of the two stars.

▲ **FIGURE 13.24**

Artist's conception of the development of the Algol close binary system.

binary system are near enough to exert significant tidal forces on each other [Section 4.4]. The gravity of each star attracts the near side of the other star more strongly than it attracts the far side. The stars therefore stretch into football-like shapes rather than remaining spherical. In addition, the stars become *tidally locked* so that they always show the same face to each other, much as the Moon always shows the same face to Earth.

During the time that both stars are main-sequence stars, the tidal forces have little effect on their lives. However, when the more massive star (which exhausts its core hydrogen sooner) begins to expand into a red giant, gas from its outer layers can spill over onto its companion. This **mass exchange** occurs when the giant grows so large that its tidally distorted outer layers succumb to the gravitational attraction of the smaller companion star. The companion then begins to gain mass at the expense of the giant.

Stars in close binary systems can exchange mass with each other, altering their life histories.

The solution to the Algol paradox should now be clear (Figure 13.24). The $0.8 M_{Sun}$ subgiant *used to be* much more massive. As the more massive star, it was the first to begin expanding into a red giant. As it expanded, however, so much of its matter spilled over onto its companion that it is now the less massive star.

The future may hold even more interesting events for Algol. The $3.7 M_{Sun}$ star is still gaining mass from its subgiant companion. Its life cycle is therefore actually accelerating as its increasing gravity raises its hydrogen core-fusion rate. Millions of years from now, it will exhaust its hydrogen and begin to expand into a red giant itself. At that point, it can begin to transfer mass *back* to its companion. Even more amazing things can happen in other mass-exchange systems, particularly when one of the stars is a white dwarf or a neutron star. But that is a topic for the next chapter.

---

the big picture | Putting Chapter 13 into Perspective

In this chapter, we have seen how the origin of the elements, first discussed in Chapter 1, is linked to the lives and deaths of stars. As you look back, keep in mind these "big picture" ideas:

- Virtually all elements in the universe besides hydrogen and helium were forged in stars. We and our planet are therefore made of stuff produced by stars that lived and died long ago.

- Low-mass stars like our Sun live long lives and die with the ejection of planetary nebulae, leaving behind white dwarfs.

- High-mass stars live fast and die young, exploding dramatically as supernovae and leaving behind neutron stars or black holes.

- Close binary stars can exchange mass, altering the usual course of stellar evolution.

my cosmic perspective One of the deepest connections we have with the cosmos is through the many elements that make up our bodies, which were formed by nuclear fusion in stars.

13.1 Star Birth

◆ **How do stars form?**

Stars are born in cold, relatively dense **molecular clouds.** As a cloud fragment collapses under gravity, it becomes a rapidly rotating **protostar** surrounded by a spinning disk of gas in which planets may form. The protostar may also fire **jets** of matter outward along its poles.

◆ **How massive are newborn stars?**

On the upper end, the most massive newborn stars are about $150M_{Sun}$. On the lower end, stars cannot be less massive than $0.08M_{Sun}$; below this mass, **degeneracy pressure** prevents gravity from making the core hot enough for efficient hydrogen fusion, and the object becomes a **brown dwarf.** Low-mass stars far outnumber high-mass stars.

13.2 Life as a Low-Mass Star

◆ **What are the life stages of a low-mass star?**

A low-mass star spends most of its life generating energy by fusing hydrogen in its core. When the core's hydrogen is exhausted, the core begins to shrink while the star as a whole expands to become a **red giant,** with **hydrogen shell fusion** occurring around an inert helium core. When the core becomes hot enough, a **helium flash** initiates **helium fusion** in the core, which fuses helium into carbon; the star shrinks somewhat in size and luminosity during this time. The core shrinks again when helium core fusion ceases, while both helium and hydrogen fusion occur in shells around the inert carbon core and cause the outer layers to expand once more.

◆ **How does a low-mass star die?**

A low-mass star like the Sun never gets hot enough to fuse carbon in its core, because degeneracy pressure stops the gravitational collapse of the core. The star expels its outer layers into space as a **planetary nebula,** leaving its exposed core behind as a white dwarf.

13.3 Life as a High-Mass Star

◆ **What are the life stages of a high-mass star?**

A high-mass star lives a much shorter life than a low-mass star, fusing hydrogen into helium via the **CNO cycle.** After exhausting its core hydrogen, a high-mass star begins hydrogen shell fusion and then goes through a series of stages, fusing successively heavier elements. As a result, the star swells in size to become a supergiant.

◆ **How do high-mass stars make the elements necessary for life?**

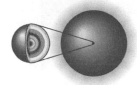

In its final stages of life, a high-mass star's core becomes hot enough to fuse carbon and other heavy elements. The variety of different fusion reactions produces a wide range of elements—including all the elements necessary for life—that are then released into space when the star dies.

◆ **How does a high-mass star die?**

A high-mass star dies in a cataclysmic explosion called a **supernova,** scattering newly produced elements into space and leaving behind a neutron star or black hole. The supernova occurs after fusion begins to pile up iron in the high-mass star's core. Because iron fusion cannot release energy, the core cannot hold off the crush of gravity for long. In the instant that gravity overcomes degeneracy pressure, the core collapses and the star explodes. The expelled gas may be visible for a few thousand years as a **supernova remnant.**

13.4 Stars in Close Binaries

◆ **How are the lives of stars with close companions different?**

When one star in a close binary system begins to swell in size at the end of its main-sequence stage, it can begin to transfer mass to its companion. This **mass exchange** can then change the remaining life histories of both stars.

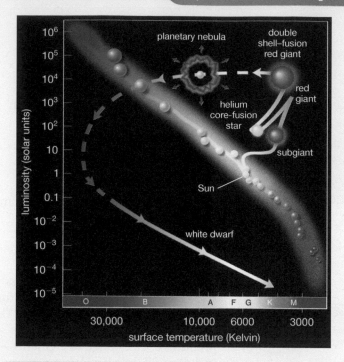

This figure, similar to the left side of Figure 13.13, shows the future life stages of the Sun on an H-R diagram. Use the figure to answer the following questions.

1. What will the Sun's approximate luminosity be during the subgiant stage?

2. When the Sun is a red giant, what will its approximate surface temperature be?

3. Just before the Sun produces a planetary nebula, what will its approximate luminosity be?

4. When the Sun becomes a white dwarf with a surface temperature similar to its current surface temperature, what will its luminosity be?

exercises and problems

 For instructor-assigned homework and other learning materials, go to MasteringAstronomy®.

Review Questions

1. What is a *molecular cloud*? Briefly describe the process by which a protostar forms from gas in a molecular cloud.
2. Why do protostars rotate rapidly? How can a close binary star system form?
3. Why does a spinning disk of gas surround a protostar? Describe key phenomena seen among protostars, such as strong *stellar winds* and *jets*.
4. What are the minimum and maximum masses for a star, and why do these limits occur? What is a *brown dwarf*?
5. What is *degeneracy pressure*, and how does it differ from *thermal pressure*? Explain why degeneracy pressure can support a stellar core against gravity even when the core becomes cold.
6. Briefly describe the Sun's life stages after it exhausts its core hydrogen. Discuss both the changes occurring in the Sun's core and the changes visible from outside the Sun.
7. Why does helium fusion require much higher temperatures than hydrogen fusion? Briefly explain why helium fusion in the Sun will begin with a *helium flash*.
8. What is a *planetary nebula*? What happens to the core of a star after a planetary nebula occurs?
9. What will happen to Earth as the Sun changes in the future?
10. What do we mean by a star's *life track* on an H-R diagram? Summarize the stages of the Sun's life track in Figure 13.13.

11. In broad terms, explain how the life of a high-mass star differs from that of a low-mass star.
12. Describe some of the nuclear reactions that can occur in high-mass stars after they exhaust their core helium. Why do these reactions occur in high-mass but not in low-mass stars?
13. Why can't iron be fused to release energy?
14. Summarize some of the observational evidence supporting our ideas about how the elements form in massive stars.
15. What event initiates a *supernova*, and why is a neutron star or black hole left behind? What observational evidence supports our understanding of supernovae?
16. Why can the lives of close binary stars differ from those of single stars? Describe the *Algol paradox* and its resolution.

Test Your Understanding

⟳ Does It Make Sense?

Decide whether the statement makes sense (or is clearly true) or does not make sense (or is clearly false). Explain clearly; not all of these have definitive answers, so your explanation is more important than your chosen answer.

17. The iron in my blood came from a star that blew up more than 4 billion years ago.
18. I discovered stars being born within a patch of extremely low-density, hot interstellar gas.

behind by a $1M_{Sun}$ star like our Sun consists mostly of carbon, since stars like the Sun fuse helium into carbon in their final stage of life.

Despite its ordinary-sounding composition, a scoop of matter from a white dwarf would be unlike anything ever seen on Earth. A typical white dwarf has the mass of the Sun ($1M_{Sun}$) compressed into a volume the size of Earth. If you recall that Earth is smaller than a typical sunspot, you'll realize that packing the entire mass of the Sun into the volume of Earth is no small feat. The density of a white dwarf is so high that a teaspoon of its material would weigh several tons—as much as a small truck—if you could bring it to Earth.

A teaspoon of white dwarf matter would weigh several tons.

More massive white dwarfs are actually smaller in size than less massive ones. For example, a $1.3M_{Sun}$ white dwarf is half the diameter of a $1.0M_{Sun}$ white dwarf (Figure 14.2). The more massive white dwarf is smaller because its greater gravity compresses matter to a much greater density. According to the laws of quantum mechanics, the electrons in a white dwarf respond to this compression by moving faster, which makes the degeneracy pressure strong enough to resist the greater force of gravity. The most massive white dwarfs are therefore the smallest.

The White Dwarf Limit

The fact that electron speeds are higher in more massive white dwarfs leads to a fundamental limit on the maximum mass of a white dwarf. Theoretical calculations show that the electron speeds would reach the speed of light in a white dwarf with a mass of about 1.4 times the mass of the Sun ($1.4M_{Sun}$). Because neither electrons nor anything else can travel faster than the speed of light (see the Special Topic on the next page), no white dwarf can have a mass greater than $1.4M_{Sun}$, which is known as the **white dwarf limit** (also called the *Chandrasekhar limit,* after its discoverer).

A white dwarf cannot have a mass greater than 1.4 times the mass of the Sun.

Strong observational evidence supports this theoretical limit on the mass of a white dwarf. Many known white dwarfs are members of binary systems, and hence we can measure their masses [Section 12.1]. In every observed case, the white dwarfs have masses below $1.4M_{Sun}$, just as our theory predicts.

◆ What can happen to a white dwarf in a close binary system?

Left to itself, a white dwarf will never again shine as brightly as the star it once was. With no source of fuel for fusion, it will simply cool with time into a cold "black dwarf." Its size will never change, because its electron degeneracy pressure will forever keep it stable against the crush of gravity. However, the situation can be quite different for a white dwarf in a close binary system.

Accretion Disks

A white dwarf in a close binary system can gradually gain mass if its companion is a main-sequence or giant star (Figure 14.3). When a clump of mass first spills over from the companion to the white dwarf, it has some small orbital velocity. The law of conservation of angular momentum dictates that the clump must orbit faster and faster as it falls toward the white dwarf's surface. The infalling matter therefore forms a whirlpool-like disk around the white dwarf. Because the process in which material falls onto another body is called *accretion,* this rapidly rotating disk is called an **accretion disk.**

In a close binary system, gas from a companion star can spill toward a white dwarf, forming a swirling accretion disk around it.

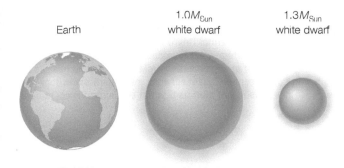

Earth | $1.0M_{Sun}$ white dwarf | $1.3M_{Sun}$ white dwarf

▲ **FIGURE 14.2**
Contrary to what you might expect, more massive white dwarfs are actually smaller (and thus denser) than less massive white dwarfs. Earth is shown for scale.

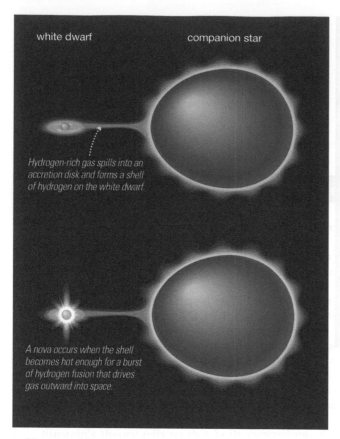

white dwarf   companion star

Hydrogen-rich gas spills into an accretion disk and forms a shell of hydrogen on the white dwarf.

A nova occurs when the shell becomes hot enough for a burst of hydrogen fusion that drives gas outward into space.

a Diagram of the nova process.

▲ **FIGURE 14.4**

A nova occurs when hydrogen fusion ignites on the surface of a white dwarf in a binary star system.

b Hubble Space Telescope image showing blobs of gas ejected from the nova T Pyxidis. The bright spot at the center of the blobs is the binary star system that generated the nova.

White Dwarf Supernovae Each time a nova occurs, the white dwarf ejects some of its mass. Each time a nova subsides, the white dwarf begins to accrete matter again. Theoretical models cannot yet tell us whether the net result should be a gradual increase or decrease in the white dwarf's mass, but if it is an increase, a white dwarf's mass might gradually approach the white dwarf limit. The day it reaches that limit will be the white dwarf's last.

Recall that white dwarfs are made largely of carbon. As a white dwarf's mass approaches $1.4M_{Sun}$, its temperature rises enough to allow carbon fusion to begin. Carbon fusion ignites almost instantly throughout the white dwarf, much like the sudden helium flash in low-mass red giants [Section 13.2] but releasing far more energy. The white dwarf explodes completely in what we will call a **white dwarf supernova.**

> A white dwarf that reaches the $1.4M_{Sun}$ white dwarf limit will explode completely in a white dwarf supernova.

Alternatively, a white dwarf may reach the white dwarf limit by merging with its binary-star companion. Ordinarily, two objects in orbit around each other will remain in those orbits unless a third object (or surrounding gas) interacts with them. However, two white dwarfs orbiting especially close together emit *gravitational waves*

> Two very closely orbiting objects will emit gravitational waves, causing them to spiral toward each other and ultimately merge.

(see Special Topic, page 373), which carry energy and angular momentum away from the binary system. The two white dwarfs therefore gradually spiral inward toward each other, ultimately merging together.

If the total mass of the two white dwarfs exceeds $1.4M_{Sun}$, the result of this merger is a white dwarf supernova.

think about it According to our understanding of novae and white dwarf supernovae, can either of these events ever occur with a white dwarf that is *not* a member of a binary star system? Explain.

Regardless of which process leads to a white dwarf supernova, the resulting carbon explosion is quite different from the iron catastrophe that leads to a supernova ending the life of a high-mass star [Section 13.3], which we will call a **massive star supernova.*** Astronomers can distinguish between the two types of supernova by studying their light. Both types shine brilliantly, with peak luminosities about 10 billion times that of the Sun ($10^{10}L_{Sun}$), but the luminosities of white dwarf supernovae fade steadily, while the decline in brightness of a massive star supernova is often more complicated (Figure 14.5). In addition, spectra of white dwarf supernovae lack hydrogen lines (because white dwarfs contain very little hydrogen), while these lines are prominent in the spectra of most massive star supernovae.

▲ FIGURE 14.5

The curves on this graph show how the luminosities of the two types of supernovae fade with time. The white dwarf supernova fades quickly at first and then more gradually a few weeks after the peak, while the massive star supernova fades in a more complicated pattern.

14.2 Neutron Stars

White dwarfs with densities of several tons per teaspoon may seem incredible, but neutron stars are stranger still. The possibility that neutron stars might exist was first proposed in the 1930s, but many astronomers thought it preposterous that nature could make anything so bizarre. Nevertheless, strong evidence now makes it clear that neutron stars really exist.

◆ What is a neutron star?

A **neutron star** is the ball of neutrons created by the collapse of the iron core in a massive star supernova (Figure 14.6). Typically just 10 kilometers in radius yet more massive than the Sun, neutron stars are essentially giant atomic nuclei made almost entirely of neutrons and held together by gravity. Like white dwarfs, neutron stars resist the crush of gravity with degeneracy pressure that arises when particles are packed as closely as nature allows. In the case of neutron stars, however, it is neutrons rather than electrons that are closely packed, so we say that **neutron degeneracy pressure** supports them against the crush of gravity.

A neutron star is a ball of neutrons just a few kilometers in radius but with a mass like that of the Sun.

The force of gravity at the surface of a neutron star is awe-inspiring. Escape velocity is about half the speed of light. If you foolishly chose to visit a neutron star's surface, your body would be squashed immediately into a microscopically thin pancake of subatomic particles.

▲ FIGURE 14.6

This X-ray image from the Chandra X-Ray Observatory shows the supernova remnant G11.2–03, the remains of a supernova observed by Chinese astronomers in A.D. 386. The white dot at the center is the neutron star left behind by the supernova. The different colors correspond to emission of X rays in different wavelength bands. The region pictured is about 23 light-years across.

---

* Observationally, astronomers classify supernovae as *Type II* if their spectra show hydrogen lines, and *Type I* otherwise. All Type II supernovae are assumed to be massive star supernovae. However, a Type I supernova can be either a white dwarf supernova or a massive star supernova in which the star blew away all its hydrogen before exploding. Type I supernovae fall into three classes, called *Type Ia, Type Ib,* and *Type Ic.* Only Type Ia supernovae are thought to be white dwarf supernovae.

▲ FIGURE 14.7

About 20 seconds of data from the first pulsar discovered by Jocelyn Bell in 1967.

Things would be only slightly less troubling if a bit of neutron star could somehow come to visit you. A paper clip with the density of neutron star material would outweigh Mount Everest. If such a paper clip magically appeared in your hand, you could not prevent it from falling. Down it would plunge, passing through the Earth like a rock falling through air. It would gain speed until it reached Earth's center, and its momentum would carry it onward until it slowed to a stop on the other side of our planet. Then it would fall back down again. If it came in from space, each plunge of the neutron star material would drill a different hole through the rotating Earth. In the words of astronomer Carl Sagan, the inside of the Earth would "look briefly like Swiss cheese" (until the melted rock flowed to fill in the holes) by the time friction finally brought the piece of neutron star to rest at the center of the Earth.

In the unfortunate event that an *entire* neutron star came to visit you, it would not fall at all. Because it would be only about 10 kilometers in radius, the neutron star would probably fit in your hometown.

> A neutron star could fit in your hometown, but its gravity would quickly destroy our planet.

Remember, however, that it would be 300,000 times as massive as Earth. As a result, the neutron star's immense surface gravity would quickly destroy your hometown and the rest of civilization. By the time the dust settled, the former Earth would have been squashed into a shell no thicker than your thumb on the surface of the neutron star.

◆ How were neutron stars discovered?

The first observational evidence for neutron stars came in 1967, when a 24-year-old graduate student named Jocelyn Bell discovered a strange source of radio waves. The radio waves pulsed on and off at intervals of precisely 1.337301 seconds (Figure 14.7). At first, astronomers could not think of any natural process that could pulse in such a clockwork way, and they only half-jokingly called the new radio source LGM, for Little Green Men. Today we refer to such rapidly pulsing radio sources as **pulsars.**

The mystery of pulsars was soon solved. By the end of 1968, astronomers had found two smoking guns: Pulsars sat at the centers of two supernova remnants, the Vela Nebula and the Crab Nebula (Figure 14.8). The pulsars are neutron stars left behind by the supernova explosions.

The pulsations arise because the neutron star is spinning rapidly as a result of the conservation of angular momentum [Section 4.3]: As an iron core collapses into a neutron star, its rotation rate must increase as it shrinks in size. The collapse also bunches the magnetic field lines running through the core far more tightly, greatly amplifying the strength of the magnetic field. These intense magnetic fields direct beams of

▶ FIGURE 14.8

This time-lapse image of the pulsar at the center of the Crab Nebula, a supernova remnant, shows its main pulse recurring every 0.033 second. The fainter pulses are thought to come from the pulsar's other lighthouse-like beam. (Photo from the Very Large Telescope of the European Southern Observatory.)

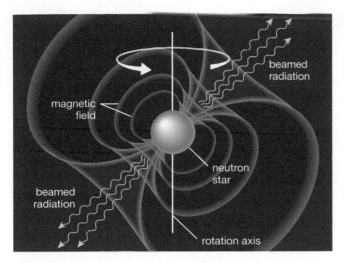

a A pulsar is a rotating neutron star that beams radiation along its magnetic axis.

b If the magnetic axis is not aligned with the rotation axis, the pulsar's beams sweep through space like lighthouse beams. Each time one of the pulsar's beams sweeps across Earth, we see a pulse of radiation.

▲ **FIGURE 14.9**
Radiation from a rotating neutron star can appear to pulse like the beams from a lighthouse.

Neutron stars can spin rapidly and emit beams of radiation along their magnetic poles, which we detect as pulses of radiation if the beams sweep by Earth.

radiation out along the magnetic poles, although we do not yet know exactly how they produce that radiation. If a neutron star's magnetic poles are not aligned with its rotation axis, the beams of radiation sweep round and round (Figure 14.9). Like lighthouses, neutron stars emit fairly steady beams of light, but we see a pulse of light each time one of those beams sweeps past Earth.

Pulsars are not quite perfect clocks. The continual twirling of a pulsar's magnetic field generates electromagnetic radiation that carries away energy and angular momentum, causing the neutron star's rotation rate to slow gradually. The pulsar in the Crab Nebula, for example, currently spins about 30 times per second. Two thousand years from now, it will spin less than half as fast. Eventually, a pulsar's spin slows so much and its magnetic field becomes so weak that we can no longer detect it. In addition, some spinning neutron stars may be oriented so that their beams do not sweep past our location. We therefore have the following rule: *All pulsars are neutron stars, but not all neutron stars are pulsars.*

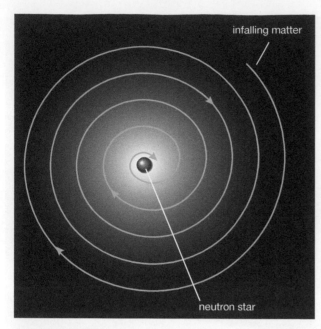

▲ **FIGURE 14.10**

Matter accreting onto a neutron star adds angular momentum, increasing the neutron star's rate of spin. The spin increases because infalling matter just above the neutron star's surface is orbiting faster than the neutron star is spinning. When this matter hits the neutron star's surface, it boosts the star's spin rate.

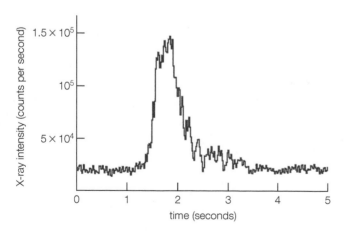

▲ **FIGURE 14.11**

Light curve of an X-ray burst. In this particular burst, the X-ray luminosity of the neutron star spiked to over six times its usual intensity in a matter of seconds.

think about it Suppose we do not see pulses from a particular neutron star and hence do not call it a pulsar. Is it possible that a civilization living in some other star system would see this neutron star as a pulsar? Explain.

We know that pulsars must be neutron stars because no other massive object could spin so fast. A white dwarf, for example, can spin no faster than about once per second without being torn apart, because a faster spin would mean its surface would be rotating faster than the escape velocity. Pulsars have been discovered that rotate as fast as 716 times per second. Only an object as small and dense as a neutron star could spin so fast without breaking apart.

◆ **What can happen to a neutron star in a close binary system?**

Like a white dwarf, a neutron star in a close binary system can brilliantly burst back to life as gas overflowing from a companion star creates a hot, swirling accretion disk around it. However, the much stronger gravity of the neutron star makes its accretion disk much hotter and denser than an accretion disk around a white dwarf.

The high temperatures in the inner regions of the accretion disk around a neutron star make it radiate powerfully in X rays. Some close binaries with neutron stars emit 100,000 times as much energy in X rays as our Sun emits in all wavelengths of light combined. Because of this intense X-ray emission, close binaries that contain accreting neutron stars are often called **X-ray binaries.** We have identified hundreds of X-ray binaries in the disk of the Milky Way Galaxy.

The hot accretion disks around neutron stars in close binary systems shine brightly with X rays.

The emission from most X-ray binaries pulsates rapidly as the neutron star spins. However, while other pulsars tend to slow down with time, the pulsation rates of X-ray binaries tend to accelerate, presumably because matter accreting onto the neutron star adds angular momentum (Figure 14.10). Some of these neutron stars rotate so fast that they pulsate every few thousandths of a second (and are called *millisecond pulsars*).

X-Ray Bursts Like accreting white dwarfs that occasionally erupt as novae, accreting neutron stars sporadically erupt with enormous luminosities. Hydrogen-rich material from the companion star builds up on the surface of the neutron star, forming a layer about a meter thick. Pressures at the bottom of this hydrogen layer are high enough to maintain steady fusion, which produces a layer of helium beneath the hydrogen. Helium fusion suddenly ignites when the temperature in this layer builds to 100 million K. The helium fuses rapidly to make carbon and heavier elements, generating a burst of energy that flows from the neutron star in the form of X rays. These **X-ray bursters** typically flare every few hours to every few days (Figure 14.11). Each burst lasts only a few seconds, but during those seconds the system can radiate 100,000 times as much power as the Sun, all in X rays. Within a minute after a burst, the X-ray burster cools back down and accretion resumes.

Neutron Star Mergers Just as we discussed for two closely orbiting white dwarfs, two neutron stars orbiting close together will emit gravitational waves, ultimately causing the two neutron stars to spiral together and merge

(Figure 14.12). The total energy released during this cataclysmic merger can be even greater than that of a massive star supernova, and it happens in an environment rich in neutrons. As a result, neutron star mergers can produce a blend of rare elements that differ from those made in a massive star supernova. Most of the neutron star matter remains gravitationally bound to the system, but some of it is ejected into interstellar space. Models of these mergers indicate that they produce most of the gold, platinum, and rare earth elements present in the universe. In other words, the gold in your jewelry was probably made by neutron star mergers.

Gold and other rare elements may have been produced in explosions resulting from neutron star mergers.

14.3 Black Holes: Gravity's Ultimate Victory

The story of stellar corpses would be strange enough if it ended with white dwarfs and neutron stars, but it does not. Sometimes, the gravity in a stellar corpse becomes so strong that nothing can prevent the corpse from collapsing under its own weight. The stellar corpse collapses without end, crushing itself out of existence and forming perhaps the most bizarre type of object in the universe: a *black hole*.

◆ What is a black hole?

The "black" in the name **black hole** comes from the fact that nothing—not even light—can escape from a black hole. The escape velocity of any object depends on the strength of its gravity, which depends on its mass and size [Section 4.4]. Decreasing the size of an object of a particular mass makes its gravity stronger and increases its escape velocity. A black hole is so compact that it has an escape velocity greater than the speed of light. Because nothing can travel faster than the speed of light, neither light nor anything else can escape from within a black hole.

The "hole" part of the name *black hole* tells an even stranger story. Einstein discovered that space and time are not distinct, as we usually think of them, but instead are bound up together as four-dimensional **spacetime.** Moreover, in his general theory of relativity, Einstein showed that what we perceive as gravity arises from *curvature of spacetime* (see Special Topic, page 373). Curved spacetime is not easy to visualize, because we can see only three dimensions at once. However, we can understand the idea with a two-dimensional analogy.

A black hole is a place where gravity is so strong that nothing—not even light—can escape from within it.

Figure 14.13 uses a rubber sheet to represent two-dimensional slices through spacetime. In this analogy, the sheet is flat—corresponding to weak gravity—in a region far from any mass (Figure 14.13a). The sheet becomes curved near a massive object, corresponding to strong gravity (Figure 14.13b), and greater curvature means stronger gravity. In this representation, the curvature of spacetime near a black hole is so great that the rubber sheet forms a bottomless pit (Figure 14.13c). Keep in mind that the illustration is only an analogy, and black holes actually are spherical, not funnel-shaped. Nevertheless, it captures the key idea that a black hole is like a hole in the observable universe in the following sense: If you enter a black hole, you leave our observable universe and can never return.

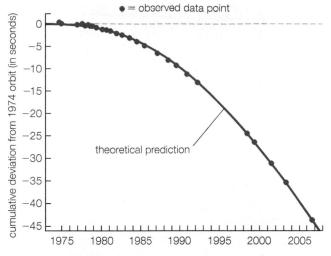

▲ **FIGURE 14.12**

This diagram shows how the orbital period of a close binary system consisting of two neutron stars has changed over the last several decades. The observed changes precisely match what we expect from a system with an orbital distance that is changing because of gravitational-wave emission. Projecting the trend into the future shows that the two neutrons stars will collide and merge about 85 million years from now. (Data courtesy of Joel Weisberg and Joseph Taylor.)

The Schwarzschild Radius

The Schwarzschild radius (R_S) of a black hole is given by a simple formula:

$$\text{Schwarzschild radius} = R_S = \frac{2GM}{c^2}$$

where M is the black hole's mass, the gravitational constant $G = 6.67 \times 10^{-11}$ m³/(kg × s²), and the speed of light is $c = 3 \times 10^8$ m/s. With a bit of calculation, this formula can also be written as

$$\text{Schwarzschild radius} = R_S = 3.0 \times \frac{M}{M_{\text{Sun}}} \text{ km}$$

Example: What is the Schwarzschild radius of a black hole with a mass of $10M_{\text{Sun}}$?

Solution: We are given the black hole's mass in solar units, so we use the second formula above and set $M = 10M_{\text{Sun}}$:

$$R_S = 3.0 \times \frac{10M_{\text{Sun}}}{M_{\text{Sun}}} \text{ km} = 30 \text{ km}$$

The Schwarzschild radius of a $10M_{\text{Sun}}$ black hole is about 30 km—roughly the radius of a large city on Earth, but containing 10 times as much mass as the Sun.

▲ **FIGURE 14.14**

Time runs more slowly on the clock nearer to the black hole, and gravitational redshift makes its glowing blue numerals appear red from your orbiting spaceship.

gradually toward the event horizon. Sure enough, the clock on the rocket ticks more slowly as it heads toward the black hole, and its light becomes increasingly redshifted. When the clock reaches a distance of about 10 kilometers above the event horizon, you see it ticking only half as fast as the clock on your spaceship, and its numerals are red instead of blue.

The rocket has to expend fuel rapidly to keep the clock hovering in the strong gravitational field, and the fuel soon runs out. The clock plunges toward the black hole. From your safe vantage point inside your spaceship, you see the clock ticking more and more slowly as it falls. However, you soon need a radio telescope to "see" it, as the light from the clock face shifts from the red part of the visible spectrum to the infrared, and on into the radio. Finally, its light becomes so redshifted that no conceivable telescope could detect it. Just as the clock vanishes from view, you see that the time on its face has frozen.

Curiosity overwhelms the better judgment of one of your colleagues. He hurriedly climbs into a space suit, grabs the other clock, resets it, and jumps out of the air lock on a trajectory aimed straight for the black hole. Down he falls, clock in hand. He watches the clock, but because he and the clock are traveling together, its time seems to run normally and its numerals stay blue. From his point of view, time seems to neither speed up nor slow down. When his clock reads, say, 00:30, he and the clock pass through the event horizon. There is no barrier, no wall, no hard surface. The event horizon is a mathematical boundary, not a physical one. From his point of view, the clock keeps ticking. He is inside the event horizon, the first human being ever to vanish into a black hole.

Back on the spaceship, you watch in horror as your overly curious friend plunges to his death. Yet, from your point of view, he will *never* cross the event horizon. You'll see time come to a stop for him and his clock just as he vanishes from view because of the huge gravitational redshift of light. When you return home, you can play a video for the judges at your trial,

If you fell toward a black hole, you would rapidly accelerate and soon cross the event horizon. But to someone watching from afar, your fall would appear to take forever.

proving that your friend is still outside the black hole. Strange as it may seem, all this is true according to Einstein's theory. From your point of view, your friend takes *forever* to cross the event horizon (even though he vanishes from view because of his ever-increasing redshift). From his point of view, it is but a moment's plunge before he passes into oblivion.

The truly sad part of this story is that your friend did not live to experience the crossing of the event horizon. The force of gravity grew so quickly as he approached the black hole that it pulled much harder on his feet than on his head, simultaneously stretching him lengthwise and squeezing him from side to side (Figure 14.15). In essence, your friend was stretched in the same way the oceans are stretched by the tides, except that the *tidal force* near the black hole is trillions of times stronger than the tidal force of the Moon on Earth [Section 4.4]. No human could survive it.

If he had thought ahead, your friend might have waited to make his jump until you visited a much larger black hole, like one of the *supermassive black holes* thought to reside in the centers of many galaxies [Section 16.4]. A 1 billion solar mass ($10^9 M_{\text{Sun}}$) black hole has a Schwarzschild radius of 3 billion kilometers—about the distance from our Sun to Uranus. Although the difficulty of escape from the event horizon of any black hole is equally great, the larger size of a supermassive black hole makes its tidal forces much weaker and hence nonlethal. Your friend could safely plunge through the event horizon. Unfortunately, anything he saw or learned on his continuing plunge toward oblivion would be known to him alone, because there would be no way for him to send information back to you on the outside.

◆ Do black holes really exist?

As was the case for neutron stars, at first most astronomers who contemplated the idea of black holes thought them too strange to be true. Today, our understanding of physics gives us reason to think that black holes ought to be fairly common, and observational evidence strongly suggests that black holes really exist.

The Formation of a Black Hole   The idea that black holes ought to exist comes from considering how they might form. Recall that white dwarfs cannot exceed $1.4M_{Sun}$, because gravity overcomes electron degeneracy pressure above that mass. Calculations show that the mass of a neutron star has a similar limit that lies somewhere between about 2 and 3 solar masses. Above this mass, neutron degeneracy pressure cannot hold off the crush of gravity in a collapsing stellar core.

A massive star supernova occurs when the electron degeneracy pressure supporting the iron core of a massive star succumbs to gravity, causing the core to collapse catastrophically into a ball of neutrons [Section 13.3]. That is why most supernovae leave neutron stars behind. However, theoretical models show that very massive stars might not succeed in blowing away all their upper layers. If enough matter falls back onto the neutron core, its mass may rise above the neutron star limit. Likewise, a merger between two neutron stars can produce an object that exceeds the neutron-star mass limit.

As soon as the core exceeds the neutron star limit, gravity overcomes the neutron degeneracy pressure and the core collapses once again. This time, no known force can keep the core from collapsing into oblivion as a black hole. Moreover, another consequence of Einstein's theory of relativity makes it highly unlikely that any as-yet-unknown force could intervene either.

Recall that Einstein's theory tells us that energy is equivalent to mass ($E = mc^2$) [Section 4.3], implying that energy, like mass, must exert some gravitational attraction. The gravity of pure energy usually is negligible, but not in a stellar core collapsing beyond the neutron star limit.

According to the known laws of physics, nothing can stop the collapse of a stellar corpse with a mass greater than about 3 solar masses.

Inside a star that collapses beyond the point where it could have been a neutron star, the energy associated with the enhanced internal temperature and pressure acts like additional mass, making the crushing power of gravity even stronger. The more the star collapses, the stronger gravity gets. To the best of our understanding, *nothing* can halt the crush of gravity at this point, so the star must inevitably collapse to form a black hole.

Observational Evidence for Black Holes   The fact that black holes emit no light might make it seem as if they should be impossible to detect. However, a black hole's gravity can influence its surroundings in a way that reveals its presence. Astronomers have discovered many objects that show the telltale signs of an unseen gravitational influence with a large enough mass to suggest a black hole.

Strong observational evidence for black holes formed by supernovae comes from studies of X-ray binaries. Recall that the accretion disk around a neutron star in a close binary system can emit strong X-ray

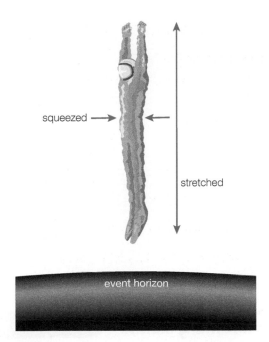

▲ **FIGURE 14.15**
Tidal forces would be lethal near a black hole formed by the collapse of a star. The black hole's gravity would pull more strongly on the astronaut's feet than on his head, stretching him lengthwise and squeezing him from side to side.

common misconceptions

Black Holes Don't Suck

What would happen if our Sun suddenly became a black hole? For some reason, the idea that Earth and the other planets would inevitably be "sucked in" by the black hole has become part of our popular culture. But it is not true. Although the sudden disappearance of the Sun's light and heat would make our planet cold and dark, Earth's orbit would not change.

Newton's law of gravity tells us that the allowed orbits in a gravitational field are ellipses, hyperbolas, and parabolas [Section 4.4]. Note that "sucking" is not on the list! A spaceship would get into trouble only if it came so close to a black hole—within about three times the Schwarzschild radius—that the force of gravity would deviate significantly from what Newton's law predicts. Otherwise, a spaceship passing near a black hole would simply swing around it on an ordinary orbit (ellipse, parabola, or hyperbola). In fact, because most black holes are so small—typical Schwarzschild radii are far smaller than those of any star or planet—a black hole is actually one of the most difficult things in the universe to fall into by accident.

Some X-ray binaries probably contain accreting black holes rather than accreting neutron stars.

radiation, resulting in an X-ray binary. The accretion disk forms because the neutron star's strong gravity pulls mass from its companion star. Because a black hole has even stronger gravity than a neutron star, a black hole in a close binary system should also be surrounded by a hot, X ray–emitting accretion disk. Some X-ray binaries may therefore contain black holes rather than neutron stars.

One of the most promising black hole candidates is in an X-ray binary called Cygnus X-1 (Figure 14.16). This system contains an extremely luminous star with an estimated mass of $19 M_{Sun}$. Based on Doppler shifts of its spectral lines, astronomers have concluded that this star orbits a compact, unseen companion with a mass of about $15 M_{Sun}$. Although there is some uncertainty in these mass estimates, the mass of the invisible accreting object clearly exceeds the $3 M_{Sun}$ neutron star limit. It is therefore too massive to be a neutron star, so according to current knowledge it must be a black hole. A few dozen other X-ray binaries offer similar evidence for black holes formed

---

extraordinary claims | Neutron Stars and Black Holes Are Real

Subrahmanyan Chandrasekhar

Theoretical calculations predicted the existence of neutron stars and black holes long before their observational discovery, but many astronomers considered these theoretical results too strange to be true.

Subrahmanyan Chandrasekhar, an astrophysicist from India, was only 19 when he completed the calculations showing that there is a white dwarf limit of $1.4 M_{Sun}$, and he boldly predicted that a more massive white dwarf would collapse under the force of gravity. He did this work in 1931 while traveling by ship to England, where he hoped to impress the eminent British astrophysicist Sir Arthur Stanley Eddington. However, Eddington ridiculed Chandrasekhar for believing that white dwarfs could collapse. Neutrons had not yet been discovered, little was known about fusion, and no one had any idea what supernovae were. The idea of gravity achieving an ultimate victory seemed nonsensical to Eddington, who speculated that some type of force must prevent gravity from crushing any object.

A few more radical thinkers took collapsing stars more seriously. A Russian physicist, Lev Davidovich Landau, independently computed the white dwarf limit

Lev Davidovich Landau

Sir Arthur Stanley Eddington

in 1932. Neutrons were discovered just a few months later, and Landau speculated that stellar corpses above the white dwarf limit might collapse until neutron degeneracy pressure halted the crush of gravity. While most astronomers found the idea of neutron stars to be unacceptably weird, two European scientists who had emigrated to California, Fritz Zwicky and Walter Baade, were not so skeptical. Without knowing of Landau's ideas, they also independently

Robert Oppenheimer

concluded that neutron stars were possible. In 1934, they suggested that a supernova might result when a stellar core collapses and forms a neutron star—an extraordinarily insightful guess. By 1938, physicist Robert Oppenheimer, working at Berkeley, was contemplating whether neutron stars had a limiting mass of their own. He and his coworkers concluded that the answer was yes and that neutron degeneracy pressure could not resist the crush of gravity when the mass rose above a few solar masses. Because no known force could keep such a star from collapsing indefinitely, Oppenheimer speculated that gravity would achieve ultimate victory, crushing the star into a black hole.

Astronomers gradually came to accept Chandrasekhar's $1.4 M_{Sun}$ white dwarf limit, because observations found no white dwarfs more massive than this. However, most astronomers held to a belief that high-mass stars would inevitably shed enough mass late in life to prevent the formation of a more massive collapsed object. Jocelyn Bell's 1967 discovery of pulsars shattered this belief. Within a few months, Thomas Gold of Cornell University correctly suggested that the pulsars were spinning neutron stars. These discoveries forced astronomers to acknowledge that nature was far stranger than they had expected. The verification that neutron stars really exist made the prospect of the still stranger black holes much less difficult to accept.

Jocelyn Bell

Chandrasekhar, who had long since moved to the University of Chicago, was awarded a Nobel Prize in 1984 for his lifelong contributions to astronomy. Landau won a Nobel Prize in 1962 for his work on condensed states of matter. Oppenheimer went on to lead the Manhattan Project, which developed the atomic bomb in 1945. Eddington died in 1944, still convinced that white dwarf stars could not collapse.

Verdict: Strong evidence supports the reality of neutron stars and black holes.

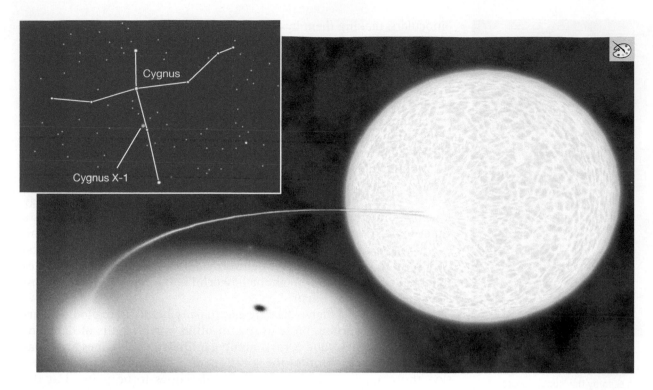

Cygnus

Cygnus X-1

from the collapse of massive stellar cores. As we'll discuss in coming chapters, an even greater body of evidence suggests the existence of *supermassive black holes*—some with masses millions or billions of times that of our Sun—residing at the centers of many galaxies, including our own Milky Way.

think about it Recall that some X-ray binaries that contain neutron stars emit frequent X-ray bursts and are called *X-ray bursters*. Could an X-ray binary that contains a black hole exhibit the same type of X-ray bursts? Why or why not? (*Hint:* Where do the X-ray bursts occur in an X-ray binary with a neutron star?)

14.4 Extreme Events

Supernovae that produce neutron stars are rare and enormously energetic events. However, the events accompanying the formation and growth of black holes are rarer and even more energetic. To identify such events, astronomers watch for extreme outbursts of energy. Two kinds of events are receiving particularly close attention: gamma-ray bursts and gravitational-wave pulses.

◆ What causes gamma-ray bursts?

In the early 1960s, the United States began launching a series of top-secret satellites designed to look for gamma rays emitted by nuclear bomb tests. The satellites soon started detecting occasional bursts of gamma rays, typically lasting a few seconds (Figure 14.17). It took several years for military scientists to become convinced that these **gamma-ray bursts** were coming from space, not from some sinister human activity, and the military then made the discovery public. We have since learned that gamma-ray bursts represent explosions of almost unimaginable power.

Gamma-ray bursts originating billions of light-years from Earth can produce afterglows of visible light (Figure 14.18) that can be seen through

▲ **FIGURE 14.16**

Artist's conception of the Cygnus X-1 system, so named because it is the brightest X-ray source in the constellation Cygnus. The X rays come from the high-temperature gas in the accretion disk surrounding the black hole. The inset shows the location of Cygnus X-1 in the sky.

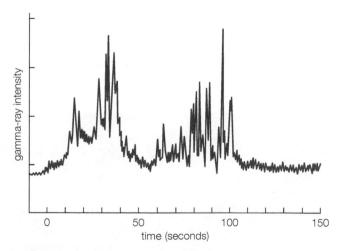

▲ **FIGURE 14.17**

The intensity of a gamma-ray burst can fluctuate dramatically over time periods of just a few seconds.

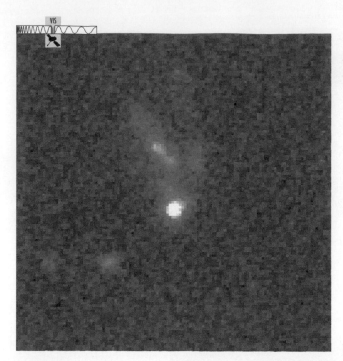

▲ FIGURE 14.18

The bright dot near the center of this photo is the visible-light afterglow of a gamma-ray burst, as seen by the Hubble Space Telescope. The elongated blob extending above the dot is the distant galaxy in which the burst occurred.

▼ FIGURE 14.19

The bright object marked "source of gamma-ray burst" in the first panel of this sequence is the visible-light afterglow of a gamma-ray burst in the outskirts of a distant galaxy (marked "host galaxy"). The light detected from this object once the initial afterglow faded showed that it had the light curve of a massive star supernova.

binoculars, making them by far the most powerful bursts of energy that we observe in the universe. If a gamma-ray burst emitted light equally in all directions, like a light bulb, then its total luminosity would briefly exceed the combined luminosity of a million galaxies like our Milky Way. Because such a high luminosity is very difficult to explain, scientists think it's likely that gamma-ray bursts channel their energy into narrow searchlight beams, like pulsars, so only some are visible from Earth. But even in this case, for a brief moment, a gamma-ray burst is far more luminous than anything else in the universe.

What could cause such massive outbursts of energy? At least some gamma-ray bursts come from extremely powerful supernova explosions. A supernova that forms a neutron star does not release enough energy to explain the luminosity of the brightest gamma-ray bursts. However, a supernova that forms a black hole crushes even more matter into an even smaller radius, releasing many times more gravitational potential energy than one that forms a neutron star. This kind of event (sometimes called a *hypernova*) might be powerful enough to explain the most extreme gamma-ray bursts.

The primary evidence linking gamma-ray bursts to exploding stars comes from observing these events in other wavelengths of light, including visible light and X rays. Some gamma-ray telescopes are capable of rapidly pinpointing the location of a gamma-ray burst in the sky, thereby allowing other types of telescopes to be pointed at the gamma-ray source almost as soon as the burst is detected. Observations like these have shown that at least some gamma-ray bursts coincide with powerful supernova explosions (Figure 14.19). In a number of other cases, gamma-ray bursts have been observed to come from distant galaxies that are actively forming new stars. Those observations also support the idea that gamma-ray bursts are produced in the explosions of extremely massive stars, because such stars are very short-lived and therefore should be found only in places where stars are actively forming.

Supernovae forming black holes probably account for most gamma-ray bursts, but there is another type whose origin has been harder to verify. Bursts of this second type last only a few seconds, making them more difficult to catch in action with telescopes for other wavelengths. Follow-up observations of these short bursts (which represent about 30% of all gamma-ray bursts) have shown that they do *not* come from supernovae. What could be causing them? The leading hypothesis is a collision in a binary system containing either two neutron stars or a neutron star and a black hole that results in the formation of a more massive black hole. Scientists are actively studying these

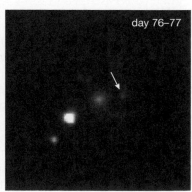

source of gamma-ray burst

host galaxy

day 13–14

day 23–24

day 27–28

day 76–77

◀ **FIGURE 14.20**
These three panels illustrate gravitational waves coming from a black hole binary. They are based on a supercomputer simulation of the final moments before the black holes merge, and time progresses from left to right. Gravitational waves are depicted in red, orange, and yellow, in order of increasing intensity. The sequence shows that the gravitational-wave intensity from a black hole binary system rapidly increases as the black holes spiral together.

short gamma-ray bursts in hopes of confirming, or contradicting, this hypothesis.

What happens when black holes merge?

We have already seen that the orbits of both binary white dwarf systems and binary neutron star systems decay because gravitational waves carry away some of their orbital energy and angular momentum. The same basic physics also applies to binary systems that consist of two black holes orbiting each other, but the greater masses of the black holes (compared to white dwarfs and neutron stars) lead to much stronger emission of gravitational waves (Figure 14.20). As with the white dwarf and neutron star systems, the two black holes can ultimately merge to make a single, more massive black hole.

Models predict that gravitational waves from a black hole binary become particularly intense during the final death spiral preceding a merger. The resulting pulses of gravitational radiation are so powerful that we can detect black hole mergers that happen billions of light-years away. The Advanced LIGO experiment (see Figure 5.24) first detected such gravitational waves in 2015 (Figure 14.21).

Scientists have detected gravitational waves from merging black holes.

▲ **FIGURE 14.21**
Gravitational-wave signal observed on September 14, 2015 by both detectors of the Advanced LIGO experiment, which are located in Hanford, Washington and Livingston, Louisiana. In order to measure the signal, the LIGO detectors needed to be sensitive enough to record vibrations (strain) of less than one part in 10^{21}. Analysis of the signal shows that it came from the merger of two black holes, each about 30 solar masses, at a distance of 1.3 billion light-years.

---

the big picture **Putting Chapter 14 into Perspective**

We have now seen the mind-bending consequences of stellar death. As you think about the bizarre objects of the stellar graveyard described in this chapter, try to keep in mind these "big picture" ideas:

- Despite the strange nature of stellar corpses, clear evidence exists for white dwarfs and neutron stars, and the case for black holes is very strong.

- White dwarfs, neutron stars, and black holes can all have close stellar companions from which they accrete matter. These binary systems produce some of the most spectacular events in the universe, including novae, white dwarf supernovae, and X-ray bursters.

- Black holes are holes in the observable universe that strongly warp space and time around them. The nature of black hole singularities remains beyond the frontier of current scientific understanding.

my cosmic perspective The idea of a black hole—something with a pull so strong that nothing can escape—is a common metaphor in popular culture, but we humans have little to fear from real black holes. They are at such great distances that their powerful gravitational forces have little chance of ever affecting us.

14.1 White Dwarfs

◆ **What is a white dwarf?**

A white dwarf is the core left over from a low-mass star, supported against the crush of gravity by **electron degeneracy pressure.** A white dwarf typically has the mass of the Sun compressed into a size no larger than Earth.

◆ **What can happen to a white dwarf in a close binary system?**

A white dwarf in a close binary system can acquire hydrogen from its companion through an **accretion disk** that swirls toward the white dwarf's surface. As hydrogen builds up on the white dwarf's surface, it may begin nuclear fusion and cause a **nova** that, for a few weeks, may shine as brightly as 100,000 Suns. In extreme cases, accretion or a merger of two white dwarfs may cause a white dwarf's mass to reach the **white dwarf limit** of $1.4 M_{Sun}$, at which point the white dwarf will explode as a **white dwarf supernova.**

14.2 Neutron Stars

◆ **What is a neutron star?**

A neutron star is the ball of neutrons created by the collapse of the iron core in a massive star supernova. It resembles a giant atomic nucleus 10 kilometers in radius and with more mass than the Sun.

◆ **How were neutron stars discovered?**

Neutron stars spin rapidly when they are born, and their strong magnetic fields can direct beams of radiation that sweep through space as the neutron star spins. We detect such neutron stars as **pulsars,** and these pulsars provided the first direct evidence for the existence of neutron stars.

◆ **What can happen to a neutron star in a close binary system?**

Neutron stars in close binary systems can accrete hydrogen from their companions, forming dense, hot accretion disks. The hot gas emits strongly in X rays, so we see these systems as **X-ray binaries.** In some of these systems, frequent bursts of helium fusion occur on the neutron star's surface, causing **X-ray bursts.** Neutron stars can also merge together, and such mergers may be the primary sources of gold and various other rare elements.

14.3 Black Holes: Gravity's Ultimate Victory

◆ **What is a black hole?**

A black hole is a place where gravity has crushed matter into oblivion, creating a hole in the universe from which nothing can escape, not even light. The **event horizon** marks the boundary between our observable universe and the inside of the black hole; the size of a black hole is characterized by its **Schwarzschild radius.**

◆ **What would it be like to visit a black hole?**

You could orbit a black hole just as you could any other object of the same mass. However, you'd see some strange effects if you watched an object fall toward the black hole: Time would seem to run more slowly for the object, and light from it would appear increasingly redshifted as the object fell closer to the black hole. The object would never appear to pass through the event horizon but instead would disappear from view as its light became too redshifted for any instrument to detect it.

◆ **Do black holes really exist?**

No known force can stop the collapse of a stellar corpse with a mass above the neutron star limit of 2 to 3 solar masses, and theoretical studies of supernovae suggest that such objects should sometimes form. Observational evidence supports this idea: Some X-ray binaries include compact objects far too massive to be neutron stars, making it likely that they are black holes.

14.4 Extreme Events

◆ **What causes gamma-ray bursts?**

Gamma-ray bursts occur in distant galaxies but shine so brightly in the sky that they must be the most powerful explosions we ever observe in the universe. Most gamma-ray bursts appear to come from unusually powerful supernova explosions that may create black holes. Less common short gamma-ray bursts may come from mergers of neutron stars in close binary systems.

◆ **What happens when black holes merge?**

Close binary systems consisting of two black holes emit gravitational waves that causes the average orbital distance to decrease with time until the black holes merge. Gravitational waves from such systems have recently been detected and represent some of the strongest evidence we have for black holes.